# Beyond Machine Man

## Who we really are and
## why Transhumanism is just an empty promise!

Arne Klingenberg

Category: Philosophy/Self Help/Spirituality & Ethics/Education/Personal Development

First Edition
First Published: March 14, 2021

Hardcover ISBN-13: 978-1-876538-06-4
Paperback ISBN-13: 978-1-876538-07-1
Ebook-EPUB ISBN-13: 978-1-876538-08-8

Published by:
Beam Publishing Pty. Ltd.
P.O. Box 405
Port Douglas QLD 4877
Australia

Phone: +61-7- 40 993 888
Email: editor@beampublishing.com
Web: www.beampublishing.com

Cover Art by: Nada Orlic, Erelis Design (www.erelisdesign.com)
Book Formatting by: Erelis Design

Disclaimer:
All information contained in this book are the personal opinions, insights and practices of the author, and are presented purely for educational purposes. There are no representations or warranties, express or implied, about the completeness, accuracy, reliability, or suitability with respect to the information contained in this book for any purpose.

Dedicated to:
*All serious seekers of truth and wisdom.*


Thank you to:
*My dear wife, Miyuki Klingenberg, for her endless patience
and loving support.*


In Memoriam:
*My dear father, Hans U. Klingenberg (14.3.1929 – 8.8.2013)*

# TABLE OF CONTENTS

# The Big Questions

Who am I? Is there life after death? And if so, where did we come from and where will we go to? Is there a God or an ultimate reality? Respectively, who or what is the intelligence behind the billions of intelligent effects we can observe?

Since time immemorial these questions have been asked by a great many, if not all, people. And a myriad of philosophers, religious proponents, and scientists of the believing, agnostic or atheistic kind have attempted to answer them, each in their own ways, to this very day.

***Who are we? And ultimately, are we going to be always alive or will we be dead forever?***
In today's official world of technocratic government, academia and media, it sure looks like the answers are already very clear. Actually, even just asking such questions aloud will expose you (or me) to total ridicule, or at best earn us an obviously condescending smile.

To proponents of *The Party Line* these questions have long been answered by accredited science and they look forward to eventually enlighten all of the dumb and superstitious who still stubbornly cling to silly notions like spirituality or worse, religion. In the meantime, they are more than happy to bless us with their benevolent rule. Or so they imagine it to be.

Will modern science really be able to prolong life by merging us with machines? Or is transhumanism just an empty promise to keep us hooked to a rather destructive and depressing way of life for the majority of people, and endless riches for a select few? Will the loudly announced technical singularity actually lead us to the promised land – eternal life and heaven on Earth? And if so, would it be for all of us or just for our well-heeled rulers and their well-paid enablers?

This book will discuss all of the above – with the exception of religious matters as that would go beyond the scope of our discussions – and attempt to show you why the final words about **who we really are** have not been spoken yet; why the current materialistic paradigm of officialdom is likely to be very wrong and how the consequences of their fundamental errors are rather dire for us as individuals and society as a whole. Moreover, we will analyze what the ultimate truths may turn out to be and the many reasons why.

We have much grounds to cover and it will be an exciting ride, so hold on and keep reading! But first, allow me a couple of quick points: while we will discuss the latest insights into various disciplines of cutting-edge science, we will aim to keep it as simple and concise as possible in the main text and refer you to the *Notes* section for direct links to the very technical aspects and other information that help us to prove the points we are making here.

You may also notice that the language of your author is colorful at times and generally a bit playful with the odd sprinkling of dark humor, despite the serious and profound nature of the topics; this is simply part of my character coupled with the belief that books should elevate, educate and entertain us all at the same time. And hopefully, you will find that I have succeeded in this endeavor!

Since my very early childhood days, I have somehow felt the answers to the big questions without actually asking them in an explicit manner. To me, whether we are always alive or not was never even a question, simply because I just *knew* how it is, or so it seemed.

My dear father was both an outspoken atheist and mortally afraid of dying, which is a very common and rather understandable occurrence among atheists, and actually even among some believers of religious faiths, as strange as that may sound right now.

I clearly remember the first time he expressed his fear of dying, of ceasing to exist – for good. It was late one night when I woke up to the sound of clonking bottles as he selected a new drink from the bar that was located just outside my bedroom. Our first conversation is still fresh in my memory simply because his 'confession' came as a total surprise to me! Until that very moment, I had simply assumed that everybody else also knew that we do live forever.

Admittedly, psychologists or psychiatrists reading the above might now rub their hands in utter glee before quickly offering a lot of insights into the hows and whys an obviously delusional child might think like this. Well, we'll see about that a bit later on while we discuss the many myths of neuroscience and psychotropic drugs, among other things, but let's just continue with the story.

I remember telling my father that there is really nothing to worry about, that for sure we will all continue to live. The good, the bad and even the ugly. He listened intently, visibly surprised, even puzzled. And yet he continued to express his many doubts and fears. Dad thought that I'm simply being a nice son trying to comfort his beloved father. Yet as much as he was certain about the truth of the matter, so was I.

Over the following months, we had many more of these late night discussions. And when it finally dawned on me that he wasn't going to change his mind on this, and that indeed there was nothing else I could possibly add to get him to reconsider, I told him that when the day will eventually come, he will likely have the best and most pleasant surprise of his life.

He smiled his kind smile, glad that I care about him yet seemingly a bit worried about my youthful ignorance. And I went back to bed, equally concerned about my Dad and his mental pain, while also wondering about his rather strange and outright depressing beliefs.

*"Knowing others is intelligence; knowing yourself is true wisdom. Mastering others is strength; mastering yourself is true power."* Lao Tzu

# Three Perspectives

Our collective consciousness is made up of endless individual thoughts, beliefs and opinions, besides countless hopes, dreams and desires, and a myriad of emotions and feelings. And yet there are a great many similarities in the way we perceive our world.

Not to judge but solely for the purpose of our discussion, let's sort human consciousness into the following three very general types of thought or awareness – a concept first introduced and elaborated upon in my second book (see chapter *Notes* for details).

Since consciousness goes far beyond mere thinking, analyzing and reasoning, we could call them *the three main modes of experiencing the world*, or simply, The Three Perspectives:

1. The Materialistic Perspective – hereafter referred to as *Machine Man* or *Homo Machina*
2. The Religious Perspective – *Believing Man* or *Homo Credo*
3. The Spiritual Perspective – *Mystic Man* or *Homo Mysticum*

Of course, these three categories or perspectives are both very broad and fluid. For example, it is certainly possible to be a religious person but also believe in mainstream science (up to a certain point, depending on their respective dogmas). And likewise there are a great many scientists who believe in a God, however defined; not every scientist is a radical physical reductionist or atheist, even though only researchers of that particular flavor seem to receive both media exposure and government grants.

*Mystic Man* too can (but doesn't have to) be deeply devout while at the same time be most interested in the latest achievements of science, in particular the amazing insights into quantum mechanics and the many challenges these pose to proponents of purely mechanical points of views. Quite naturally, *Homo Mysticum* has a tendency to come up with far broader interpretations of science than the typical materialistic scientist or medical doctor.

By making the three distinctions, we certainly don't wish to assign any moral or other values whatsoever. That would be irrelevant anyway as the quality of our individual lives, the sum total of our beliefs and the resulting consciousness is a most personal experience. And as such it is beyond criticism by third parties – for as long as we don't harm others, of course.

So let's take a look at the main differences between the three perspectives and how these outlooks shape the corresponding realities experienced:

1. *Machine Man* or *Homo Machina:* People who *think* that they *are* their body – ruled by a more or less intelligent brain, aided and abetted by a better or worse set of DNA. This is the purely materialistic perspective, incessantly propagated and promoted by academia, governments, and the mainstream media. According to reductionist Machine Man, "We are just smart animals."

2. *Believing Man* or *Homo Credo:* People who also identify themselves as their body but *believe* that they somehow or another *have* a spiritual eternal soul. It is believed to be somewhere, deep down and hidden within themselves. This is the religious perspective and it is mostly based on scripture, faith, and cultural traditions.

3. *Mystic Man* or *Homo Mysticum:* People who *know* that they *are* the eternal spiritual soul, but are temporarily having a human experience in a body made out of flesh, blood and bones. This is the mystical perspective, based on real personal experiences made and the subsequent insights gained. The essential point here is the need to have made profound personal experiences, so simply reading a book by Deepak Chopra (et alia; insert any name of a New Age or Personal Development guru) or believing a holy book of any kind just won't do as it is still taken on faith.

*So who is right and who is wrong? Is there a right and wrong? And why does it matter so much?* The ways we feel, think and talk are all influenced by our overall consciousness; it literally determines how we see and experience the world we live in today. Our macro perspective largely decides what choices we make in our life and how we act; the kind of things we do and equally, those things we *don't* do!

In other words, the overall quality of our lives greatly depends on our deepest-held beliefs. The perspective we more or less consciously choose decides much about the degree of our success; how healthy, wealthy and happy we will be in life. Therefore it is rather crucial to get it right. Not just for each one of us on an individual level, but also for society as a whole.

The primary example of course is how we deal with the fact of our own mortality and the losing of our loved ones. How we approach and deal with this inevitable and tough reality of life has a great influence on how we live our lives, including how happy we are. Let's see how the three differing perspectives produce dramatically different results:

1. ***Machine Man:*** Adherents of this belief system think that when they die, well, they will be dead. Forever. They believe that they basically cease to exist, respectively turn to fertilizer and worm fodder. This is the realm of both agnostics and atheists; they harbor great fears about their own eventual deaths and increasingly so as they grow older. They also suffer major psychological repercussions like anxiety or depression. The death of loved ones too affect them greatly; often they are and remain inconsolable. The most common solution to deal with this subject is self-medication with copious amounts of alcohol and both legal and illegal drugs. The idea is to not even think or talk about it because it is just too frightening or painful to bear; ***Homo Machina*** well and truly hates to talk about death or the dead. Suppressing thoughts or memories and simply trying to move on is the usual method, yet that is not an easy task, even while being intoxicated (and sometimes particularly so). Another approach is trying to run away from death by being extremely health-conscious, but of course that is neither a guarantee of good health nor will it necessarily prolong life. And

at the latest with advancing age, all of their fears and worries will simply return with a vengeance.

2.  ***Believing Man:*** Homo Credo generally approach their own mortality far more optimistically, regardless of the countless different forms and flavors of their particular beliefs. Believing people mourn their dead yet at the same time they believe – to various degrees – that the deceased person continues to exist as a soul, hopefully in some sort of heaven, of course. And they are fairly sure that by living a pious life they will be enabled to join their loved ones in paradise and live together happily ever after. ***Homo Credo*** usually talk about their souls as being something different than they are at present, yet they will magically turn into that very thing upon death (saying things like: he bared his soul, speaking to my soul, wake up your soul, I feel it in my soul, I have sold my soul, SOS – save our souls, we ***have*** an eternal soul that will never die, I am the captain of my soul). Some believe in having a soul that goes to heaven, but that their current physical bodies will eventually become resurrected , somehow (from the already decomposed atoms?), and that they will become again that body and live forever here on planet Earth. No matter what their individual beliefs may be, what is common is the general self-identification as being their physical bodies, which oddly enough is fundamentally the exact same belief as the ones held by atheists and agnostics (a.k.a. Machine Man). And yet, research findings consistently show that Believing Man generally tends to be happier and otherwise more stable in terms of their emotions than Homo Machina. It comes as a result of their faith and relationship with God (however defined), which of course gets decried and ridiculed by atheists as having, or needing to have, an imaginary friend.

3.  ***Mystic Man:*** Mystics who identify themselves as eternal beings of energy may also deeply miss the person, spirit or soul who has passed away and will honor their dead bodies, yet at the same time they continue to feel connected with a beloved person through their mutual bands – and means of communication – of love. They are ***totally sure*** about seeing their loved ones again rather soon,

knowing full well that time, after all, is very relative; indeed they are already looking forward to it! This state of consciousness simply helps to be far more relaxed and happy in the current here and now – devoid of all fears of dying and much of the heartache that comes with the losing of loved ones. **Homo Mysticum** is also not in the least burdened by the assorted religious dogmas that induce fear or gloom and doom in order to control people. It therefore enables a life of real freedom and great joy, provided it is actually authentic upon having personally experienced spiritual realities.

*"Our ideas about death define how we live our life."* Dag Hammarskjöld

Who is right and who is wrong is therefore the wrong question to ask. The more important question should be which one of the three perspectives will make us the most happy, healthy, wealthy and wise we can possibly be.

Our overall fears and worries in life either increase or decrease, all depending on this underlying perspective. And likewise with having real peace of mind and generally being in high spirits, or not. Perhaps, in the end it doesn't really matter whether our big picture view is only based on personal illusions or not; in terms of finding real happiness and success in life, what works best is obviously the right philosophy. While a life of chronic unhappiness indicates the need for a fundamental change of perspective.

We already mentioned that the three general perspectives are both broad and fluid in nature. This is especially so with the passing of time. When we're still young, we never even think about growing older. But eventually we all do. Time waits for no one. And life in itself, with all its many challenges and occasional difficulties, is a great teacher. So our core beliefs are quite likely to change over time.

Some agnostics or atheists will turn to religion for comfort. And some Believing Man will turn into atheists because they are very upset with God for losing a loved one, ignoring their prayers, or a host of other reasons. Sometimes *Homo Machina* and *Homo Credo* will make deeply mystical experiences that will completely change their outlooks and lives, giving them the deep certainty and peace of mind of *Homo Mysticum*.

***Current science is telling us in most certain terms that we are our bodies.*** This mainstream scientific view is promoted by governments via state schools, the higher education system, and by giving research grants only to approved scientists and researchers. Despite the many question marks raised by the latest insights into the totally mysterious and absolutely astonishing worlds of quantum physics, the reductionist and mechanical belief system is also promoted by mainstream media – sponsored by the 'almighty' pharmaceutical industry and other companies and organizations harboring all kinds of self-serving interests.

Alternative views are generally excluded or decried as heresy, respectively ridiculed as being just the playgrounds of the uneducated and unwashed masses that still need to cling to superseded superstitions. Supremacists of the atheistic kind privately – and increasingly publicly – consider the spiritual or religious to be rather dumb, people with both a low IQ and education. Welcome to the world of technocrats.

At best, people who experience different kind of realities are thought to be mentally unstable or simply a bit confused. The cause is said to be some kind of a still unproven yet much-believed-in chemical imbalance in their brains (more on this to come!), and therefore they are in urgent need of medication. Or at least, some form of sedation to keep them quiet and docile. In any case, when it comes to making all the important decisions in our modern societies, these people have to be ignored. Let the enlightened experts and smart technocrats decide what is best for them... or so they'd like it to be from now on.

But let's start to gently rattle this narrow cage of thought and inquiry and look a bit closer into the assorted absurdities of the absolutist views of *Homo Machina*. We will ask many questions and look into a lot of the evidence that portrays very different perspectives. First however, I'd like to entertain you with a story about **the adventures of Paul Schmitz, an incredibly unlucky**

**racist** whose life is about to be turned upside down. Completely. And most dramatically so.

It is an entirely fictional story, and although the conclusions reached are for real and hopefully meaningful to you as well, it is written in a rather lighthearted way, and is best read with a good dose of humor and a twinkle in the eyes.

There is absolutely no offense intended in any way whatsoever. However, allow me a word of warning: at times our story may appear to be(come) a bit morbid, perhaps even bordering on the macabre. So the fainthearted may need to 'fast-read forward' and skip some of the seemingly gory bits. But try to bear and read it with a grin or better, be simply amazed and amused! The 'tough' parts are actually illustrating some points rather nicely, perhaps even in a self-evident way. So here we go with the tale:

# The Unfortunate Racist

*Paul Schmitz* woke up feeling grumpy. His Jewish neighbor's wife must have cooked something smelly last night and he could swear the unpleasant odors were still wafting up the stairways. He hated Jews. And women were inferior beings anyway. They were only good for some things. Like you know. Plus cooking. And cleaning. Or bearing children to proudly follow in the footsteps of the righteous path as outlined by the Fuehrer and the Party. With bravery and honor.

Paul was a proud card-carrying member of the New Germany Party, the leading neo-Nazi organization that was spreading rapidly, particularly in the former East. He was looking forward to go to the party meeting tonight. Talk about the glorious past and the even more glorious future to come. And drink beer with his comrades, of course. Lots of beer.

Paul considered himself to be a good man. A good German patriot from good old Allemanic stock. He used to be a hard worker, before he was laid off from Allianz Stahlwerke, the large steel factory in Dresden that used to employ thousands of young hopeful Germans. Before those stinking Chinese communists started to sell the stuff at dumping prices, far below costs. Furious, he took a deep drag from his cigarette. His dark thoughts were suddenly interrupted by a sharp coughing attack, taking away his breath.

He was the archetype of the Aryan race. 100 percent. Tall, strongly built with fair skin, short-cropped, blond hair and piercing blue-eyes that moved quickly, revealing a sharp intellect, a man of high intelligence. Or so he thought. Paul just knew that his race was superior to all the others. The only purpose of colored people was to serve. Him and his compatriots. The New Reich that was about to be unveiled, destined to rule the world. Of course they would first need to weed out the unwanted elements. Like the Jews. Gypsies. And definitely those godless homosexuals. The weak and unclean.

Paul didn't like blacks either. Those smelly Africans and devil worshipping Muslims. Totally useless eaters, all of them.

He left his apartment early this morning, after a hearty breakfast of German rye bread, assorted cold cuts of meats and cheese, washed down with copious amounts of strong coffee. He was scheduled to present himself to the Arbeitslosenamt, the local Bureau of Labor, to sort out some paperwork and talk about those elusive new job prospects. As he crossed the street he turned to yell at a passing refugee from Sri Lanka: "Go home, you stinking pig!" and was immediately hit and run over by the speeding bus that appeared seemingly out of nowhere.

Witnesses were shocked as the accident scene was messy. Really messy. Blood and gore was just everywhere. And everyone agreed that there was no way the poor guy could have survived this.
Three months later the doctors woke Paul Schmitz from his induced coma and told him how lucky he was. That all his bones were completely shattered, but thanks to the availability of a donor they could replace the bones of his arms and legs with new ones. They had to use some artificial parts as well for his elbows, hips and knees. Plus some arteries. All *Made in Germany*, of course.

He was in agony and pain. Terrible pain. And yet he was glad to be alive, that the Teutonic gods had spared him so that he could continue to be of service to The Reich.
*Who was the anonymous donor*, he wondered one morning, feeling a bit better, almost euphoric, after the pain killers had fully kicked in. *It's such a noble and generous thing to do*, he thought and decided to ask his nurse.
'I can't reveal any personal details for privacy reasons. Only that he was a Turkish engineer who passed away suddenly from a heart attack a few hours earlier,' nurse Gertrud replied.
'He was listed on the German Registry of Organ Donors,' she added.

It hit Paul like a hammer. *He must have been a bloody Muslim!* he thought, feeling both alarmed and uncomfortable.

'You're a very lucky man, Herr Schmitz. There were actually two donors that helped to save your life,' his nurse continued. 'You have lost all your blood in the accident and during the ensuing operations, but there was a donor with the exact same blood type and rhesus factor who died just the night before.'

'Is there anything you can tell me about him,' Paul asked quietly.

'Only that it was actually a woman, still very young,' Gertrud offered and paused, looking sad before continuing, 'She was a student at the local university who committed suicide when her visa was cancelled and she was about to be deported back to Somalia, her home country.'

Slowly the news sunk in. It was a *woman* who had saved his life, and not only that, to top it off, it was a *black* woman! Paul started to suddenly feel delirious, not sure whether he was actually awake or just dreaming.

'You must rest now, Herr Schmitz,' his nurse ordered with her soft but resolute voice.

'Herr Professor Doktor Heinzmann himself is visiting soon to check your progress. He's the very best transplant surgeon in Dresden, indeed all of Saxony. Without him, you surely wouldn't be here now,' she added.

Paul suddenly felt weak and mentally drained. *David Heinzmann is a Jewish name, for sure,* he realized. He could not believe his luck, or should he say bad luck? First, his new bones were from a Muslim Turk. Second, all his blood came from a black African woman. And third, his new lease on life was given to him by a Jewish doctor. *It must be a dream. A very bad dream,* he thought before passing out.

A few months later Paul was well enough to be released. He started to drink even more than before his accident. Three to four litres of strong German beer a day washed down with a bottle of Doppelkorn, a popular German Schnapps with an alcohol content of 38% ABV. It helped him to feel better, for a while. Until he threw up after one of his many coughing fits. He still enjoyed a pack or two of his favorite cigarettes with his drinks, but inhaling was starting to get really painful at times.

These days he didn't feel too good about himself. He was confused about what had happened to him. He still attended all meetings of the New

German Party but he didn't dare to tell his comrades about what the nurse had told him. The truth about his donors. How would they react if they knew that he now had black African blood pulsing through his veins? Or that his bones once carried a Muslim, one of these filthy Turks that robbed good Germans of their jobs...

One morning, the pains in his abdomen got simply too much to bear and he finally called for an ambulance. His breathing was very painful too. Even worse, he had again discovered blood in his sputum.

He was really unlucky. The attending doctor diagnosed him with a severe alcoholic cirrhosis needing a liver transplant real soon. It was the only way he would survive. Then Paul suddenly got lucky. An organ donor was taken to the hospital for some urgent medical attention, but was pronounced dead on arrival.

Three surgeons and one anesthesiologist operated on Paul for 12 hours, assisted by several supporting nurses. When Paul awoke it was again nurse Gertrud who looked after him and told him the good news.
'Herr Professor Heinzmann and his team did again a very good job on you and all went well. There should be no complications and you should be out of here in no time,' she said with a warm smile.
'Do you know...?' Paul tried to ask her, but his voice trailed of.
'All I can tell you is that it was the generosity of an itinerant traveler, a Gypsy from Romania, that saved your life,' Gertrud said.

**By now, our proud German Neo-Nazi – once a 100% member of the Aryan race – was 'reduced' to being only 77% of his former glorious self.** (Transplanted bones now made up 10% of his body weight, assorted man-made medical supplies 3.5%, blood a further 7.5%, and the Gypsy liver another 2%.)

Upon his recovery and release, Paul had recurring nightmares and felt generally uneasy and nervous during the days. To know that his body was now composed of other people's body parts deeply disturbed him. He still attended the weekly party meetings with his fellow comrades but could no longer partake in the important drinking rituals that bonded them together.

Instead he had developed a taste for sugary food. He would gobble down any sweet stuff he could find, from chocolates and cakes, to cookies and pies, all washed down with lots of sodas. It helped him to feel better. To cope with his destiny.

During rehabilitation he was introduced to some basic relaxation and breathing techniques, so one day he decided to give it another try. He eventually overcame his animosity and joined yoga lessons given by an Indian teacher in one of the public housing estates that housed refugees from around the world. One evening the class was just about to conclude when they heard loud yelling and shouting followed by several big bangs. And suddenly the entire building was engulfed in flames and Paul fell unconscious, overcome by toxic fumes and the omnipresent smoke.

When he awoke in hospital, he was in pain. Terrible pain. Nurse Gertrud told him that they had to replace all his skin as he suffered from third degree burns to most of his body. He was suffering too much to ask her, but she already knew what Paul Schmitz wanted to know.
'It was a Chinese chef who just died from mushroom poisoning. The poor man collected local mushrooms that looked just like an edible Chinese delicacy, unfortunately ours are most poisonous,' she said, before adding, 'Lucky for you his wife donated his entire body for organ transplants.'

'What happened,' Paul asked weakly, writhing in agony.
'It was an arson attack by members of the New Germany Party. These neo-Nazi racists threw Molotov cocktails into a refugee home and killed 9 people, 22 got severely wounded, including yourself,' Gertrud revealed.
Paul remained silent, too surprised and shocked to say a word, and looked away. He didn't know, nobody had told him. Maybe his colleagues didn't trust him any longer?
'Police were able to arrest several members, but unfortunately, some could get away,' she said, before adding wishfully, 'I hope they will catch these cowards, put them in jail and throw away the keys!'

*By now, our proud card-carrying member of the New Germany Party – once 100% a member of the Aryan race – was further reduced to being*

**only 61% of his former glorious self.** (Transplanted skin now made up 16% of his body weight.)

Over the coming months Paul made good progress, his wounds were healing rather nicely thanks to the careful attention he had received from the wonderful staff at the Universitätsklinikum "Carl Gustav Carus", the University Hospital in Dresden. He had become quite friendly with his primary care physician, Professor David Heinzmann, a warm and jovial personality who liked to cheer up his patients with a joke or other words of encouragement. It was easy to like him and Paul almost forgot to mind the fact that Doctor Heinzmann was Jewish, once even presenting him with a beautiful box of delicate hand-made candles to celebrate Hanukkah, the Festival of Lights.

One day however, the good professor was very serious while he addressed Paul as he had tough news to convey.
'The bad news is that various test results have conclusively shown that there is life-threatening damage to both your heart and lungs,' the doctor said with a somber voice.
'You are suffering from pulmonary arterial hypertension caused by your lifelong smoking and the further damage sustained in the incident at the refugee asylum,' he continued and added, 'All that toxic smoke didn't help,' shaking his head slowly.
'The good news is that a heart–lung transplant will cure it,' he said a bit more cheerfully, before saying, 'And fortunately we have already identified a suitable donor whose organs are a perfect match for you.'

Once the procedure was done and Paul awoke from his narcosis, he looked at nurse Gertrud with asking eyes, but remained quiet.
'I shouldn't be telling you this, but it was an American Rabbi who was on a speaking tour in Europe and while visiting Germany, he suddenly passed away in his sleep,' she told him. 'May he rest in peace, Shalom.'
Paul looked bewildered but said nothing, drifting back into a drug-induced haze.

When he was released a few months later and went back to his former life, all seemed to be the same, but nothing really was. He still felt like he was the same person as ever, yet he looked rather differently at the world and its people. Paul continued to attend all weekly meetings of the New Germany Party, but now he did so as a police informer, secretly recording all proceedings and otherwise collecting evidence to be used against party leaders, and perhaps more importantly, the shadowy group of financiers behind them.

Paul had become active in bible-study groups, still attended regular yoga lessons, and participated in meditation classes given by Tibetan Buddhists. He desperately needed to come to terms with the upheavals in his life. Was there a reason why he was so unlucky yet fortunate at the same time? What was it that motivated all these people to be so kind and generous with their fellow human beings to donate their own bodies, in selfless service to mankind and science? He needed to understand the reasons why. He started to ponder the big questions in life. Is there life after death? Or are we dead forever and ever? Where do we come from and where do we go to? Who are we anyway? What was life all about? Is there a meaning to it all?

He knew now that the hateful activities and goals of his former colleagues were a total travesty to humanity, so very wrong, and he felt ashamed for his past contributions to that cause. He felt that he had an obligation to make up for his egregious mistakes and was determined to now play his part to stop them once and for all.

Paul had developed a severe form of diabetes over the last year, no doubt as a result of his ongoing and seemingly never-ending appetite for sweets and sugary soda waters. Kidney damage was aggravated by the strict regimen of immunosuppressive drugs he needed to take every day to suppress his immune system and prevent the rejection of the various organ transplants he had received. He was told the bad news during one of his many follow-up visits to the hospital.

'Unfortunately, we have diagnosed diabetes mellitus type 1, due to destruction of the beta cells in your pancreas, and very soon, it will cause complete renal failure,' Professor Heinzmann said with a stern expression on his face. 'By good luck, we have identified a suitable donor and are ready to immediately transplant both kidneys together with the pancreas,' he continued.

Later, Paul learned from nurse Gertrud that his anonymous benefactor was a visiting tourist from Korea, a Reverend of the Rainbow Alliance of Christ, who had unexpectedly passed away from AIDS related complications.

While he was recovering, final investigations by State Police and the Federal Office for the Protection of the Constitution had proceeded at a rapid pace and they were able to make a large number of spectacular arrests. They had dealt a crippling blow to the leadership of the New Germany Party and its financial backers.

Upon his renewed release from hospital and the ensuing months, Paul had become a star witness for the prosecution in a series of widely televised trials. It was decided that the best way to deal with radical racists was to fully expose the utter ugliness of their thoughts and actions, for all to see and ponder about. Paul now received a lot of hate mail and threatening phone calls. Police were providing him with around the clock security, but protection details were called off once all proceedings came to their successful conclusions.

One early morning Paul was walking towards his favorite café on Leipziger Strasse, enjoying the crisp fresh air that heralded a beautiful autumn to come, when he was suddenly confronted by three skinheads sporting their trademark shaven heads and military attire. They quickly surrounded him and without much ado started to beat him up. Viciously, without mercy. Their heavy boots kicked him relentlessly, and finally trampled on his face, beating it to a pulp. They only relented when they heard the approaching sirens of the alerted police cars rushing to the scene.

Once Paul was awoken from prolonged emergency and reconstructive surgeries, he was told the good news that at just the right time a matching donor could be found and that he now had a brand new face, ears and teeth, looking all handsome now. Plus that it was most unlikely now that a future wanna-be-attacker would actually be able to recognize him as Paul Schmitz. 'Do you know...,' he started to ask nurse Gertrud.

'He was an Indian computer wizard who died of acute alcohol poisoning when they celebrated the takeover of their startup by internet giant, Boozle,' she offered with an understanding voice.

*By now, our no-longer proud and former card-carrying member of the New Germany Party – once 100% a member of the Aryan race – was further reduced to being only 55% of his former glorious self.* (Transplanted heart and lungs, kidneys and pancreas, face and ears, plus a set of brand new teeth now made up 6% of his body weight.)

With the money and new identity papers given to him by the German government, Paul decided to travel the world, in search of answers. The biggest question on his mind was who he really was, his identity. After all, his sense of self, or body image, was rattled to the very core, his world and deeply held beliefs were thoroughly shaken and stirred, completely turned upside down.

Originally, he was a 100% German male, straight, and nominally only, a Christian. Now he wasn't sure who or what he was. After all he had the bones of a Turkish engineer who happened to be a practicing Muslim. Blood by a black African student girl pulsed through his veins. It was cleansed by a liver, courtesy of a Romanian Gypsy, and powered by the heart and lungs of an American Rabbi. His body was covered with the skin of a Buddhist from China, and cleansed by the kidneys and pancreas of a gay Korean Christian. The face he now wore was compliments of a Hindu computer guru from India, and assorted body parts were Made in Germany, Made in Japan, Made in USA, and of course these days, the ubiquitous, Made in China.

Paul spent the next six months in an ashram in Bangalore, India, to practice yoga techniques as taught by the old masters since time immemorial. He then immersed himself in Zen meditation in a Buddhist temple outside of Kyoto, Japan. The following months he spent working and studying the Kabbalah in a Kibbutz outside of Tel Aviv, Israel. Thereafter he moved on to a mountain retreat in Turkey to learn about Sufism, the esoteric dimension of Islam. His search for answers finally led him to a Catholic monastery hidden away in the pristine countryside of Italy. There he started to write down the lessons he had learned from his painful ordeals, and the insights into life and death he subsequently gleaned while traveling around the world.

His thoughts and life experiences took form over the coming months and were ultimately published as a book by a large publishing company in New York. It turned into an international bestseller, making Paul lots of money. A large part of it he donated to worthy causes. Like organizations that help to combat the scourge of racism or otherwise promote respect, peace and understanding among the people co-inhabiting planet Earth.

Furthermore, he bought nurse Gertrud a beautiful house in the leafy outskirts of Dresden. And Doctor Heinzmann – being the avid sailor – was very happy to receive a luxurious yacht complete with its own mooring in a posh North Sea resort town.

This fantastic tale of *The Unfortunate Racist* tells us many things, some are quite obvious and others a bit less so, at first. In the next chapter we will analyze what it means and gain some important first insights that will help us along the way to unravel the mystery of who we really are.

# First Conclusions

While Paul highly respected the advancements, even wonders, of modern science and medicine, he realized that we cannot just be our physical bodies.

There must be more to us than solely being a perfectly constructed and most efficiently operating machine that is controlled by a more or less intelligent brain... luckily for us, no matter how smart we may think we are, all of the really crucial bodily functions are steered autonomously via the autonomic nervous system, so our opinion or approval is neither required nor asked for!

*Paul's body now only consisted of about 55% of its original parts*, and yet he felt that he was exactly the same person as ever before! We could have easily continued the story by coming up with further dramas that required even more of his body parts to be replaced. For example, another little incident by say a scorned lover with a pair of scissors that now required a full penis, scrotum and testicles transplant (already a medical reality), and so on. But let's keep moving and see what kind of insights we might gain from his new reality.

Paul was the very same person as he was on that fateful early morning that started so badly. Sure, his thoughts had changed a lot alongside the both dramatic and traumatic experiences he went through. *Nevertheless he was still the very same person with his own individual character traits, a distinct personality, and very personal likes and dislikes, hopes and dreams. He did not suddenly assume or assimilate the differing personalities and preferences of his many donors.* Nor did his memories change from his own to partly his combined with partly the various memories his assorted benefactors had accumulated during their lifetime.

Yet, if we were solely our bodies and the sum total of its parts, then we would have to expect exactly such an outcome. Paul would be such a total mash-up of people, the seven generous donors, that it would require an entire team of psychologists for a great many years. They would need to analyze a wide spectrum of conflicting memories and disentangle the various personalities now inhabiting Paul's body and occupying his mind. That obviously did not happen, which leads us to our first insight that we must be more than just a body composed of trillions of cells.

Machine Man has somewhat understandably reduced us humans to a mere collection of chemical compounds swimming in mostly water – all held together by certain applications of the laws of physics, biology and biochemistry, some of which were partly proven and others simply assumed.

Fact is that the reasons why the many highly complex systems that make up our bodies have assembled and now live, repair and replicate themselves, all automatically and with the utmost efficiency, cannot yet be fathomed. To this very day, scientists essentially *explain it all with their absolute yet unproven belief* in sheer luck, pure coincidence, and the order out of chaos theory. Their scientific conclusions could be cheekily summarized like this:

1. *Some say that somehow something came out of nothing and acted upon the nothing to produce everything, all for no reason.*
2. *Some say that life was created for no reasons by an endless streak of good luck involving dumb and dead matter that nobody made out of nothing.*

Thereafter, these initial but ongoing feats of magic are believed to be further enhanced by the drive to survive: survival of the fittest is said to have powered evolution, even though, from this point of view, simple organisms would survive just fine and perhaps even better on their own, by remaining fully autonomous. So why should or would an accidentally derived single cell organism suddenly want to turn itself into a plethora of highly complex organisms?

A great many if not most people now believe that this is all they are. Bodies. Only a mass of chemicals, atoms and molecules that had randomly assembled over millions of years. A collection of meat and bones that will turn to dust and sooner or later fertilize the crops that will feed future generations.

Which brings us to yet another way of looking at the matter. The body you see in a picture of yourself say at age ten is not at all the same body as the one you see in a picture at age twenty! Strictly speaking, *Homo Machina* who fully identifies himself as being his body, will have to admit that ***the person in the earlier picture is actually already dead***. Gone. Turned to dust and so on.

How come? Simply because the cells in our bodies change entirely at differing intervals. There is a constant dying and renewal of cells taking place, all without us even thinking about it, respectively missing or mourning the parts that have already died. Furthermore, all of the sub-atomic particles ***within*** the atoms that make up the cells of our bodies change and get replaced with fresh ones too. Continuously.

And likewise it is with water. The total amount of water in an average person is about 60% of his body weight. This water is never the same, it continually changes. It is used in various bio-chemical processes, gets eliminated via our kidneys, or evaporates both through our breathing and perspiring. We need to replenish it every day. Yet we are not water. The dilution of ourselves by the ever changing water does not change our personality, thoughts and beliefs, hopes and dreams, feelings or memories.

Water comes and water goes in an never-ending cycle on a both local and global scale. The same is true with oxygen: normal blood oxygen levels in humans are between 95-100 percent. The different gases that make up the air we breathe constantly enter and leave our bodies. And so do the many micro-nutrients that constantly come and go. None of them dilute, diminish or change who we really are.

Biological life is a constant recycling process. The elements that make up the food we eat, digest and absorb into our bodies will get eliminated in the form of urine and stool. So now, just for fun but with a serious undertone, let's imagine a racist Ku Klux Klan member who was born in San Francisco and hates everybody. Everyone who is not white that is.

He doesn't realize that his father's body was quite possibly made up of the atoms and molecules that were once part of a Chinese railroad worker, and Jewish refugees escaping the Holocaust, plus some African Americans who escaped their slave masters on a cotton farm and moved West to participate in the big gold rush. His father consisted of all the people this proud but dumb KKK member has chosen, or been conditioned, to hate.

Maybe today his very own body partially consists of the very same elements that were once excreted by certain 'undesirables' after a particularly good meal, or regurgitated upon the consumption of a few drinks too many! All atoms and molecules get recycled, sooner or later, without exceptions. So even if the above or Paul's dramatic story doesn't yet convince diehards who like to cling to the absolute beliefs of Machine Man, it may hopefully point out the very real fallacies of racists.

The cells that make up our bodies could have come from anywhere and anybody who has previously lived on planet Earth. From the good, the bad, and the ugly. Physically speaking, we're all in this together, living on the same boat, respectively planet, that is floating in this particular part of the Universe.

The atoms and molecules making up our bodies could very well have been part of the body of an animal too. From maggots to dogs or pigs, and so on. Who knows, maybe the atoms that once made up the brains of a chicken, or its excrement, are now actually part and parcel of a racist's brain? Just kidding...

And yet, the whole ideology of racial supremacy is just so very ridiculous and hilarious (besides sad) that one simply has to make a bit of a joke about its proponents. After all, there is a French bonmot that aptly says, "C'est le ridicule qui tue," which means *ridicule kills*. We can and should apply this practice to all really bad ideas. Including the proposals of idiotic, corrupt or power-hungry politicians.

In this spirit of caricature, try to imagine the face of a very proud Brahmin (a member of the upper caste in India) who absolutely despises untouchables Dalits (the lowest caste) upon being told by his family guru that his own body actually consists of molecules of both dogs *and* dog eaters. Or picture the highly credentialed, superbly learned yet totally arrogant professor, a proud upper-class member of a race with an *assumed* superior intelligence, who is suddenly told by the laboratory department that his brain is actually made up of the molecules of a 'stupid cow' and a 'dumb ass.'

The list of funny examples could be endless, so let's leave the matter to your own vivid imagination. But we can safely conclude that *racism is a rather silly and unenlightened concept – even when considered from a purely materialistic perspective in life.*

Actually, even the most ardent racist would not refuse the gift of an organ transplant if he knew that it came from someone of a different race, creed or culture. Who would say 'No thanks' while facing a life or death situation? Who would say 'No' even in a lesser emergency and turn down say a replacement eye, tongue or penis? Or who would refuse to receive a life-saving blood transfusion if they knew that the blood actually came from a despised fellow member of the human race?

Maybe the racial origin of donated blood or organs should be told to every transfusion or transplant recipient – to help everyone understand the futility, silliness, even idiocy of racism (besides its ugliness). We could actually honor and celebrate the people who give this ultimate gift on a public website (on a voluntary basis), perhaps even with their picture and biography. This would encourage more people to become a donor. And it would also help to bring about increased awareness that currently, we are indeed all unique members of the human family.

Racism is ignorance about some very basic principles of science. Ultimately, racism is ignorance about our true identity, about who we really are. Hopefully, the conclusions we can draw from the above examples, or the insights derived from the vivid tale of Paul's trials and tribulations, will help to further the understanding that we are interconnected and dependent in a myriad of ways.

And this is even so when we look at the world purely through the 'eyes of matter' only, the physical reductionist understanding of Machine Man, or *Homo Machina*.

To knowingly be in this cycle of nature means to be a part of the rhythm of the universe. Our planet Earth is one of trillions of planets and stars 'out there'. Or is it really 'in there?' Is there an even larger reality looming beyond what we can perceive with our telescopes?

The microcosm of cells, molecules and atoms within our bodies also form galaxies of proportions that are totally beyond a single cell's ability to comprehend. This is even more so when we delve into the realms of the subatomic worlds that are composed of super-tiny parts and particles, like leptons, electron muon and tauon neutrinos, pion, kaon, K and eta mesons, protons, neutrons, lambda sigma, xi and omega baryons.

So, are we our physical bodies? Just pieces of meat, blood and bones? The answer is, No. We must be something else, or at least something more. Let's keep investigating!

# The DNA Question

Since a great many of the physical atoms and molecules that make up our bodies keep changing every moment of every day, perhaps what defines us or turns us into who we are is our DNA? Some proponents of Machine Man philosophy think that at least parts of our identity can be explained with this underlying software that regulates the growth of our cells.

Let's have a brief look into what science says about DNA:

1. Our genome (genetic material) can be compared to a cookbook that contains the instructions to make many kind of dishes; it is a book with 23 chapters (or chromosomes).

2. Instead of paper it is made up of the chemical deoxyribonucleic acid (DNA), a two-stranded molecule shaped like a double helix that consists of *four letters*, basic building blocks or nucleotides: *A* (adenine), *C* (cytosine), *G* (guanine) and *T* (thymine).

3. Each of the 23 chapters contains 48 to 250 million letters (A,C,G,T) without spaces, so **the book consists of a total of over 3.2 billion letters**.

4. The book includes about 20'000 different recipes (genes or short sequences of DNA) holding the instructions for the making of proteins in our bodies, like muscle cells, neurons, keratin (hair protein), haemoglobin (oxygen-carrying blood protein), and so on.

5. However, only about 2% of the human genome provides instructions for making proteins. 98% of human DNA consists of both ***non-coding*** and ***highly repetitive*** sequences (some are repeating over 1.1 million times); it is commonly called junk DNA as it appears to have no discernible (a.k.a. known) biological function.

6. Humans have one of the smallest genome of all living beings. For example, onions and garlic have 5 times more DNA than we do, other plants 50 times, and salamanders 20 times more. Amoeba

dubia, a single-celled eukaryote, has 670 billion base pairs of DNA making its genome 209 times larger than ours.

7. The reasons for the presence of so much non-coding DNA and the extraordinary differences in genome size (called C-value) among species represent a long-and-still-standing mystery known as the "C-value enigma."

8. Genes are continuously mutating; most of the mutations in the functional portion of the genome are actually harmful or damaging (called 'deleterious'). Furthermore, oxidative DNA damage happens over 10'000 times per cell per day, while other damage can be caused by exposure to radiation or various kind of chemicals.

Many people still believe the popular myth that their genes fully determine their physical features or personality, thanks to sensationalist but wrong headlines in the news. Some even worry that their genes are deciding their actual destiny, whether they will develop a particular disease or not.

But reality shows that **what could potentially happen does not actually have to happen**, for a variety of reasons. Some people may have a genetic propensity for heart disease yet will never develop heart problems (perhaps even though a parent or grandparent did). Others however who didn't have such a predisposition may nevertheless have serious issues with their hearts.

Life is continuously changing so things are rarely if ever written in stone. Perhaps it really is just like with the recipes in a cookbook; we can always adjust the instructions to suit our own particular tastes or circumstances, the availability of ingredients, and so on.

New research has shown that at least parts of our genetic material is actually changing somewhat during the course of our lives. Identical twins were long thought to be identical since they developed from just one fertilized egg, thereby originally containing the same set of genetic instructions. And yet, over the course of their lifetimes, even their genes will not completely stay the same.

*"I believe that the genome that you're born with is not the genome that you die with—at least not for all the cells in your body."* Carl E G Bruder, eminent geneticist.

Despite their initially equal DNA, identical twins are very often very different in their physical features, their personality and health. Therefore, our genes alone cannot be the one and only deciding factor in life.

**Epigenetics** has become the most exciting field of research over the last twenty years; it literally means **upon genetics**. Epigenetic factors control the actual expression or function of genes by switching some parts on and off (becoming active or dormant), or dimming a section here and there.

To a very large degree our genes are thereby regulated by environmental factors like our diet, and even the quality of our mother's diet, or whether she smoked or drunk alcohol during her pregnancy. Other important factors are our stress levels or social interactions with others, where we live, when we sleep or whether and how much we exercise.

New research into behavioral epigenetics suggests that even our emotional well-being (e.g. receiving plenty of maternal love or not) results in actual physiological changes in our gene expressions. Not to speak of its further psychological effects.

Some New Age authors go as far as saying that the latest insights of epigenetics show that we can directly influence our genes and their expression with our thoughts. That of course is vehemently denied by materialistic scientists. Who is right or wrong there?

Common sense would say that **they are both right and wrong at the same time**. Our individual thoughts are changing all the time, sometimes our thoughts are very positive and optimistic for one second, and rather dark and negative the very next. Therefore it would not make much sense to leave important biological matters like cell renewal or growth in the hands of our fickle minds that change on a moment to moment basis.

However, a persistent reduction in stress via meditation and other relaxation techniques has shown positive results in our gene expressions. And vice versa! So by learning to control and calm our minds, being happy within ourselves, and without by having mostly peaceful and pleasant interactions with other people, we can indeed influence the epigenetic expressions of our DNA.

It is therefore not a short term instant type of effect by our individual thoughts as that would be pretty chaotic and likely rather detrimental to our health. But still, it is an enduring and cumulative effect that is growing in size and importance over time. So small thoughts don't matter, but our continuous thoughts that become deeply held beliefs with all the associated behavior, do matter greatly.

How and where we live, what we think and feel, what we eat and drink, how we interact with people and the world, how much sleep or rest we get, and so on, does indeed control our genes. In other words, we have much to say in the matter. Therefore we can already conclude that we are not our DNA, or merely DNA-controlled biological robots.

The DNA in our individual cells does not think things through but rather executes a program. Or rather, many programs. It doesn't have personal desires or make decisions for us. Every moment of our lives we obviously can and do make fully independent conscious decisions and thereby we influence certain outcomes.

And that of course involves free will. In other words, there must be someone, like you and me, who independently thinks and freely makes decisions, thereby exerting our individual free will. Yes, I know. Free will is one of the latest attempted victims of Machine Man as they seriously deny that it even exists. As often, contrary to common sense. But let's leave that easily-debunked theory for the chapter *Neurofiction*.

So just how special or important is our DNA anyway? Let's see. Chimpanzees are our closest living evolutionary relatives with a 96 percent genetic similarity, the Abyssinian cat is 90% similar, while bananas share about 60% of our DNA.

The difference in the genetic makeup of all human beings is only 0,1 percent. In other words, in terms of DNA we humans are 99.9 percent identical. And yet, we are all totally different beings in every sense of the word. No one is alike and that is true way beyond the merely different genetic or biological make-up.

Data scientist Riccardo Sabatini demonstrated that a printout of *the human genetic code would fill about 262'000 pages, out of which only 500 pages are unique to each one of us* as an individual person.

The well documented phenomena of *twin strangers* (doppelgänger, or double-walker) may also add some insights here. There are people who are quite literally doppelgangers of each other. They really look alike even though they are totally unrelated and live in very different parts of the world. So, since even strangers with biologically unrelated DNA can look pretty much the same, we could say that after all, our individual genetic code does not seem to turn us into who we really are.

Overall, the divergence in DNA between people is so small that it simply cannot explain the vast and total difference in our personalities. In terms of our characters, we really are totally unique. Our likes and dislikes, our thoughts and feelings, our dreams and desires, our strengths and weaknesses, our choices and creations, and our memories and experiences in life really are very different from anyone else's. Regardless of the almost total sameness of our human DNA. Or even the fully identical DNA of identical twins.

We have seen in the story of *The Unfortunate Racist* that Paul has only about fifty percent of his original body parts left. Prior to his many organ and tissue transplants, Paul's body contained 100% of his original DNA. But by now he would have lost about half of it. The missing parts all had his own individual DNA codes, but these are now gone.

If the total person and personality called Paul Schmitz were just the sum total of his DNA and so much of it is now gone, quantitatively speaking in terms of the total number of cells, he simply could not be his complete original self anymore. He would only be about 50 percent of his former self, with much of his memories, intelligence, abilities and overall consciousness missing to the point that even his own mother would not recognize him anymore. Not to speak of he himself!

There is only one way this practically 50 percent loss of DNA and its corresponding personality problems would not stand up to this train of thoughts. This possibility however is not even being suggested by the most ardent of Machine Man scientists. There simply is no genetic or other mechanism conceivable, not to speak of available, to do such a feat! But just for fun and purely analytical reasons, let's indulge in this potential fantasy anyway.

Quite simply, we would have to postulate that every single moment, every single memory would need to get inscribed and stored in every DNS helix of every single of our 37 trillion cells on a continuous 24/7 basis (even while we sleep because we can still remember some of our dreams even decades later) as we continuously make new experiences and thereby create ever more memories. That would actually be the only way to say that we would not lose 50% of who we are if indeed we were our DNA.

*"Study of the genetics of human memory is in its infancy."* Wikipedia

Coming back to reality, there is an additional matter we need to consider. Paul's remaining fifty percent of DNA got mixed up and convoluted with all kinds of DNA strands by strangers, of the people who had so generously donated their body parts.

And of course, the cells of those body parts contained ***their*** own set of DNA. So, if some members of the Machine Man tribe would be correct in their assumption that we are all just expressions of our individual DNA, then ***the seven donors physiological and psychological identities would now also be included in the actual Paul of today.***

He would therefore also possess and express their assorted character traits, their distinctive personalities, individual hopes and dreams, besides bits and pieces of their manifold memories, knowledge and abilities. Therefore, he would be a total mash-up or mixture of a person and have a complete identity crisis or psychosis for the rest of his life. Never really knowing who is who, what, where and when.

All of the organs and tissue Paul has received were **Allografts**, the term used for transplants between **two genetically non-identical members** of the same species, as are most human tissue and organ transplants. Due to this genetic difference, the recipient's immune system will identify the organ as a foreign object that needs to be eliminated. To prevent such transplant rejection, patients will have to take **immunosuppressive** drugs for the rest of their lives, thereby lowering the body's resistance.

Nevertheless, this foreign DNA or 'external software' is now present in Paul's body and continues to do its job in the mitosis and other cell functions of the transplanted organs and tissue – without producing mental or psychological dramas. Or physical deformities.

If we really were our DNA, then Paul would be a totally different person with a completely changed personality today. And yet he isn't. And neither is anyone else of the great many real-life people worldwide who have actually gone through these life-changing procedures over the last seven decades.

Yet another fun way to look at the DNA question is this: *our bodies consist of about 37 trillion of individual cells* (of about 200 different types), however the number of microorganisms that share our bodies is far greater.

This so-called *human microbiome* consists of about *100 trillion microbial cells* – it is the sum total of microorganisms living on the skin, in the saliva and mucosa of our mouths, in our lungs and eyes, in the biliary and gastrointestinal tracts (they include bacteria, fungi, and archaea), and many other places.

All of these microorganisms make up between 1-3% of our total body mass. *The real remaining percentage of Paul's own original DNA is therefore even lower than the 55 percent* previously calculated.

*Foreign bacterial cells outnumber human cells by a factor of ten to one.* Some estimates say that it is 'only' three to one because the estimated number of human cells is 37 trillion rather than 10 trillion. Regardless, Machine Man himself concedes that we humans are indeed more bacteria than we are ourselves! Furthermore, when we consider that the genome size of every single bacterial cell is by magnitudes larger than one of our own cells, we could say that *we are literally swamped by foreign DNA*, potentially leaving a number of rather interesting open questions. And more morbid thoughts. Like, who is who and what is what?

Actually, it gets even more crowded: *the human virome is estimated to contain a staggering 380 trillion viruses* of all kinds. DNA and RNA viruses, bacterial viruses (bacteriophages), eukaryotic viruses, endogenous retroviruses, archaeal viruses, and so on.

Research about the human virome is still in its very infancy. Yet it is already known to be a predominant component of the microbiota in our intestines, and rather than making us sick, it contains a huge amount of crucial information; it seems to play a fundamental part in the healthy functioning of our immune systems. So there sure is plenty of all kinds of mostly unknown DNA swirling around in our bodies, doing a great many things we don't know much about! (Imagine some scary music here.)

*Fortunately, it doesn't look like these legions of foreign entities have any say about who we really are when it comes to our personalities, individual desires and so on.* However they still greatly influence the health of our bodies and thus the quality of our lives. For example, the hundreds of kinds of bacteria in our intestines are producing over thirty types of neurotransmitters, including one that is touted to be the 'happy' molecule serotonin (more on that to come in chapter *Neurofiction*).

So, our physical DNA slightly changes over the course of a lifetime. And, how our DNA is epigenetically expressed or applied changes even more. Continuously. Furthermore, we are hosting hundreds of trillions of cells and biological agents containing lots of foreign DNA.

And yet all this DNA and the many ongoing changes will not result in a modification of our character or identity. It seems to be a bit like changes in software. It results in deterioration and improvements. Software performs important functions in a computer, yet it is different from the hardware part of it. And similarly, it is not the user of the computer or the programmer who has coded it.

Our genes are the software of the cells while our overall body is the biological version of hardware. We are both the users and up to a point the programmers of biological machines. But we are not the machines.

In conclusion, are we our DNA? Or partly foreign DNA? Are we the recipes or assembly manuals of our proteins, the instructions of a cookbook? Just strings of deoxyribonucleic acid that are only partially useful, highly repetitive, widely damaged and arguably badly designed, besides somewhat changing and controlled by the whims of our environment, respectively our behavior and lifestyle choices?

The answer is again, No. We must be something else, or at least something more. We'll have to keep looking!

# Brain Matters

We have already come to the preliminary conclusion that we are unlikely to be just sophisticated pieces of flesh and bones, or strands of DNA of which more than 98 percent is non-coding. So maybe it is all happening 'up there'? Since Paul still has his original brain, we now have to answer the obvious question: *are we our brains?*

Is it the brain that makes us who we really are? A great many people certainly seem to think so, professionals and amateurs alike. After all, the human brain is by far the most complex organ; it forms the center of our nervous system that consists of the actual brain, our spinal cord, and a variety of peripheral nerve cell clusters (ganglia).

But we also have a kind of *second brain* that is in our intestines and contains an amazing 100 million neurons which is more than what we have in our spinal cords. Commonly we call it 'gut instincts' while experts of neurogastroenterology refer to it as the 'backup brain' because it works independently of any control by the brain. It is thought to influence our moods, what kind of diseases we get, and even some of our decision making.

Furthermore, and perhaps most importantly, we also have *a third 'little brain' in our heart*. An estimated 40,000 neurons form its own intrinsic nervous system which is directly linked via the 80-90% afferent vagus nerve to the brain, which means that it sends eighty to ninety percent of the information signals from the heart, lungs and digestive tract to the brain with only about 10 to 20% going the other way. Rather contrary to what one might think.

So the heart is not just a pump and probably a lot more important for our overall health and quality of life than is currently being acknowledged. Indeed, the heart, long considered to be the seat of love, feelings, and even wisdom, was shown to be closely involved in intuitive extrasensory perceptions in a clinical trial, as we shall see later in chapter *Beyond Machine Man*. For now, we could say that a happy heart is likely to also be a healthy heart that will ensure the perfect functioning of our brains.

Much insight into the brain has been gained since the 1990s that was proclaimed to be the *Decade of the Brain*. In the meantime, many previously cherished dogmas got overturned. And at least initially, ever more fancy promises were made – most enthusiastically and loudly by the mass media, pharmaceutical industries, and other self-interested parties.

Moreover, a very wide range of 'new' sciences were born, respectively simply went through a commercial rebranding exercise. The word 'Neuro' got suddenly added in front of almost too many disciplines to count just because it attracted a lot more attention and thus bigger investments. It's a bit like the currently fashionable word 'blockchain' that guarantees any company ever more injections of new funds by perhaps gullible investors.

Let's have a brief look at some of the refurbished science: the rather boring field of economics got spruced up and became *neuro*economics, promising to solve the mystery of how economic decisions are made by looking deep inside the brain. Then we now have the exciting discipline of *neuro*marketing that wants to forecast the tastes and behavior of fickle consumers who often do the most unexpected.

Machine Man philosophy has become *neuro*philosophy that claims to be able to resolve the mind and consciousness conundrum with the latest of neuroscience. *Neuro*theology of course is not too far behind trying to explain away people's stubborn belief in a God of any kind by simple neuronal activity somewhere in the brain. Other examples of modernized disciplines include *neuro*architecture, *neuro*psychology and *neuro*aesthetics...

Social justice warriors are not to be outdone either and talk about *neuro*sexism, while armchair warriors in the Pentagon already salivate over the prospects of *neuro*wars that could further flood their coffers with freshly printed money.

We will closely look into the promises, facts and myths of neuroscience and other matters of the mind and consciousness in the following chapters. Here, we will first focus on purely biological reductionist views of our brains and what the latest research really says about our identity. Or rather, what is doesn't say.

There are different kind of cells that make up our brains:

Cell types like blood vessels or non-neuronal glial cells surround the actual nerve cells, or neurons, in the brain and other parts of the nervous system. Their function is to supply neurons with oxygen and nutrients, destroy pathogens and remove dead nerve cells. They renew normally through mitosis and therefore we can apply the very same insights we have already made in chapter *First Conclusions* while discussing Molecular Turnover.

For more than one hundred years, brain scientists **believed** that these non-neuronal cells (called neuroglia) would not be involved in the actual communication process of signals between neurons. Modern research however has discovered that they do indeed modulate neurotransmission, thus overturning long-held scientific theory – perhaps making posthumous fools out of renowned scientists who at the time loudly ridiculed their more freethinking fellows (a.k.a. open-minded or real scientists), now proved to be correct.

Equally so, for hundreds of years it was said and believed that brains cells, or neurons, are always the very same and don't renew anymore after a certain age. Hence the popular saying that we just got a bit dumber upon destroying some of our brain cells after a good night out drinking a bit too much.

And yet, it has now been conclusively shown that neurons also continue to grow, change and renew. This adult neurogenesis (birth of neurons) is an ongoing process where neural stem cells (NSCs) create new neurons in the dentate gyrus of the hippocampus and the subventricular zone lining the lateral ventricles (and according to some experts in the neocortex as well). For normal healthy adults this process continues throughout old age.

Another cherished belief bites the dust: we do indeed live in interesting and amazing times!

*"Interestingly, stem cells are found not only in these regions, but also have been isolated from areas that are non-neurogenic such as the septum, striatum, spinal cord, cerebral cortex, corpus callosum, and optic nerve and eye. In culture, these cells are multipotent and can give rise to neurons and glia. However, cells isolated from areas outside of the hippocampus and subventricular zone require high levels of FGF-2 [a gene encoding a protein of the Fibroblast Growth Factor family] in order to give rise to neurons, rather than only glial cells."* (Neurogenesis in Adult Brains by Fred H. Gage and Henriette Van Praag)

So how important is our brain? Quite obviously it seems to be rather important despite the fact that we have no clue about most of its ascribed functions, never mind what is being said by some, or believed by many, as we shall see!

**Could we live with half a brain?** Yes, as incredible as that may sound, we can!

Hemispherectomy is an operation where one half of the brain (a cerebral hemisphere) is surgically removed, disconnected, or disabled. Since 1923, it has been successfully performed hundreds of times. And perhaps best of all, this rather radical surgery does not affect who we really are!

A patient's personality, memory, or sense of humor is the same as before. There is no part that has suddenly gone missing. Relatives and friends will still instantly recognize the person and be able to continue their previous relationships just like before the operation.

At worst there are only minimal changes in cognitive function (concerning the mind). But normally, patients show actual improvements; they test above average in intelligence tests and have otherwise increased intellectual capacities. Like superior language skills, despite the removal of the left hemisphere which is believed to contain the classical language zones.

So why is someone with half a brain still the same person? Machine Man scientists say that it only shows that the brain has a great deal of extra capacity without giving any evidence of how or why that would be so. Other scientists however freely admit that such an argument is simply a dodgy excuse for those who cannot explain something or accept facts that are contrary to their deeply-held beliefs!

Perhaps this is a good time to clean up a few more commonly held myths. Like the one that says that we only use ten percent of our brain: all *research clearly shows that there are no inactive areas in our brain and that we use the full 100 percent of it.*

Furthermore, it is an established fact that evolution excludes any and all wastefulness. Our brain was shaped by natural selection just like other organs; it only weighs two percent of our body's weight yet uses about 20% of its energy to function!

Therefore, brains are metabolically very expensive to both grow and operate. Evolution would simply not permit the wasting of resources by building a totally inefficient organ that is only very moderately used. Organisms with such high cost brains that operated with only 10% power would naturally get deselected and thereby excluded from the gene pool.

Another old but inaccurate belief is the 19th century tale that some of us are 'left-brained' and others are 'right-brained,' that the right hemisphere of the brain is about emotions and creativity while the left side is all about logic, analysis and reason. Fact is that *there is no hemispheric dominance* and that both hemispheres work together.

Also, *many parents still falsely believe* that the first three years of their child's life is the most important for the development of the brain and that an 'enriched environment' is needed to enhance the capacity for learning. And that failing to provide rich and diverse stimuli will put their children at a disadvantage because they would have lost intellectual capacities that cannot be recuperated later in life.

Fact however is that ***our brains keep growing, changing and adapting throughout our lives.*** The widely accepted conclusions of neuroplasticity demonstrate continuing changes both in individual neurons as well as larger-scale reorganizations (cortical remapping) of our brains based on external stimuli from the environment (which includes potential injuries), as well as our thoughts, emotions and behavior.

We have already talked about people living with half a brain. ***Could we live without a brain and still function normally***? That really sounds like a silly question, doesn't it?

And yet, it does happen. It is a well-established medical fact: there are people who function perfectly well, essentially without having a brain!

*"There's a young student at this university, who has an IQ of 126, has gained a first-class honors degree in mathematics, and is socially completely normal. And yet the boy has virtually no brain."* Professor John Lorber, British neurologist at Sheffield University, UK.

Hydrocephalus is a medical condition that was already described by Hippocrates more than 2000 years ago. The term is derived from the Greek words *hydro* (water) and *kephalos* (head) and refers to an accumulation of cerebrospinal fluid within the brain which causes increased pressure inside the skull. It can affect newborns as well as adults. While there are some theories, the actual causes of hydrocephalus are still not understood.

During infancy, the condition prevents the brain from growing so the person has very little or no brain tissue at all. In adults, it causes the brain to shrink. Computed tomography scans (CAT scans) of the above-mentioned student showed only a ***one millimeter thin layer of brain cells*** while the rest of his skull was filled with cerebrospinal fluid.

Cerebrospinal fluid (CSF) is a colorless body fluid in the brain and spinal cord; it keeps the brain tissue buoyant, acting somewhat like a shock absorber to prevent injuries. It also delivers nutrients to the brain cells and removes waste. CSF circulates between the cranium and spine and compensates for changes in the amount of intracranial blood volume.

While these functions are surely important for the basic biological functioning of the brain, there are no suggestions that CSF might be involved in any of the higher brain functions like thinking, and so on.

*"Scores of similar accounts litter the medical literature, and they go back along way, but the important thing about Lorber is that he's done a long series of systematic scanning, rather than just dealing with anecdotes. He has gathered a remarkable set of data and he challenges, **How do we explain it?**"* Patrick Wall, British neuroscientist and Professor.

Dr. Lorber has documented more than 600 scans of people with hydrocephalus and categorized them into the following four groups: a) almost normal brains b) 50-70% of the cranium filled with CSF c) 70-90% filled with CSF, and d) where **95% of the cranial cavity was filled with cerebrospinal fluid.**

Less than 10% of the studied cases were in the last, most severe category. Half of the people in this group were seriously retarded, yet the other half had **IQs higher than the average 100.**

Critics say that there must be some kind of error in the interpretation of the CAT scans, without saying how, where or why such mistakes could have been made. Professor Lorber himself conceded that he did not quantify the exact amount of missing brain cells and stated:

*"**I can't say whether the mathematics student had a brain weighing 50 grams or 150 grams, but it is clear it is nowhere near the normal 1.5kg** and much of the brain he does have is in the more primitive deep structures that are relatively spared in hydrochephalus."*

He added, "The cerebral cortex of the brain is probably responsible for a great deal less than most people imagine."

Fact is that there are people living absolutely regular lives without having many or any brain cells. And yet they are able to function perfectly normal in society, indistinguishable from anyone else; they have families, jobs, and so on.

Another most amazing fact is that there is no medical explanation as to why people with this condition are able to feel sensations like hot and cold, have a sense of touch, can speak and understand spoken words, hear and see things, or have full motor control – when **the areas thought to be responsible for these functions are devoid of neurons**, and instead, are only filled with cerebrospinal fluid.

The cerebral cortex, normally filled with brain cells, **is believed to** play an important role in cognition and perception. Processes **are thought to** include attention, formation of knowledge and memory, solving problems and making decisions, comprehension of language, evaluating and judging, general awareness, personality and consciousness.

And yet there are perfectly well-functioning, intelligent people with a cerebral cortex full of a liquid that has nothing at all to do with any of these functions. And the very brain cells that are thought to provide them are completely or mostly absent.

It is important to note that essentially **all scientific beliefs about what really happens in our brains are not really proven facts; they are only theories, models and ideas.** There is no proof of any of these working assumptions. Some scientists believe certain theories while others have postulations of their own. The language used by neuroscientists is always vague for this very reason, from Wikipedia:

*"A widely accepted **theory** regarding the function of the brain's prefrontal cortex is that it serves as a store of short-term memory. This **idea** was first formulated by... Theories of frontal lobe function can be separated into four categories: Single-process **theories**, Multi-process theories, Construct-led theories, Single-symptom theories... **Other theories** include..."*

*"Scientists **have indicated** an integral link... Shimamura proposed Dynamic Filtering Theory to describe the role of the prefrontal cortex...Miller and Cohen **proposed** an Integrative Theory of...The two **theorize** that... conclude that the implications of their theory can explain... Once **the concept** of working memory was established... these neuropsychological findings **contributed to the theory**..."*

*"Several studies **have indicated**... It **is believed** that at least some of the human abilities to feel guilt or remorse, and to interpret reality, are dependent on... It is also **widely believed** that the size and number of connections in the prefrontal cortex relates directly... And it is **theorized that**, as the brain..."*

So, are we our brains? Perhaps the answer is not fully conclusive yet, but it sure looks increasingly unlikely: if we can indeed live without or much of a brain, we must be something else, or something more.

Let's delve deeper and look at many more facts, besides exposing further fiction!

# Neurofiction

Many believers of the Machine Man theory of life believe that the advancements in neuroscience have already answered much of what is to be discovered about our brains, with the rest to be discovered very soon.

This total myth has been, and continues to be, highly promoted by the mass media and other self-interested parties. In the USA alone, the corporate media receives more than six billion dollars per year in advertising money from a highly unscrupulous pharmaceutical industry that likes to imply that they do know what their highly profitable psychotropic drugs are doing to the human brain, even though they don't have much of a clue (as we shall see in chapter *Medical Tales* and its extensive chapter *Notes*).

Academies of science in turn want to keep receiving large amounts of government money, so it literally pays to eternally keep people's hopes high by making a lot of promises. The sad truth is that **all** research grants paid for by our tax dollars only goes to Machine Man projects, no matter how silly or outright laughable they may be. So as a matter of course, their undertakings are **always** of a physical reductionist, mechanical and materialistic nature.

The bureaucratic and technocratic elite likes to think, or rather, **believes**, that strictly reductionist scientists are the only smart ones (when the actual reality and the judgment of history is not so kind). Therefore, any alternative explanation is simply being ignored or ridiculed. And any alternative research proposal has absolutely no chance to get funded, no matter how smart or promising its design may be.

The time-poor medical profession too likes to prescribe psychoactive pills for any and all ills that are falsely attributed to the brain. Indeed, there are many studies that show how these highly dubious and dangerous drugs are well and truly over-prescribed (some toddlers get drugged-out before their brains even have a chance to start developing). That the pharmaceutical companies have well-established very close and most generous relationships with doctors is perhaps not a coincidence either.

Silicon valley billionaires also love to peddle the story of a technological singularity where we will merge with smart machines and augment our mental and physical abilities to the point of living happily ever after on planet Earth. Soon, very soon, we can all forget about disease or death. Well, at least the wealthy who can afford it all, and get to eternally rule us all. Or so they hope and dream their grandiose yet futile dreams (as we shall see).

Hollywood producers jumped on the bandwagon too and made movies that suggest that we are so very close or indeed already able to download our brains into external computer hard drives. And so many of the totally uninformed but nevertheless fully convinced and converted currently believe it all.

One social media contact of yours truly, a computer security specialist, has recently published an article warning about the acute dangers of hackers (private or otherwise) being able to access our minds and download our passwords. Such is the state of hype, promise and expectation. And we shall happily debunk it all within these pages!

The sum total of all this most enthusiastic reporting on amazing brain breakthroughs falsely raised hopes among the public that new cures will be available very soon, or are already available. The problem is that nothing could be further from the truth. And nobody has an interest to tell the truth. Quite to the contrary.

***All proponents of the Machine Man explanation of life have philosophical, political or profit motives to keep promoting their fantasies.*** So any and all proof that their narrative could be totally wrong will not get any exposure. It simply pays to keep us in the dark. And it is also far easier to keep a forever fearful but eternally hopeful population under control. Just dangle a carrot in front of the donkey and you won't need to use the stick.

Machine Man says that our brains create our minds and that all mental problems are due to some kind of biological or biochemical defect within our skulls. In other words, it's all happening up there, or not, because of some sort of deficiency or abnormality. And yet, to this very day, ***there is not even one single biological test available that could determine a psychological problem of any kind.*** Despite the countless billions of mostly other people's money (a.k.a. taxpayers) already spent.

The task force assigned to find some kind of biological marker to include in the latest, fifth-edition of the *Diagnostic and Statistic Manual (DSM-5)* failed miserably, despite the huge efforts made by a rather unholy alliance between assorted scientists and the marketing departments of pharmaceutical giants.

This 947 page reference book is published by the American Psychiatric Association (APA) and constitutes the principal (and essentially global) authority for all psychiatric diagnoses and treatment recommendations. Naturally, the pharma industry is most interested to find biological or chemical origins for just about every mental disturbance (real, imagined or invented) as it enables them to sell more of their psychoactive concoctions.

To their utter disappointment, there are no clinical chemistry or medical biochemistry tests to be found that could diagnose any psychological disorder. And neither could anything be identified through genetic tests or the latest kind of brain imaging tests.

***There is absolutely nothing that can actually show the difference between a totally healthy person and a person suffering from schizophrenia, depression, dementia, anxiety, agitation, mania, paranoia, psychosis, bipolar disorder or any other mental disorder.***

In other words, modern psychiatry and psychology still needs to use the very same old methods as ever before to determine what could possibly be wrong: they need to talk with patients and their relatives, have them answer questionnaires, and do clinical observations.

What about those colorful pictures we get to see in the media? Don't they prove that neuroscientists know exactly what is going on in the brain, that they can literally watch our neurons firing (the changing of the frequency of electrical discharges) while we are thinking? They said so on TV, right? Let's see what is actually possible and what is not.

But first, let me acknowledge and appreciate the amazing technical knowledge, professional insights, logical arguments, and meticulous research of Swiss neuroscientist, pharmacologist and whistleblower, Dr. Felix Hasler, in his book *Neuromythologie.*

It is a highly referenced work and proved to be an invaluable source of knowledge and information in the writing of this chapter. Indeed, it is a book that pharmaceutical companies likely want to banish and stay hidden in obscurity! (Currently available in German only; see chapter *Notes* for more information.)

Since 1980, Magnetic resonance imaging scans (**MRI**) are able to **show the anatomy of the brain and its structures**, a bit like an X-ray. These structural imaging machines need careful calibration and are prone to mistakes. And so are the people who operate them. Or those who **try to make sense** of the images obtained. Radiologists even invented the term **UBOs – unidentified bright objects** – to refer to whatever they can't explain.

Yet MRI scans can only help us identify actual anatomical problems like the appearance of a brain tumor, its potential spreading, a physical injury, or a brain anomaly (like the ones we have discussed in the previous chapter, *Brain Matters*).

In the beginning of the 1990s, *functional Magnetic Resonance Imaging* (*fMRI*) machines were introduced to neuroscience that purport to measure the actual functioning of our brain, venturing beyond its mere anatomy and structure. While this sounds impressive at first, we need to understand what is actually being measured and what is not.

In short, ***it only measures the difference in blood flow.*** The **theory** behind fMRI technology is that sections of the brain are active where there is more blood flow. That in turn shows a higher consumption of oxygen in those areas.

The brain does not store either oxygen or glucose, its primary source of energy. Therefore both ingredients need to be constantly supplied via our blood. So as neural activity increases in certain places, the local blood flow increases too. And oxygen-rich blood will replace oxygen-depleted blood about two to three seconds later.

Does that mean that scientists can actually watch or even understand our brain at work in real time as it is implied by some and believed by many? No, not at all.

***The famous colored pictures are only obtained after the completion of the actual measuring,*** by performing complex mathematical calculations on a computer. The pretty pictures ***are just a graphical depiction of the statistical distribution of time-dependent blood flows and oxygen consumption.*** In other words, they are only a visualization aid and not the real-time measurement or depiction of neuronal activity of the brain.

In animal brains it was shown that most of the time there was indeed a correlation of brain activity and oxygen consumption. However, other studies have revealed the very opposite: ***an increase in neuronal activity sometimes leads to less rather than more blood flowing*** – as measured by a tightening of blood vessels instead of their expected expansion.

Put simply, the very theory (of hemodynamics) behind fMRI technology could be wrong, or only partially right.

So while evaluating euphoric media reports about the latest brain breakthroughs we really need to distinguish between serious and populist neuroscientists: the latter are usually the ones making outlandish and highly publicized claims, while the former are far more realistic, modest and quiet.

Indeed, many of them have actually become neuroskeptics; they fully realize the old adage that the more you do know about something, the more you are aware of how little you really understand.

Fact is, not everyone who plays around with a fashionable neuroimaging device understands the actual assumptions that were made, the as of yet totally unproven nature of theories, or the many technical limitations involved.

Some, or perhaps most of them, are simply psychologists who are not really qualified in the fields of neuroscience or neurobiology that require detailed knowledge of physiology, anatomy, biochemistry, besides the molecular biology of neurons and neural circuits. Not to speak of the other areas of expertise involved in fMRI scans like radiology, mathematics, or statistics.

*These scans are simply prone to many kinds of mistakes.* From faulty human designs, incorrect interpretations, apparent simplifications, flawed designs or erroneous process decisions, to a variety of technical errors, structural or statistical correlation problems, and unproven assumptions, like the assignment of certain anatomical areas of the brain to specific fMRI signals.

A seriously funny illustration to highlight the false-positive rates inherent in fMRI studies was made at the 2009 Human Brain Mapping conference, where a team of mischievous scientists presented the results of fMRI scans that subsequently became famous as *The Salmon of Doubt*.

Craig Bennett, Abigail Baird, Mike Miller, and George Wolford put a large salmon into a fMRI scanner and showed it pictures of people hugging or shaking hands, etc. Afterwards, they did the usual statistical interpretation of the scan results. And indeed, pictures showed a higher brain activity in certain parts of the fish brain. The hilarious part of the story is that *the fish was actually already dead* before the scan even began!

The authors of the study simply wanted to demonstrate the importance of making a *multiple comparisons correction*, a frequent omission and source of errors that is capable of showing brain activity in a dead fish. Oops.

Psychological research using fMRI scans are based on the **assumption of the localization of function**: they try to assign specific mental functions to particular areas in the brain, despite the lack of any evidence for this assumption!

Dr. Hasler points out that this is essentially like trying to get to know the functions of various computer programs by measuring the consumption of electricity while the computer performs these functions.

For example, **the anterior cingulate cortex** (ACC) is thought to be the link between emotions and cognition ('the mental action or process of acquiring knowledge and understanding through thought, experience, and the senses'). **Yet the ACC gets equally activated in a whole range of completely unrelated situations:**

Like, when people get tickled while being scanned. When lovers are freshly in love. While undecided voters looked at pictures of a certain female politician who kept failing in presidential elections. When men got reminded that they are indeed mortal. When women were asked to choose a potential sexual partner.

Or when optimists imagined positive developments. While vegetarians looked at pictures of animals getting abused. When multi-lingual persons have to choose the right words. When people addicted to food received a chocolate milk-shake. And so on and so forth.

**Another problem is that of wrong timing** of what and when something actually happens: the results of fMRI scans are measured **as an average over several seconds**. The actual haemodynamic response (dynamics of blood flow) however takes a few hundred milliseconds. And constant changes in neuronal activity happen in a few milliseconds only!

And while scanners may eventually be improved in terms of speed and accuracy, that would still not change **the fundamental issue: the indirect and therefore imprecise measuring of what is going on.** It simply takes time for blood flows to change and oxygen or glucose absorption to register.

Besides, each person's body is very different at the time of measuring too. From its age to its current health condition, and a variety of other ever changing, individual and therefore incomparable circumstances.

Indeed, **one absolutely fundamental tenet of the scientific method is the requirement of reproducibility** and replicability. Will the results be the same the next day when scans are done under the same conditions? Will they be the same when scientists use another fMRI machine altogether? The short answer to both questions is: no, not at all.

Meta-research ('research on research') of many fMRI studies showed **an error rate of seventy-eight percent** when different machines were used. In other words, the positive correlation where there was an **average** overlapping of active brain regions was only twenty-two percent (it was only seven percentage points higher when using the same scanning device).

And importantly, the tests performed were always very simple in nature to the point of being rather trivial. For example, test subjects had to follow a basic rhythm by tapping with their fingers; **experiments involved no complex mental functions** like analyzing problems or making big decisions, and the like.

A further major issue is that **there is always a lot of background noise going on which needs to be deducted simply because our brain is always very active even in its supposed resting state.** Furthermore, its energy consumption increases only by a few percentage points even while performing complex cognitive functions.

So the problem is how to measure the regular activities of body and brain, respectively to know what exactly needs to be deducted. So **all of the pretty pictures have first gone through a subtraction process** (besides everything else as described above and more) **to hopefully eliminate all unspecific brain activations that are assumed to not be involved.**

Dr. Hasler likens it to the measuring of a yacht with only its captain aboard, then measuring the yacht again by itself to find out how much the captain weighs. Or to this simple formula from an actual fMRI study: what delayed oxygen consumption happens in the brain when a person is in love plus everything else *minus* another person not in love plus everything else!

In summary, *neuroscience cannot determine if or where there is something physically wrong in the brain or a particular area of the brain when a patient suffers from a mental problem* like depression or anxiety, and so on.

There is not one single piece of evidence that there are any biological or biochemical reasons for bipolar disorder, schizophrenia, or any other mental disorder featured in DSM-5 (the 'bible' of the American Psychiatric Association). And neither are there any tests available to determine so, including fMRI and other neuroimaging devices (like PET; positron-emission tomography that also measures the blood flow with the tracer oxygen-15).

Any and all suggestions that colorful pictures of a brain show specific brain activities that can be assigned to specific cognitive experiences of an individual person are completely wrong. It is not at all clear what we actually see or the reasons why.

These pretty pictures may have convinced the public that scientists actually know and understand full well what they are talking about when in reality they don't; *the pretty pictures of our brains are after all pretty useless.*

Neuroscience to this very day knows next to nothing about how our brain really works and nothing at all about our mental processes; what happens when we think and analyze, feel and dream, are aware of our environment or conscious about our inner life, when we consider complex matters or make difficult decisions, and so on.

Again, are we really just a product of our brains like Machine Man claims without offering any shred of actual evidence besides the fictitious notion of seeing is believing? And why are they so adamant to demand our equal and total devotion to their rather dogmatic beliefs?

The deeper we look into their empty claims and promises, the more it starts to look just like any other religion – to be believed at your own risk.

But let's keep investigating further; we still have a lot more interesting grounds to cover and many rather amazing insights to gain!

# Medical Tales

By its very definition, Machine Man totally and absolutely believes in reductionist science, or physicalism, the notion that everything in this world is purely physical in nature. Yet curiously, while they sure like to loudly profess that science is the one and only way to provide any and all answers in life, they actually often fail to adhere to some of *the most basic principles* of the scientific method.

*Like the constant questioning of our assumptions and the consequent pursuit of facts, no matter where they may lead.* Even if they do contradict previously established theories that over time have merely turned into closely cherished dogmas – to be challenged or contradicted only at the peril of one's current or future employment prospects.

So quite naturally, Machine Man also believes that Western medical science is the only way to heal our bodies, despite the availability and age-old practice of often more effective natural methods (especially as there are usually no negative side effects). But since their mechanisms are beyond Machine Man's current comprehension, any form of alternative medicine gets downplayed or outright ridiculed.

This chapter is not meant to be negative about medical science or to diminish its many actual achievements over the last one hundred years or so. However, we do need to be aware of its limitations; what does modern medicine really understand and what it doesn't; where does it excel and where it doesn't.

Why? Because it claims to be the one and only authority with the proper understanding to treat our bodies and even minds. Ultimately, it also asserts to know who we really are, again to the total exclusion of every other explanation. And it offers the assurance to eventually be able to solve the problem of all disease and mortality itself. Highly promoted proponents of transhumanism are promising the necessary breakthroughs to come real soon.

But of course, they have been saying that for decades already; the timetable of 2025 or 2030 has now been quietly postponed to 2045, the onset of the technical singularity that promises mind uploading and to otherwise overcome the imaginary physical limitations of our bodies and brains. In other words, immortality is always near, very near. Hurray hurray. Or so they keep dreaming, telling and selling.

Machine Man likes to point out that in the old days, prior to the advent of modern science, people always died very young. And of course they have some statistics at hand to prove their point, all the while forgetting the old but true adage about the three kinds of lies: 'lies, damned lies, and statistics.' Put differently, it all depends on who put together the statistics, respectively who paid for it.

Yes, nowadays far less babies die at birth or their earliest months and years, mostly thanks to a better regime of hygiene by midwifes and doctors, less malnutrition, and certain medical improvements (in prenatal or postnatal care, and at childbirth itself). So, having less of the very young succumb at an early age, automatically improved longevity records. Whereas before, and particularly during the darker part of the Middle Ages, a higher infant mortality rate resulted in the dramatic lowering of the overall average lifespan.

Medieval Christians were told that the body is evil, so washing was not at all encouraged or even thought to be important. And of course, frequent wars didn't exactly help the general populace who were sent to do the actual killing and (early) dying for the wars instigated by the assorted aristocratic elites in Europe. Nor did some silly superstitions about the evil nature of cats that helped to further spread and prolong epidemics (the widespread killing of cats helped to dramatically increase the numbers of disease-carrying rodents).

Nowadays, most people believe that only very few of our ancestors got to live beyond the age of thirty or forty. Nobody has told them that a great many people also lived to a ripe old age. And that was long before the introduction of much-hailed vaccines, and the like. Here's a little sample list of the lifespan of historical figures:

| | | |
|---|---|---|
| Pittacus | 640–568 BC | 72 years |
| Solon | c.638–558 BC | c.80 years |
| Lao Tzu | 604 BC–531 BC | 73 years |
| Pythagoras | c.570 BC–495 BC | c.75 years |
| Buddha | c.563–483 BC | c.80 years |
| Confucius | 551 BC–479 BC | 72 years |
| Aeschylus | c.525 BC–456 BC | c.69 years |
| Hippocrates | c.460BC–370 BC | c.90 years |
| Sophocles | 497/6–406/5 BC | 90–92 years |
| Antiphon | 480 BC–403 BC | 77 years |
| Euripides | c.480–c.406 BC | c.74 years |
| Socrates | 470–399 BC | 71 years |
| Lysias | 459–380 BC | 79 years |
| Xenophon | 431–355 BC | 76 years |
| Isocrates | 436–338 BC | 98 years |
| Plato | 428–348 BC | c.80 years |
| Aeschines | 389–314 BC | 75 years |
| Cato the Elder | 234–149 BC | 85 years |
| Epictetus | 55 AD–135 AD | 80 years |
| Anthony the Great | c.251–356 | c.105 years |
| Athanasius of Alexandria | c.296–373 | c.77 years |
| Saint Jerome | c.347–420 | c.73 years |
| Saint Augustine of Hippo | 354–430 | 76 years |
| Saint Isidore of Seville | c.560–636 | c.76 years |
| Saint Hildegard of Bingen | 1098–1179 | 81 years |
| Albertus Magnus | c.1193–1280 | c.87 years |
| Madhvacharya | 1199–1278 | 79 years |
| Roger Bacon | c.1214–1294 | c.80 years |
| Bridget of Sweden | 1303–1373 | 70 years |
| Thomas à Kempis | 1380–1471 | 91 years |

| | | |
|---|---|---|
| Kabir | 1398–1518 | 120 years |
| Askia Muhammad I | c.1443–1538 | c.95 years |
| Leonardo da Vinci | 1452–1519 | 67 years |
| Nicolaus Copernicus | 1473–1543 | 70 years |
| Michelangelo | 1475–1564 | 89 years |
| Francis Bacon | 1561–1626 | 65 years |
| Galileo Galilei | 1564–1642 | 78 years |
| Owen Feltham | 1602–1668 | 66 years |
| Madeleine de Scudéry | 1607–1701 | 94 years |
| Francois de La Rochefoucauld | 1613–1680 | 67 years |
| Roger L'Estrange | 1616–1704 | 88 years |
| John Locke | 1632–1704 | 72 years |
| Madame de Maintenon | 1635–1719 | 84 years |
| Thomas Sprat | 1635–1713 | 78 years |
| Sir Isaac Newton | 1642–1727 | 84 years |
| Gottfried Wilhelm von Leibniz | 1646–1716 | 70 years |
| Jeremy Collier | 1650–1726 | 76 years |
| Christian Wolff | 1679–1754 | 75 years |
| Emanuel Swedenborg | 1688–1772 | 84 years |
| Voltaire | 1694–1778 | 84 years |
| Lord Chesterfield | 1694–1773 | 79 years |
| Saint Ignatius of Laconi | 1701–1781 | 80 years |
| Benjamin Franklin | 1706–1790 | 84 years |
| Samuel Johnson | 1709–1784 | 75 years |
| Denis Diderot | 1713–1784 | 71 years |
| Immanuel Kant | 1724–1804 | 80 years |
| Marquis de Sade | 1740–1814 | 74 years |
| Johann Wolfgang von Goethe | 1749–1832 | 83 years |
| Joseph Joubert | 1754–1824 | 70 years |
| John Quincy Adams | 1767–1848 | 81 years |
| August Wilhelm Schlegel | 1767–1845 | 78 years |
| Andrew Jackson | 1767–1845 | 78 years |
| François-René de Chateaubriand | 1768–1848 | 80 years |
| Baron Alexander von Humboldt | 1769–1859 | 90 years |
| William Jay | 1769–1853 | 84 years |
| William Wordsworth | 1770–1850 | 80 years |

| | | |
|---|---|---|
| Hosea Ballou | 1771–1852 | 81 years |
| Ludwig Tieck | 1773–1853 | 80 years |
| Friedrich Wilhelm Joseph Schelling | 1775–1854 | 79 years |
| Geert Adriaans Boomgaard | 1788–1899 | 111 years |
| Michael Faraday | 1791–1867 | 76 years |
| Margaret Ann Neve | 1792–1903 | 111 years |
| Jean Antoine Petit-Senn | 1792–1870 | 78 years |
| Thomas Carlyle | 1795–1881 | 86 years |
| Amos Bronson Alcott | 1799–1888 | 89 years |
| Ralph Waldo Emerson | 1803–1882 | 79 years |
| Benjamin Disraeli | 1804–1881 | 77 years |
| Henry Wadsworth Longfellow | 1807–1882 | 75 years |
| Ann Pouder | 1807–1917 | 110 years |
| Giuseppe Garibaldi | 1807–1882 | 75 years |
| Oliver Wendell Holmes | 1809–1894 | 85 years |
| Harriet Elisabeth Beecher | 1811–1896 | 85 years |
| Samuel Smiles | 1812–1904 | 92 years |
| Berthold Auerbach | 1812–1882 | 70 years |
| Louisa Thiers | 1814–1926 | 111 years |
| Miriam Bannister | 1817–1928 | 111 years |
| Demetrius Philipovitch | 1818–1928 | 110 years |
| Delina Filkins | 1815–1928 | 113 years |
| Louis Pasteur | 1822–1895 | 73 years |
| Thomas H. Huxley | 1825–1895 | 70 years |
| Mark Twain | 1835–1910 | 75 years |
| William Winter | 1836–1917 | 81 years |
| Auguste Rodin | 1840–1917 | 77 years |
| Charles Henry Parkhurst | 1842–1933 | 92 years |
| Mahatma Gandhi | 1869–1948 | 79 years |

Many of these personalities were outstanding scientists, philosophers and artists, part of the clergy or otherwise spiritually inclined. One could say that being particularly intelligent and educated is quite possibly a factor in the attainment of a longer life. Some of them were also members of the elite or at least got sponsored by the powerful and wealthy – with all the privileges that it entails.

We can still observe this essential truth today: the more money and material comforts (like better food and health care, no hazardous work, less stress and more rest) we are able to enjoy, the longer we are likely to live. And vice versa. But of course, no matter what we do or don't do, there are no guarantees in life. It all depends on many factors. Perhaps most of all, on our general state (peace) of mind.

So what is the current situation? Well, life expectancy in all Western countries (including Japan) has notably declined over the past two decades, and particularly so in the USA and the United Kingdom. In 2018, the British Medical Journal published a long term study that showed increasing death rates across all racial and ethnic groups, men and women alike.

US doctors actually came up with a rather disturbing term for the economic and social causes of this barely reported public health crisis: "shit-life syndrome." (Sorry for their language.) With an ever widening income and wealth gap and a deliberately hidden high (real) inflation rate, people get ever more destitute and depressed, eat a diet of highly processed foods (a.k.a. fast or sadly, fat food) lacking in real nutrition, and resort to taking the highly addictive 'wonders' of the pharmaceutical industry that come with a myriad of toxic side effects.

Indeed, both legal and illegal drug overdoses were the leading reported cause of increased mortality, closely followed by alcohol-related problems, suicides and multiple organ diseases (like liver and heart conditions or cancers).

Nowadays, so many misinformed yet trusting people literally **outsource their health** – surely the most important of our assets – to their doctors and pharmacists, rather than taking charge of it themselves and making the necessary lifestyle changes that are not only far cheaper, but also much more effective and long-lasting. Besides far safer by a large order of magnitude.

A study by the Mayo Clinic and Olmsted Medical Center found that nearly 70 percent of all Americans are on at least one prescription drug, and more than half take two; twenty percent of all Americans are even on five or more prescription drugs.

While Americans account for only about five percent of the global population, they buy over 50 percent of pharmaceutical drugs. And a grand total of 80 percent of all prescription painkillers. Sadly, drug overdose has now become the leading cause of death of Americans under 50, with two-thirds of those deaths from prescription and non-prescription opioids.

Who is to blame? Obvious over-prescriptions by overworked doctors? People in need of pain relief who suddenly become addicted to the fatal point of respiratory failure? Thrill or euphoria seekers who miscalculate dosages and are ignorant of side effects?

Immoral and greedy pharmaceutical companies that pay to display never-ending direct-to-consumer ads (only allowed in the USA and New Zealand)? Or their well-endowed and thus powerful lobbyists, respectively essentially corrupt members of Congress (or Parliament) who turn a blind eye to all the misery caused by unnecessary prescription drugs?

Let's see what an honest high-profile insider had to say about the state of modern medicine:

*"The medical profession is being bought by the pharmaceutical industry, not only in terms of the practice of medicine, but also in terms of teaching and research. The academic institutions of this country are allowing themselves to be the paid agents of the pharmaceutical industry. I think it's disgraceful."*
Dr. Arnold Relman, a Harvard professor of medicine and editor of The New England Journal of Medicine (*NEJM*) from 1977 to 1991.

Of course, none of the above facts or practices are ever mentioned by Big Pharma in their glitzy advertisements. And neither are the most horrendous toxic side effects caused by their chemical concoctions (the less harmful ones are typically read by a speed reader).

Even seemingly harmless *pleasure-enhancing pills* (sildenafil, a.k.a. Viagra) come with a wide range of rather common reactions like headaches, the sudden reddening of the face and neck, impaired vision (e.g. blurred vision, intolerance to light, seeing everything tinted blue or red, sometimes permanently so!), back pain and indigestion, dizziness and nausea (or worse still, a fatal drop in blood pressure, heart attack, stroke or the sudden loss of hearing).

What about **antidepressants** that are admitted by its manufacturers to actually **cause depression**? Besides anxiety or impotence (Viagra anyone?), weight gains, suicidal tendencies (a black box warning is now required for all SSRIs to warn about the increased risk of suicide in people younger than 25), and too many more to mention here.

Speaking of weight gain: another one of countless pills causing just that is the cheerfully named *Abilify*, the top-selling drug ingested by millions of Americans. The manufacturer also warns of the danger of suffering a stroke, and wants people to go to the emergency ward if they encounter: "high fever, stiff muscles, confusion, sweating, changes in pulse, heart rate and blood pressure, that may be signs of a condition called neuroleptic malignant syndrome (NMS), a rare and serious condition that can lead to death." Oops!

Furthermore, its maker warns that this popular antipsychotic may also cause **uncontrolled movements of face, tongue, lips and/or other parts of the body** – a serious condition called tardive dyskinesia. And perhaps worst of all, **these shocking symptoms may – admittedly! – never ever stop.** Even if people cease taking the pills, or sometimes, **because** they do stop taking them!

Other anti-depressants or antipsychotic drugs are also causing tardive dyskinesia; we can increasingly see high profile people of all kinds suffering from it, displaying its symptoms while they are on live TV. It's not a pretty sight.

Another important and equally disturbing fact that always gets excluded from the happy ads is that neither the Food and Drug Administration (FDA) nor the manufacturer of *Abilify* actually knows what makes it work. The

USPI label on the bottle admits: *"The mechanism of action of aripiprazole is unknown."* Read that again and try not to be puzzled!

So perhaps it would be more appropriate to state that '*this drug may cause schizophrenia, bipolar disorder and depression, rather than actually treat it.*' That indeed is likely to happen once all of these **uncontrolled movements** start; the literal shaking and stirring of its many unsuspecting users. Or any of the many other adverse effects not mentioned here.

*"It is simply no longer possible to believe much of the clinical research that is published, or to rely on the judgment of trusted physicians or authoritative medical guidelines. I take no pleasure in this conclusion, which I reached slowly and reluctantly over my two decades as an editor of the New England Journal of Medicine."*
Dr. Marcia Angell, Physician and longtime Editor-in-Chief of The New England Journal of Medicine (*NEJM*), a prestigious peer-reviewed medical journal.

*Do pharmaceutical companies even know what they are doing?* As in really know? Do they even remotely understand our complex bodies and brains? And are they designing their drugs being fully aware about what they really do and how they actually work? While we sure would like to think so, here's another fact that never gets mentioned in all of their euphoria-inducing advertisements:

*Most of the drugs they make and we take were discovered by accident, not design!* Sadly, that is simply a historical truth. Entire books by highly knowledgeable pharmacologists have been written on this subject, listing sheer endless examples (as always, see the extensive chapter *Notes* for more information on all the points made herein).

Once we fully grasp this reality, we are likely to become a lot more skeptical before taking our daily poison pills, respectively put our faith in the empty promises of longevity or outright immortality made by highly publicized transhumanists. Becoming fully aware of how little the people we consider to be real experts and professionals actually do know, should really be a wake-up call for all of us. Or a warning.

Here's just a short list of accidentally discovered drugs, with the emphasis on psychoactive drugs, to emphasize how little modern medicine, pharmacology or neuroscience understands about what is happening in our brains:

1. Chlorpromazin (sold as Thorazine and Largactil) was developed as a new antihistamin to treat allergies, but by sheer chance became the word's first antipsychotic to treat schizophrenia, bipolar disorder, ADHD, etc. Henri Laborit, a young French marine surgeon, experimented with drug cocktails to sedate patients before surgery and noticed its euphoria and indifference inducing properties with test subjects.

2. Meprobamate, sold as Miltown by Wallace Laboratories and Equanil by Wyeth (besides more than 100 other trade names like Amepromat, Quivet, Zirpon, etc.), became the first best-selling psychotropic drug in the 1950s. While developing a new broad spectrum antibiotic, chemist Frank Berger noticed that laboratory rodents calmed down considerably without knocking them out. Thus it was turned into a minor tranquilizer, became very popular among Hollywood stars, and subsequently, was frequently sold out across the country; it was prohibited only in 2012 due to its addictive nature and serious side effects!

3. Librium (Chlordiazepoxide), a sedative and hypnotic of the benzodiazepine class (as is Alprazolam, sold as Xanax among others), used to treat anxiety, nervousness, insomnia or withdrawal symptoms, was also discovered by pure chance (involving mice that stayed calm even while they received electro-shocks!), upon experimenting with derivatives of synthetic colors in the hope of finding something useful; it is also highly addictive; serious side effects include an increased risk of death!

4. Iproniazid (sold as Marsilid, Rivivol, Euphozid, Iprazid, Ipronid, Ipronin) became the world's first antidepressant, although it was originally developed for the treatment of tuberculosis. But

doctors treating tuberculosis patients noticed how they've become unusually energized and happy.

5.  Imipramine (brand name Tofranil, among others), became a tricyclic antidepressant (TCA), but was originally meant to be an an antipsychotic due to its similar chemical structure to Chlorpromazin (see point one above).

***Not even one of all these psychotropic medications came about as the result of deliberate rational drug design based on existing scientific insights or cutting-edge research.***

What about Prozac and the many other brands (Paxil, Seroxat, Zoloft, etc.) of the SSRI (selective serotonin reuptake inhibitor) class of antidepressants? Besides being a huge financial success story for its manufacturers, there is not all that much else that could be said in terms of positive news. Other than perhaps noticing the outstanding skills of both their marketing and legal departments.

Despite its name that implies that it only works selectively, it is not selective at all because it interferes with a whole range of neurotransmitters (including dopamine). And, the very basis of its assumptions are not proven in any way: to this day, ***there is absolutely no scientific proof about their theories of a lack of serotonin, or any other neurotransmitter for that matter (like norepinephrine), as a cause of depression or anything else.***

***"We have hunted for big simple neurochemical explanations for psychiatric disorders and have not found them."***
Kenneth S. Kendler, Banks Distinguished Professor of Psychiatry, Professor of Human Genetics, and Director of the Virginia Institute of Psychiatric and Behavioral Genetics at the Virginia Commonwealth University, and one of the highest cited psychiatry researchers.

*"To propose that researchers can objectively identify a "chemical imbalance" at the molecular level is not compatible with the extant science. In fact, **there is no scientifically established ideal "chemical balance" of serotonin,** let alone*

*an identifiable pathological imbalance."* Jeffrey R. Lacasse, Jonathan Leo, medical researchers and authors.

*"Although it is often stated with great confidence that depressed people have a serotonin or norepinephrine deficiency, the evidence actually contradicts these claims."*
Elliot Valenstein, Professor Emeritus of Psychology and Neuroscience at the University of Michigan in *Blaming the Brain*.

In other words: *The continually proclaimed and therefore very widely believed story about a chemical imbalance in the brain that needs to be corrected is pure fiction*; there is no scientific basis or factual evidence at all. Actually, the very opposite is true: *these drugs are causing an imbalance of neurotransmitters in the brain*, often with devastating consequences, including the aforementioned repetitive, involuntary movements of the tongue, lips and other parts of the body (tardive dyskinesia), or akathisia (the inability to stay still because of a continuing feeling of inner restlessness and uneasiness).

Talking about being messed up! Or a chemical imbalance. Actually caused by the said to be cure for a non-existent calamity. To top it all off, independent research found the success of SSRIs as a treatment to be *"clinically insignificant"*. In other words, they are essentially just an expensive placebo that comes with many free side effects.

*"[We must] abandon the simplistic hypotheses of there being either an abnormally high or abnormally low function of a given neurotransmitter."*
Avrid Carlson, Nobel Prize in Physiology or Medicine in 2000 for his work on the neurotransmitter dopamine.

So is it all mostly a case of trial and error? Are we humans just more or less elaborate versions of guinea pigs? To be freely experimented upon and forever milked for profit? Maybe it will work, maybe it won't, or worse. It raises the question of which part exactly of the age-old medical principle of *Primum Non Nocere*: *"First do no harm"* is not being understood anymore and why?

*"Whenever a doctor cannot do good, he must be kept from doing harm."*
Hippocrates

Historically speaking, medical science always involved a great deal of trial and error. In ancient times and throughout the Middle Ages, doctors were convinced that trepanning – the drilling of a hole into the skull – is the best way to cure epileptic seizures, migraines and mental disorders.

And not too long ago, psychiatric conditions were quite commonly treated with a lobotomy, the severing of most connections to and from the brain's prefrontal cortex and the anterior part of the frontal lobes (e.g. it was practiced in China until its prohibition in 2004). In 1949, the originator of the procedure (controversially) received the Nobel Prize for Physiology or Medicine.

The treatment was found to reduce 'the complexity of psychic life.' As in: less spontaneity or responsiveness, reduced self-awareness and self-control, general inertia or feeling emotionally blunted, besides a restriction of the patient's intellectual range.

Nowadays, mental disorders are predominantly treated with psychoactive pills. So it sure sounds like a great improvement to getting a hole drilled in the head, or willy-nilly having bits of our brains chopped off. And yet, when we closely examine the actual mental effects of these pills, they sure look and sound remarkably like the above-mentioned **reduction in the complexity of psychic life:** feeling emotionally blunted, neither particularly depressed nor ever happy, slow reaction times, and so on.

We really do outsource our physical and mental health and well-being at our own risk: in 2016, an eight year Johns Hopkins Medicine study concluded that more than 250,000 people in the USA die every year from **medical errors**, making it **the third leading cause of death right after heart disease and cancer** (another study published by the Journal of Patient Safety put the number at more than 400,000 per year).

Of course, nowadays all medical professions are essentially businesses that seek to and need to make money. That simply is the name of the game in our world. And surely, most doctors and scientists really do have the best of intentions, genuinely wanting to help other human beings. But they too are only human. And therefore, and understandably so, they are also not immune to being wrong yet stubborn, both greedy and corrupt, or misguided yet arrogant.

After all, it is not too long ago that doctors ridiculed anyone who proposed that ulcers are caused by bacteria – which turned out to be true – simply because the academic consensus insisted that it was caused by sheer stress or overly spicy food. The list of other such (and even worse) follies could easily fill an entire (and thick) book of its own.

Yes, medicine has come a long way since the early days. And particularly so for all trauma related injuries. Fixing broken bones and other rather mechanical repair works are done remarkably well (and incidentally, these are the only areas of medicine your author would ever trust with his own body).

And yet, fact is that modern medicine has promised us cures for cancers for a great many decades, yet *there are ever more patients year after year, never less*. And likewise with mental health cures: despite insane growth rates and record numbers of people taking psychotropic drugs, there are ever more depressed and anxious people in the world, never less: over the last twenty years *the number of officially disabled mentally ill* (and therefore on government disability rolls) in the United States *has tripled*.

The absolute numbers of both patients and health-related costs increase every single year at a record pace. So where exactly are the much touted advancements of science actually happening? As in really happening; actually observable and independently measurable?

Well, one could argue that scientific progress does indeed happen: mostly in military hardware or surveillance software and a variety of related electronic gadgets (that seemingly make life easier albeit likely to the detriment of our mental and physical health). In other words, there are ever more efficient ways to kill or control ever more people.

Proven holistic ways to heal for good are not exactly being advertised or otherwise getting promoted by the media. To put it mildly. There is simply no profit in natural products. Or just too little for too much work. Therefore, pharmaceutical giants and a great many of their retail merchants (a.k.a. doctors) always and most resolutely discourage any and all competition. Often to be enforced by law, for the greater good (of their bank accounts).

So overdiagnosis of patients, overprescriptions of pharmaceutical products, or totally inappropriate and unnecessary surgeries do happen every day in every country. Many if not most of the drugs people get fed (or ask for) not only do not work, but actually do harm. And quite often, irreparably or terminally so.

Probably most doctors really do believe in the wonders of the methods they apply and the prescriptions they supply. Medical schools after all only teach the pure philosophy of Machine Man: everything can be reduced to physical reasons, including our minds.

And quite likely, the majority of well-meaning but overworked doctors (who generally only receive a rudimentary education in pharmacology to begin with!) may simply not have the time to keep studying medical journals or following the latest research reports. Instead, many seemingly just trust what the medical sales representatives tell them, perhaps listening only with one ear about the latest and greatest success stories from their clinical trials – all paid for and screened by, well, mostly themselves.

You know, 'We are the champions, my friend.' Or, 'Trust me,' said the cat to the mouse.

*"The case against science is straightforward: much of the scientific literature, perhaps half, may simply be untrue. Afflicted by studies with small sample sizes, tiny effects, invalid exploratory analyses, and flagrant conflicts of interest, together with an obsession for pursuing fashionable trends of dubious importance, science has taken a turn towards darkness."*

Dr. Richard Horton, Editor-in-chief of the Lancet, the world's most respected medical journal.

In summary, we have to ask whether we will ever be able to have full confidence in the purely for profit physicalist model of today's medical system. Hopefully, that day will eventually come. Soon.

***The day pharmaceutical companies can willfully design and make drugs that are totally free of any and all negative side effects is the time we can trust that they truly know what they are doing.*** Not one day earlier. And that is certainly not today. Or in the foreseeable future.

For transhumanism to succeed would require that the medical sciences fully understand our bodies and brains. In an entirely holistic manner that does no harm whatsoever. How else could they possibly propose that we will soon live longer, better or forever?

And as we have seen, the current state of both science and medicine is not even close to obtaining such a deep, all-encompassing knowledge.

But let's continue our exploring and look some more into what is really real and what is not!

# The Reality

The biggest mystery of modern medicine and neuroscience is the **Placebo Effect** with confirmed successful healing rates of up to ninety percent. Even though its curative powers are very well-researched and documented, there is simply no explanation that could possibly fit into the narrative of the current purely materialistic way of thinking that pervades all sciences. And indeed, today's society as a whole.

Studies into the placebo effect have even come to the conclusion that *many conventional treatments are only effective because of their placebo effect.* And nothing else! As we have seen, examples are antidepressants and other psychiatric drugs. However, it also includes fake Parkinson's and diabetes medicines, placebo treatments for multiple sclerosis, allergies, asthma, migraine headaches, ulcers, and so on. Like bold men starting to grow hair again!

A placebo (Latin for 'I shall please') could be a simple sugar pill, pretend surgery, fake acupuncture, or an ineffective saline infusion. And what is perhaps the most amazing part of it, these fake treatments also seem to work when we *knowingly* take a placebo! We know that we actually get fooled or fool ourselves, and yet it still works!

Of course, we have not heard about these extraordinary and most astonishing facts in any pharmaceutical promotions, or the paid advertorials that masquerade as news these days. Nevertheless, even ancient doctors and healers already knew about this mysterious reality a great many years ago:

*"Natural forces within us are the true healers of disease."* Hippocrates (460 BC-370 BC)

We also need to emphasize the reality that the placebo effect works its wonders completely *without adverse effects* of any kind. Furthermore, *it costs nothing at all*. Or not very much. Hence the rather deafening silence by the modern medical establishment.

*"When you look the papers up, you often find the drugs didn't even work better than a placebo. And no one tested how they worked in combination with the other drugs. Just taking the patient off everything can improve their health right away."*
Dr. John P. A. Ioannidis, Professor of Medicine and of Health Research and Policy at Stanford University School of Medicine, Professor of Statistics at Stanford University School of Humanities and Sciences.

*Machine Man doctors insist that everything has a physical cause, explanation and cure.* And yet, an inactive placebo has the proven ability to actually change the chemistry and circuitry of a patient's brain. In other words, *a physically inactive intervention produces a positive physical result!*

There is simply and absolutely no way to explain this observable phenomenon with the current materialistic paradigm that claims to be science but really is rather scientism: "Slavish imitation of the method and language of science" Nobel Prize winner F.A. Hayek, respectively "the aping of what is widely mistaken for the method of science" Karl Popper.

Why does the brain of patients suffering from Parkinson's disease release a flood of the neurotransmitter dopamine upon the taking of a placebo pill? Why do fake painkillers still result in the discharge of pain-relieving endorphins in our brains? And why do simple sugar pills actually lower blood pressure?

Or perhaps even stranger, *how do we explain the success of a placebo 'sham' surgery when the actual physical problem was not addressed at all?*

Patients who were suffering from osteoarthritis of the knee – a real physical ailment resulting from the breakdown of joint cartilage and underlying bone – were cured when a simple superficial skin incision was made rather than any actual surgery performed. And yet the positive results obtained were the very same as with any of the patients who did go through the real procedure.

And likewise for patients with angina pectoris. Dr. Leonard Cobb Jr, a cardiology specialist and Professor Emeritus, performed pretend surgery by merely making a small incision on the surface of the chest. He found that it equally increased the blood flow to the heart muscles of patients as when he actually did carry out the full surgery (by tying knots in the arteries).

In short, reductionist science has no plausible explanation of the reasons why the placebo effect is happening; not in general medicine and even less so in cases that normally require real physical surgery to change something in our actual skeletons.

The latest research trying to find out what could be happening on a cell communication level once the process of healing had already started, indicates (for as of yet unknown respectively unproven reasons) that the placebo effect actually gets hindered or disturbed by the simultaneous taking of real active pharmaceutical drugs. Advertise that, please.

*"To do nothing is also a good remedy."* Hippocrates

Surely, it all looks a bit like magic, but that of course does not exist in the playbook of Machine Man. Alright, let's not invoke or talk about magic. Or religion and the like. *So is it a matter of mind over body?* Well, according to materialistic doctrine, there is no such thing as the mind. Such beliefs are merely wishful thinking or superstitions by the unenlightened.

Speaking of which, until the Age of Enlightenment (or Reason), people in all cultures and throughout recorded times generally believed that the mind is separate from the brain. That it is something more, bigger, greater, going beyond the mere three-dimensional reality of the physical brain. Or indeed, that it is not even bound by the restraints of time.

Modern medicine however is convinced that the mind is the same as the brain. That it is solely a function of the brain. And that everything we think or feel and do emanates from the activities of our brain cells, including our consciousness. To Machine Man, all we are or think we are, is just an illusion made possible by the brain. That's it folks.

Real and therefore unbiased scientists however are required to partially or totally reconsider their theories, models and assumptions whenever there are serious contradictions in their scientific observations or test results. That however is obviously not always the case.

Today, many scientists, perhaps or probably for pecuniary reasons, simply lack the natural curiosity that is still inherent in children. Or the young who sincerely seek to unravel the mysteries of life. *Just because something cannot be explained or measured does not mean that it does not happen or exist.* So all too often, secular believers have become just as dogmatic as their religious counterparts. Even if they like to call themselves scientists.

*"Miracles are not contrary to nature, but only contrary to what we know about nature."* Saint Augustine

*The placebo effect is proof positive of the power of our beliefs.* This is obvious because we can observe the real-world results of beliefs; patients do get well despite the lack of active medicines or real surgical interventions. The power of our beliefs is further demonstrated by the fact that the deeper the beliefs are – in other words, the more convinced the patient is – the better placebos work.

For example, sham injections and creams seem to have a stronger effect than sugar pills. Capsules work even better than tablets, bigger pills work better than smaller ones, and the more doses a day we take, the better the results will be. It all adds to the credibility of a treatment and thus the strength of our beliefs. With placebo surgery topping it all. It is simply hard to argue or disbelieve when you have a real little scar on your chest that proves that you indeed had surgery, even though you didn't!

Furthermore, many of us do believe that if something costs more, it must be better. That is a deeply ingrained belief in our societies. A study by

Duke University scientist Dan Ariely and a team of collaborators at the Massachusetts Institute of Technology found that a fake pill that was said to cost $2.50 per dose had a success rate of 85 percent in reducing the pain of test subjects. However, those who were told that their pills cost only ten cents had 'just' a 61 percent success rate.

Numerous studies have shown that it greatly matters if we do believe our doctor, or not. The more convincing they are, the better the result will be. So doctors who give their patients a sugar pill and say, 'This **will** relieve your pain,' were far more successful than those who just said, 'This **might** help you.'

*"The art of medicine consists in amusing the patient while nature cures the disease."* Voltaire

Words and rituals of a therapeutic act can change the actual chemistry and circuitry of patients' brains, heal their knees and restore the blood flow in their hearts. And so on and so forth. That is simply and totally amazing. *The placebo effect demonstrates both the power of our beliefs and the importance of the strength of our beliefs.*

*Another proof positive is the Nocebo Effect* (nocebo – Latin for 'I shall harm') which is the other side of the coin: *negative attitudes and beliefs will result in harmful consequences, even to the point of a premature death.*

Many double-blinded clinical trials have demonstrated that patients suffered real physical side effects just because they were warned that the fake medicines they were about to take may cause such side effects. And so it often turned out to be.

Patients who were given harmless saline injections but were told that it was chemotherapy duly started to throw up and lose hair. Mere sugar pills were reported to seemingly cause memory or taste disturbances, tiredness or muscle weakness, nausea or colds, ringing in the ears and many other symptoms. All solely based on patients' expectations following their doctor's cautionary advice.

The same principle has been demonstrated by Vodoo deaths where people were told that they were cursed by a witch doctor in a black magic ritual; those who believed it duly died.

'Medical hexing' by doctors has repeatedly shown to produce similar results: healthy patients who were **mistakenly informed** that they will die within three, six or twelve months, did indeed pass away in the 'allocated' time frame they were given. Autopsies later confirmed that there was nothing physically wrong with them.

Twenty years ago, I wrote in my first book about my own experiences with friends and loved ones who were told by their doctors to get their affairs in order as there was simply no hope left. Some of them did not believe the dire prognosis and lived another twenty, even thirty years. Others did believe it and sure passed away, as they were told.

Placebos and nocebos demonstrate both the healing and destructive power of our beliefs; they can literally make or break us. Therefore *it is important to be very careful what we believe,* and to protect our minds from harmful influences by nefarious and even well-meaning people, both recurring subject matters in all of my writings:*"Dare to discover and discard all self-defeating beliefs."* Or, *"Happiness is a direct function of our beliefs."*

*The placebo and nocebo effect proves both optimists and pessimists right*: one has predominantly positive expectations and the general belief that things will turn out all right, and the other, well, just the opposite.

All of this raises quite a few interesting and perhaps rather revealing questions, all relevant in our quest to find out who we really are and to show why transhumanism certainly is just an empty promise.

*Who is it who believes?* According to the beliefs of Machine Man it is the brain. To them, all thoughts are just the result of the brain's electrical or biochemical activity. Beliefs are, by definition, thoughts that we hold to be true.

***Does the brain really believe anything at all?*** Can pure lumps of flesh, blood and matter think both rational and irrational thoughts, and then decide to believe that some thoughts are more true than others? And if so, for what purpose? What are the reasons why?

To Machine Man, it first comes down to our personal survival, followed by the long term preservation and progress of our own family, and thereafter, the protection of our extended families or tribe and country. Survival is always the primary and dominant name of the game. Everything else is supplementary.

Maslow's famous hierarchy of needs stipulates that our physiological needs (homeostasis, food, water, sleep, shelter, sex) always come first, before any of the other, more optional wants will be addressed. He proposed the following order of priorities: safety, belonging and love, social needs, self-esteem, and finally, self-actualization, which includes altruism and our spirituality.

So first things first: ***Every individual living being wants to live and thrive for as long as possible.*** This most basic of instincts seems to be hardwired into the core of all species, from a simple amoeba all the way to us humans, the most complex of all organisms. Even corporations want to survive and keep increasing their profits, forever. Obsolete government departments too want to keep going and expand ad infinitum; they never ask for smaller budgets, very much to the contrary.

Natural selection or survival of the fittest (Darwinism, the theory of biological evolution) are at best only distant afterthoughts as few if any of us are consciously thinking about making evolutionary improvements that are measured in the millions of years.

First and foremost, most of us care mainly for our own personal lives, not the abstract concept of our tribe or species. Normally, we cooperate only if it is in our best self-interest. Or if we are coerced by force, which makes it also in our best interest: the interest of not having to pay a fine, go to jail, or worse.

So if Machine Man is right and the placebo or nocebo effects were just functions of the brain, *why would the brain ever want to believe something that is detrimental to the health of itself?* And since beliefs would matter to the brain for the very reason of survival, why did it *not* believe some positive, life-affirming thoughts a bit earlier – before a life-threatening disease could actually have manifested itself? Are some brains simply a bit masochistic or suicidal?

*Why would a brain ever decide to engage in extremely dangerous* (besides totally unnecessary) *activities that could potentially endanger its own survival?* Like climb up Mount Everest or base jump down a mountain. Why do some people (respectively their brains, in the language of Machine Man) literally work themselves to death in Japan (and elsewhere)? Or compete in triathlons beyond the point of exhaustion, to their actual demise?

Or why would a brain decide to sacrifice its own life for the survival of others as countless examples of heroic acts have shown throughout times and the world? Many people have perished trying to help even total strangers, sometimes knowing full well that they are actually going to die in the process. Are such heroic acts just the result of some chemicals coming together and randomly decide to stop living once and for all, for no reasons at all, going totally against all primary instincts?

Why would the brain decide to sacrifice itself, against its own best self-interests? Or otherwise decide to commit suicide? We have seen that there is no evidence of any kind about chemical imbalances or a sick brain (other than tumors and the like). The brain doesn't even feel any pain while it is being cut up during brain surgery!

Is the brain making decisions that will lead to its very own destruction because it thinks that it should not survive any longer because of its inferior or defective genes? Because it made some mistakes that made other people sad or mad and it feels guilty now? Or to make way for another superior organism that is better suited to the continuation of its species or tribe? If so, how would it know that, and why should it care?

Imagine this discussion: 'What happened to John Doe? I haven't seen him in a while?'

'Ah well, the brain that thought to be John Doe believed that its life is not worth living anymore or not particularly conducive to the betterment of our species, and therefore decided to terminate itself by jumping in front of a train.'

That is how absurd it can get in Machine Man land where the brain is all there is, and it either makes or breaks us, supposedly for no reasons at all since ultimately, everything that exists or happens is just a random act of chance.

Who is it who overrules the most primary survival instinct? The brain? *Really? **The brain's one and only function is to keep the overall organism alive, fully intact and well.*** First by keeping up all essential biological functions (called homeostasis), and second, looking after its physiological needs. Finding shelter, food, water and the like. The rest is optional.

So why should or would the brain ever abandon its primary mission and risk or end its life? According to Machine Man, all decisions are made by the brain alone; there is nothing or nobody else! So let's just say for a moment that the answer is that it is a sick brain that makes those bad or mad decisions, even though we can't actually measure or diagnose a mentally diseased state in anyway whatsoever. Nevertheless, let's just blame the brain.

However and inexplicably, the very same supposedly diseased brain is making perfectly rational and totally smart decisions about all kinds of complex aspects of life every single day – at the same time as it makes a perhaps silly and surely risky decision, like taking up base jumping from high mountains as its new hobby.

Why or how could it be that the brain makes very intelligent investment decisions to ensure a comfortable future in the morning, and in the afternoon pursues a really high risk activity that is highly likely to jeopardize its own life?

Or let's assume that you are aware of having made a bad or outright silly decision in life. And who doesn't, occasionally, yours truly included. Should you feel bad about yourself or even a bit guilty?

Well, ***according to Machine Man there is no you at all***; you are just an illusion made up by the brain – for no explained or clear reasons! So if you say 'Silly me' or 'My silly brain' or 'My brain is a bit slow today', perhaps after a few drinks too many, ***that is only the brain's illusion that tells itself that it is a bit silly.*** And again, supposedly, the brain is doing that for no particular or understandable reason whatsoever. What a silly brain indeed!

Ah, the convolutions, contortions and concoctions by the smart brains of Machine Man scientists and philosophers are seemingly endless. Simply amazing.

Never mind and don't worry, we are not done yet. Not by a very long shot as there is so much more to be said and concluded. So keep reading and hopefully, smiling here and there!

# Illusions

Life is all about choices. We experience this reality in our daily life, everywhere and all the time. Choices, choices, choices. Sometimes there are only a few options available, yet quite often, we are faced with seemingly endless choices. And choices require decisions. Somebody has to make all these decisions. You know, be in charge and choose. It's kind of like a full time job.

Who is it who thinks and deliberates about the many aspects involved in any given issue? Who is it who thinks carefully about the available options and weighs up the potential consequences of a decision to be made? Who makes all these more or less complex deliberations, evaluations and choices?

As you know, according to Machine Man scientists and philosophers, it is solely the brain who thinks all thoughts and makes all subsequent decisions. *To them, there is no such thing as free will, despite our daily rather self-evident experience to the contrary.* They believe that free will is – like you, respectively your illusory sense of self – just an illusion. Again, without offering proof of any kind.

*Their idea is that all of our decisions were already made by a mystical subconscious mind* – whose existence is as of yet unproven too. *And thereafter, this mythical entity will inform another imaginary being – the conscious mind – about its decisions.* The conscious mind is who you think you are, but actually aren't, in their assessment. Remember, to Machine Man, you are just an illusion made up by the almighty brain.

So there is no free will. All that was willed was done without you being involved. Believe it or not, but many celebrated luminaries like Albert Einstein, Thomas Huxley or Charles Darwin did believe just that, or slight variations thereof. It is known as *The Zombie Argument* whereas a human is considered to be a conscious automaton, a self-operating machine where the brain causes all kinds of behavior **without conscious intention.**

**Zombians** – as adherents to the Zombian point of view are called – believe that consciousness can only become aware of intentions later on, without being able to cause anything. To them, consciousness simply observes the intentions that were already produced by the subconscious mind milliseconds earlier (a subspecies of Zombians admits that consciousness can overrule some unconscious decisions).

The modern basis of such belief is a rather simple (perhaps more aptly named simplistic) experiment that asks its test subjects to move their arm **and** press a button at any time of their choosing **and** notice the time when they think that they have first decided, or willed, to make that movement. That alone makes it already invalid in my assessment because we are talking about **four or five different actions, not one**: decide to move the arm, press the button, look toward the clock, and notice – plus remember – the time.

And while believers say that they have monitored the brain activity of the part of the brain that is generally **believed** to control the movement (of pressing the button), that is also pure speculation. There is no proof of any kind. It is just wishful thinking. Like believing in the Tooth Fairy. As we have previously noted in chapter *Neurofiction*, all brain imaging devices are very unreliable at best, and **the timing of what is being measured is off by seconds,** while they assume and claim to know what's going on within a **few milliseconds!**

The time lag issue alone means that we don't really know which parts of the brain were already active or newly activated. What when and where exactly which one of the multiple actions – rather than the alleged singular action – has happened or is happening is pure speculation. And so is claiming to know the one and only reason why, out of sheer endless potential explanations or possibilities.

**But that whimsical and supposedly scientific experiment is being used to state with the full magnitude and absolute authority of science that there is no free will.** Incredible but true.

Of course, the zombie argument goes totally against basic common sense and our daily experience of well and truly knowing what we want, intend and choose. We all know that we really are making free choices whenever we have the opportunity to make such free choices, whenever we are not coerced by some external factors. From the simple, mundane and trivial to the complex, important and crucial.

At night, I can choose to sleep early or stay up late, regardless of my brain telling me that the body really needs some rest. In the morning, I can choose what to eat for breakfast or to skip it altogether, despite my stomach rumbling. After work I can choose to do sports, watch some TV instead, or do both at the same time. I can choose to cook a healthy dinner at home or order some fa(s)t food takeaway.

In the bigger picture view of life, I can choose to predominantly have a victim's or a victor's attitude. I can study hard and work diligently to make lots of money, perhaps often being a bit tired or stressed out in the process. Or I can choose to take it easy in life and regularly go fishing with my friends, drinking beer all day long, without having too many worries but instead, lots of fun in the sun! Samba si, trabajo no.

Or let's say you had a lifelong best friend, but for some reasons you had a big argument and haven't spoken in years. Suddenly you meet on the street. Now you have many choices how you could act or not.

You could ignore your former best buddy and walk straight past him/her/ it while making a poker face. You could also say, 'Hello, how are you?' or just smile and say nothing. Or frown and say nothing. You could extend your hands and shake hands only. Or shake hands and exchange a brief or extended hug. You could propose to go for a coffee or a beer or have an early lunch. You could give the former friend a punch on the nose or a kick in the bum. You could exchange phone numbers and mutually promise to be in touch shortly. There are so many different ways to behave!

Is it your brain that decides how to react one way or the other? And if so, why would it choose one particular way over any of the other? None of the above examples have anything to do with the brain's survival or any other biological necessity. Not to speak of survival of the fittest. Why should the brain care about this person, simply another body that is not important for its own functioning or life in any way whatsoever?

The very fact that I can go out and do bad deeds anytime I wanted to is proof that we have free will and free choice. I could take a nice bottle of wine and visit my neighbor to discuss issues of mutual concerns in a friendly, respectful and fun setting. Or I could decide to go over there and express my displeasure with a baseball bat and hit him over the head a few times to make sure he won't play loud music again while I'd like to have my beauty sleep.

There are always many ways and choices to deal with problems. Some are rational, others not at all. Some make sense while others are totally self-destructive, contrary to our own best self-interest. Is that just another silly brain?

Sometimes we make quick and easy decisions, and at other times we don't. Mostly it depends on how many options we have to choose from at a given moment, the state of our knowledge or information about things, our actual desires or intentions, and the nature of our character.

***Indeed, the very indecisive among us are further proof of free will***; they keep thinking and evaluating options, sometimes seemingly forever, until they finally, finally make a decision! ***So they who? Who is the they?*** Who are the people we like to call procrastinators? Just slow brains? A collection of slow-circuited brain cells that can't make up their 'collective minds' (whatever that is supposed to mean)?

Nevertheless, the undecided and wavering are usually among the highly intelligent who consider complex and intricate issues others might not even think about. So they, and not their brains, are very carefully thinking and evaluating their options before deciding.

Who is it who seeks additional information before making an important decision? Who logs into the computer, visits Google and does some searching? Machine Man says: 'Oh, that is not you. That was your brain's intention, choice and action. Not yours.' And who decided to scroll down the many websites presented, click on a few search results (while opening separate tabs on your browser), and read some bits and pieces of information here and there, thinking about what might be useful or truthful? Again, supposedly, that was not you!

That was all decided and executed by your brain via its mythical creation, your subconscious mind, that then informed *you* about the brain's decisions. Oh, but sorry, and of course, that is not you either. It really should read like this: *The brain's illusory creation of a subconscious mind later informs yet another illusion, the conscious mind, of the decisions it took.* Got it? It's simple really, once you get used to confused thinking.

*Real science however does not and cannot show proof of any kind that a materially real or mentally imagined subconscious or unconscious mind actually exists.* Neither a neuroscientific Zombian version nor the mythical one proposed by psychoanalysts.

*There is simply nothing or nobody in our brains who exercises greater power, or has outright control, over who we really are. All such talk is just talk and theory only.* Pure imagination, wild speculation or just wishful thinking (a.k.a. psychological projection), without a shred of evidence. This is the scientific reality.

The (still) many disciples of Sigmund Freud and Carl Jung would now surely protest and disagree. Vehemently. The idea and the term of the unconscious or subconscious mind was actually first introduced by the 18th-century German Romantic *philosopher* Friedrich Schelling. A bit later, the *poet and essayist* Samuel Taylor Coleridge – a lifelong opium addict – introduced the concept to the English-speaking world (there is no moral judgment intended, but it is a relevant fact nonetheless).

Freud initially talked about the *subconscious* mind, but later changed the term to the *unconscious* mind. Both he and Jung popularized the concept, without offering scientific proof of any kind; they speculated that unconscious processes must exist simply because we do have dreams, laugh about strange jokes, or reveal the truth through slips of the tongue.

And sorry, that is not a joke. Oops, that must have been your author's slip of the tongue!

Repressed emotions, memories or desires are also offered as evidence, and so are instinctive reactions or automatic thoughts, behavior and skills. Proponents claim that these activities happen automatically and are not available to our conscious introspection – contrary to the actual real-life experience of most people (we will discuss these claims in coming chapters).

Sigmund Freud was a longtime compulsive user of cocaine (for over 15 years) and liberally prescribed it to his well-heeled mostly female clients; he believed that its stimulant and analgesic properties would somehow be helpful to deal with their assorted mental issues like anxiety and depression (as per his 1884 paper 'On Coca' and various other articles, see chapter *Notes*).

He supplied cocaine to his siblings, friends and colleagues, besides his fiancée, Martha Bernays, 'to make her strong and give her cheeks some color.' He also prescribed it to his morphine-addicted friend, Dr. Ernst von Fleischl-Marxow, who thereafter turned into a cocaine addict as well.

It is not about morality or a lack of respect or good manners to point out these and other perhaps sordid facts. It is simply a necessity. A public figure who lives an extraordinary life making extraordinary claims deserves, even demands, extraordinary scrutiny.

And especially so if whole generations of psychiatrists, psychologists and philosophers – many of whom now fashionably call themselves neuroscientists – over more than one hundred years have been taught to believe in these evidence-free claims. Not to speak of the thoroughly misguided general public who to this very day believes in this quackery, often with rather dire consequences to their mental health, and sometimes their very life.

So, the obvious question arises of how seriously should we take the ideas, dreams, visions and sexual fantasies or obsessions (cocaine is a powerful aphrodisiac) of heavy users of seriously mind-altering drugs like opium or cocaine? Is there any value other than perhaps demonstrating their personal mental problems and the power of projection onto others?

And, how seriously should we really take Freud's theories or practices of psychoanalysis when in a letter to Martha, he freely admitted to never having cured any of his patients (read the well documented and highly authoritative biography *Freud: The Making of an Illusion* by Frederick Crews; see chapter *Notes* for details)?

**"Patients only serve to provide us with a livelihood and material to learn from. We certainly cannot help them."** Sigmund Freud

He really meant that: "My most important client is just now going through a kind of nervous crisis and might get well in my absence," wrote Sigmund Freud, in a 1890 letter to his close friend and colleague, Wilhelm Fliess, about why he couldn't pay him a visit now.

Carl Jung not only believed in the unconscious (albeit a more positive version) but in a mythical collective unconscious too. Like his mother he also had two personalities: Personality Number 1 (as he called it) was as a contemporary Swiss schoolboy and Personality Number 2 an 18th century man of authority, influence and dignity, wearing buckled shoes and a white wig, traveling in a coach.

Was his own split personality the basis for his beliefs in the theory of a split mind? To be projected to all of us too? Did his lifelong self-analysis and search for an imaginary unconscious via self-induced hallucinations lead to his at least temporary psychosis and schizophrenia?

Well, perhaps his close contemporaries were right after all to call him more of a mystic than a scientist. He famously said: "Until you make the unconscious conscious, it will direct your life and you will call it fate."

*That sure sounds a lot like fear-mongering and fatalism*: 'You are on autopilot, my friend. So there is no need to make an effort. Just sit back, relax and enjoy the show of your life. Easy. And when you feel a bit uneasy, just pop this pill or that, or the whole lot of them. You can also talk to one of our skilled magicians who will sort through your perhaps confused but entirely imaginary emotions, and we will tell you what to do. Just in case you are not so happy with what your unconscious mind came up with for your viewing pleasure!'

New Age gurus and their followers also love to talk about the sub- or unconscious, ascribing it both great positive abilities that need to be unlocked, and terribly destructive powers that need to be overcome. Besides praying to this imaginary yet allpowerful subconscious, they also like to pay homage to a divine higher self that they need to talk to or meditate about.

Most unsurprisingly, most of today's neuroscientists (meaning mostly mere psychologists) believe, and believe is the key word, that an as of yet unidentified unconscious virtual pilot created by the brain, somehow also controls the biological computer that is the brain, that also generated a somewhat conscious illusion that is who we think we are, and is just able to observe and notice what we are allowed to notice.

They believe in magic but call it science. We will have to talk some more about this folly later on in chapter *Beyond Machine Man* because there are so many real-life, and often most dire, consequences of their fantasies. Mainly on an individual level, but sometimes in public life as well. It really is time to put an end to this myth that causes immense suffering and confusion. Luckily, there is hope that others have started to understand this as well:

Mandatory unconscious bias training in the Civil Service has now been scrapped by the British government after an assessment of the practice concluded that **it not only didn't work, but actually increased people's prejudices.** Small wonder unconscious training doesn't work because it just doesn't exist! There is no unconscious mind. Furthermore, focusing our minds on no matter what it may be, will make that object of our focus simply stronger and therefore more prevalent. That is a reality we can all observe and experience.

As far as actual science goes, **Homeostasis** is the one and only proven (besides obvious) sum total of processes of which we are not aware of, where we could indeed say that something, actually everything, happens on an unconscious level. Our brain, together with the central nervous system, independently takes care of life-sustaining functions and keeps all crucial biological conditions within a certain homeostatic range.

Things like maintaining our body's core temperature, fluid balance, blood glucose and pH levels, sodium and potassium concentration, calcium and iron levels, arterial blood pressure and oxygen content, neurotransmission and cerebrospinal fluids, gene regulation or the neuroendocrine system, and so on.

Luckily it is our brain that is **mostly** in charge of all that; we don't have to deliberate and choose, and our approval is not welcome or required either!

Why mostly only? Because many homeostatic aspects are getting influenced by the choices we consciously make by executing our free will. Sometimes we want to cool down our bodies during a heat wave and drink too much ice water (or cold beer) in an already freezing cold room. So our system will have to adjust to these conditions as well as possible. But still, we may suffer certain consequences like catching a cold (and/or having a hangover) as we knowingly chose to go beyond a certain healthy limit.

We can and do overrule this normally autonomous system (of which we are not directly aware of ) via our willpower. Taking pharmaceutical drugs also meddles with the independence and efficiency of this system, both with their intended and unintended results. Such conscious intervention or interference may be for the better at times, but often and probably mostly, it is for worse; nature after all usually knows better.

Ultramarathon runners (and others) frequently go beyond what their bodies and brains can endure. The brain will always inform us that we really should take a break or drop out of the race altogether. The whole body is aching and screaming from exhaustion. Yet someone, an obviously determined or stubborn person, freely decides to overrule all concerns and keeps running anyway. And sometimes they do drop dead in the process.

What's that all about, just brains running amok for no reasons? Was it just the silly brain's fault? Hardly, because it did inform and warn us about the impending dangers by giving us ample warning signs. ***Inform whom? Did the brain just inform and warn itself for hours on end*** (say, in a marathon), ***then continuously overruled itself until the entire system and body collapsed and died?*** Or, did the brain warn the actual person inhabiting the body? The real us. The who we really are. Who has freely choses to ignore all warnings.

***The big question is: who wills?*** Who uses willpower to overrule the brain? It can't be the brain itself as its primary mission is to ensure the survival of the entire organism. Why would it overrule itself, respectively get overruled by its fictional creation – the alleged yet unproven subconscious or unconscious mind – and go jump off mountains or worse?

Why are there or how could there be battles of will if there would be no willpower or free will? We can experience it ourselves or witness it all the time. World-class tennis players use their sheer willpower to win; they direct their exhausted or injured bodies to keep going, no matter what.

Besides, it's a mind's game: all athletes at the very top know full well that above a certain level of physical skills, it is all about maintaining their peak mental conditions. Once they lose their focus, once they lose the will to win, they will simply lose. It's as simple as that.

In a very hard-fought tennis match we can often witness the very moment of surrender, the loss of a player's willpower; we can visibly discern the difference between the determined winner-to-be and the having-already-surrendered player soon to be vanquished.

Experienced martial artists too learn to control and direct their minds, and thus bodies, while facing their adversary or battling exhaustion and pain. To keep one's mind focused, sharp and determined in a game of psychological warfare, requires the willpower to not give up, to keep going, to stay determined to win. Who is it who is so very determined? Who wills?

And who controls the mind, or learns how to do it? **We can all learn to control our thoughts.** There are many kinds of meditation techniques that are proven to calm down our racing thoughts and emotions, to overcome panic and fear, to help us become and stay more focused. **Somebody is obviously deciding to do that and then actually doing it.**

Who is it who focuses the mind? Just a collection of brain cells or synapses randomly firing together for no rational reasons or particular purpose but the sudden desire to better focus its make-believe creations, the mythical unconscious and conscious minds? Really?

And if so, **what about those fully-functional people with basically no brain**, as we've discussed in chapter *Brain Matters*? Who is it there who makes all the decisions, who thinks, feels and evaluates things before making their choices? Who is it here who dreams, desires and wills? Obviously it can't be the brain since that is essentially non-existent.

Rational questions deserve rational answers. At least they should motivate further inquiries and research. Asking smart questions after all is part and parcel of the scientific method.

So far however, supposedly rational Machine Man has presented us only with rather irrational and entirely unproven theories that go both against our rational minds and quite obvious personal experiences. Empirical evidence is also an essential part of the scientific method, and it clearly shows that indeed, we do have free will.

At least those who still take the time and make the effort to think and feel for themselves.

Now let's continue our exploration and look into other important parts of ourselves, aspects that have also been elusive of any real answers, yet may nevertheless reveal more about the puzzle of who we really are.

# Feelings

Our emotions, feelings and desires are often or perhaps mostly overriding our analytical thoughts. Every day we make decisions based on emotions and feelings, often against our much better judgment to the contrary. In other words, logic gets overruled by emotions.

This is true even for the smartest people I have met, those who have well and truly convinced themselves that they are one hundred percent rational beings only. That they are not emotional-driven in any way whatsoever. And yet, the evidence of their day-to-day decision-making proves otherwise. Sometimes very much so. Even if they themselves are not actually aware of it.

Why are emotions oftentimes dominating and overriding our thought processes? Well, it seems to indicate once again that there is someone 'in there' steering. Someone must make those evaluations based on what they want, what they desire from the bottom of their hearts.

Most of us are able to feel any or many of the following emotions, in alphabetical order: acceptance, admiration, affection, anger, amusement, anguish, annoyance, anticipation, anxiety, apathy, appreciation, arousal, avarice, awe, boredom, confidence, contempt, contentment, courage, curiosity, defeat, depression, desire, despair, disappointment, disgust, distrust, ecstasy, embarrassment, empathy, enthusiasm, envy, euphoria, excitement, fear, frustration, generosity, gratitude, grief, guilt, happiness, hatred, hope, horror, hostility, humiliation, interest, insecurity, jealousy, joy, loneliness, love, lust, outrage, panic, passion, pity, pleasure, pride, rage, regret, rejection, remorse, resentment, sadness, self-confidence, shame, shock, shyness, sorrow, suffering, surprise, tenderness, triumph, trust, wonder, and last but not least, worry.

What causes this myriad of emotions? And who feels them? Of course, Machine Man has no other answer than the usual one: our brains do!

Surprise, surprise. But joking aside, does modern science have any clue about what exactly causes our emotions? Where and how are they generated and stored or retrieved and relived? The simple but definite answer is that the latest state-of-the-art science does not know any of the answers.

*"Emotion is a mental state variously associated with thoughts, feelings, behavioral responses, and a degree of pleasure or displeasure. **There is currently no scientific consensus on a definition.**"* Wikipedia

While reading this non-explanation, remember that whenever scientists talk about the mind or mental states, they do mean the physical brain (to sometimes include the entire nervous system) because that is all there is to it in the opinion of Machine Man. As discussed, modern proponents also mean an illusory kind of mind, a type of mirage or make-believe construct that is said to be there, somewhere, but again, is just the product of a brain.

**There is no consensus about emotions but of course and as always, there are theories. Lots of them.** While reading through the summaries below, one could quite easily be forgiven to mistake them for the works of novelists or science fiction writers. And yet we are looking at what is considered to be the cutting edge of science. Let's find out more about the ideas of the brightest minds to date.

**Physiological theories propose that physical reactions within our bodies produce feelings and emotions as a secondary response only.** The James–Lange theory was proposed in the late 19th century by William James and Carl Lange and is still influential to this day. It says that an external stimulus like encountering a dangerous animal is triggering a pattern of physiological responses; **the heart rate increases and the breathing accelerates first, and only afterwards, is the brain interpreting these responses as fear.**

According to this theory, it is a matter of you are trembling therefore you feel afraid; you tremble first and only then will you realize that you are actually afraid. Wow. To these scientists it is not that you are afraid while walking down a dark alley in the middle of the night and start to tremble if you feel well and truly scared. Nope; you start to tremble while walking alone in the dark, and then you become afraid.

That however – and quite obvious to most of us – is not how it works. Besides, anyone who was ever afraid knows that there are different degrees of fear, and that sometimes we may be afraid but are far from physically trembling. Sometimes we also feel fear even though there is no real reason or external trigger to be afraid.

Furthermore, while exercising, our heart and breathing rates increase just as well yet we do not feel afraid in the least. While making love, we also breathe faster, our hearts are racing, we may even sweat and tremble, and *we experience a whole range of complex emotions, all at the same time.* But it rarely, if ever, includes fear.

The Cannon-Bard theory of emotion is another physiological theory. Walter Cannon and Philip Bard theorized that physical responses could not by themselves be responsible for our emotions because they were too slow and subtle to account for the often fast and intense nature of our feelings. So they've concluded that an emotion-evoking event triggers both a physiological response and a conscious experience of an emotion at the very same time.

Yet reality shows that there must be other factors at play. We can watch dangerous animals in the safety and comfort of a zoo, yet not feel any fear whatsoever. *Someone, a conscious being, obviously makes the distinction between different types of dangers, how real they are and how acute.* A man can also feel a bit lusty without having to walk around with bulging pants all the time. In other words, we can feel emotions without having any simultaneous or noticeable physiological response!

The Two-factor theory by Stanley Schachter and Jerome Singer states that first we encounter an emotion-invoking event and then we experience an emotion. So first we notice a snake in the garage, then the heart starts to race, then the brain scans the place to find out why the heart suddenly pumps faster, notices the snake, and finally interprets and labels the pounding heart as the emotion of fear. Simple, isn't it?

We can only hope that the brain never makes an error in its interpretation and mistakes the emotion of fear with the emotion of love. Imagine to see the snake but the silly brain somehow confuses the pounding heart as a sign of affection, and orders the muscles of the body to bend over, pick up the snake and give it a big hug and kiss. That would be quite a macabre sight to behold.

There is a whole range of cognitive theories that assume the involvement of cognitive activity in the creation of emotions. They suggest that at first the brain must make an appraisal, judgment or evaluation of a situation before an emotion can happen. One very influential theory was formulated by psychologist Richard Lazarus, who proposes the following order of events:

1. Cognitive appraisal: someone sees a snake, then cognitively assesses it as a danger.
2. Physiological changes: the brain activates the adrenal glands which pump adrenaline into the blood stream, resulting in an increased heartbeat.
3. Action: the person starts to feels the emotion of fear, then decides how to react. Like starting to scream and run away, or freeze up in panic.

Essentially, the theory is saying that the brain thinks first before we are able to feel an emotion. So we can't ever fall in love with someone in a split second or a heart beat. Nope, first we must assess that this person is worthy of our tender feelings – for reasons like good looks, nice smells, a sexy smile, beautiful eyes, similarity to our mother or father, and so on and so forth – before we can actually feel any loving feelings. Sounds right?

And no, we're not only talking about physical attraction or sexual urges here, but also really falling in love. Despite the fact that we actually don't particularly like certain physical or mental features about the other person.

Unconditional love. It happens (including to yours truly). Without having to think it through first.

It also assumes that in step three, the action step, there is someone who can make a decision, someone who decides what the best course of action would be upon feeling afraid. A fight, flight, freeze or hide response. But the same Machine Man scientists say that there is nobody but the brain who makes decisions. And that what we think is us is just a mirage, a conscious illusion or a mere observer who is conscious about what is happening without actually being involved. And only later on, after some delay.

In other words, their theories keep contradicting themselves all the time and in so many ways. ***We can't have it both ways. Either there is a conscious sentient being in charge of it all, or it's all just the brain doing all kinds of things***, either at random by sheer chance, for no reasons at all, or as a result of the drive to survive.

There are also neurological theories suggesting that some kind of activity within the brain eventually leads to an emotional response. Essentially, it's the same mystery or miracle explanation often favored by religious people:

*The brain is supposedly doing something that is unspecified and unclear as of today's knowledge, yet this unspecified and unclear activity still produces one of the seventy-seven very specific and clearly defined emotions* we have identified above.

Reality however is that ***we always know why we feel certain emotions or have particular feelings.*** At least most of us do. These are not generated by chance but as specific reactions to what is happening in our lives and environments. The only real question is how honest we are with ourselves; how good we are with introspection and self-reflection, how easily we can admit our own mistakes, or how much we'd like to fool ourselves.

We always know why we are sad, what exactly makes us particularly happy or mad. Usually we can easily identify the reasons why. At least if we wanted to!

We also have instant feelings that simply cannot be caused by the long-winding and time-consuming process described in the many theories about emotions. *We can and do feel things instantly.* As in right away. Upon meeting someone for the first time, we immediately like or dislike that person. Later we may analyze or speculate about the reasons why, but nevertheless, we feel it instantly.

*There is no delay or time* for all kinds of biochemical or electrical things to happen first on an atomic or subatomic level. Or all the evaluations and assessments and feedback loops that are said to happen before we feel what we feel.

What do these assorted theories have in common? For a start, they are all making assumptions about what really are only instincts or learned reflexes. *Their theories all use fear as their chosen example. And fear is a very basic instinct only.* It is not a complex or complicated emotion like the many we may strongly and simultaneously feel about people we have known and interacted with over many years, even the course of a lifetime.

So just imagine the many more fantastic theories and outlandish explanations we can look forward to in the future to come, once scientists dare to venture into the most complex of emotions, or even combinations thereof!

Another common thread is that they like to use encountering a snake as their favorite example, which is a universal but learned fear. Most of us learn to fear snakes from a very young age on; children's books or TV programs tell scary stories or show us frightening pictures; parents, grand parents and preschool teachers all tell us to be careful and, well, afraid. So it is not particularly surprising to develop fear as a consequence.

*Yet despite all empirical evidence to the contrary, most theories prefer to assume genetic components for our emotions.* Without offering any evidence. Imagine what would happen if a little baby grew up with snakes as playmates simply because their parents like them so much to keep them as pets. Such people do exist. Already in the crib, the baby learns to play with the snake, they like each other's company and all is jolly and good. How would that be possible if there were a genetic reason to fear snakes?

***Many of us know that we can overcome our fears.*** I was terribly afraid of snakes too, but now, having lived in the Australian rainforest for more than two decades, I only get mildly annoyed, not afraid, when I have to catch yet another one inside our house and move it to the outside. My fear of heights I conquered by making the private pilot's license. My fear of sharks came about only upon watching the Jaws horror movie at age twelve. Before that I've never feared them in the least. And I got over it by obtaining a diver's license.

Last but not least, we can notice that almost all theories about emotions were and are postulated by psychologists who lack a real medical training. Asking questions and pursuing theories in the pursuance of truths is of course very important. But merely making assumptions and jumping to much publicized conclusions without evidence is not science.

With all due respect, but we have to acknowledge the fact that their entire profession is really mostly about coming up with theories, just like storytellers. Their very foundation is not actual hard cold science but mere subjective speculations, assumptions, projections, hypotheses, conjectures, interpretations, mythical archetypes, and the like.

All of it is based on an entirely fictional split mind story where non-existing unconscious mental processes are ***believed*** to happen upon analyzing people's dreams, jokes or slips of the tongue. And yet this fabled unconscious mind is supposed to be more powerful than our conscious mind. Believe it at your own risk!

Machine Man psychologists (and most of them are of the Machine Man persuasion) also ***believe*** in emotional circuits in the brain that are said to be responsible for very specific emotions. So they propose a brain circuit of fear or a circuit of anger, one for sadness, and so on. Of course they have zero evidence to offer, but never mind. Another perhaps a bit more advanced view is that multiple brain networks work together to create a single emotion. But again, there is no proof of that either.

The theory of constructed emotion is yet another of the most recent scientific theories trying to explain why we experience emotions. It was proposed by Lisa Feldman Barrett, a University Distinguished Professor of Psychology at Northeastern University, who describes its simplified version as follows:

"In every waking moment, *your brain uses past experience*, organized as concepts, to guide your actions and give your sensations meaning. When the concepts involved are emotion concepts, *your brain constructs instances of emotion*."

Of course, this begs the question about *what type of emotions the brain could possibly come up with when we have a first time experience of some kind*, something that has never ever happened before, or we have not yet learned about in any way whatsoever. What then?

What if we never had the experience of losing a loved one? Once told about the passing of a very dear person, our brain has therefore no such experience to recall and construct the most profound feelings of sadness and loss. So we shouldn't or couldn't be sad or feel devastated, right? Well, the answer is obvious. And proves the theory wrong.

Alright, perhaps we remember a movie featuring a dearly departed, where the actor became visibly and terribly sad. So maybe our brain will now also be able to come up with the emotions of sadness. But what if we are so young that we didn't yet see such a sad story in a movie? Or what if we actually feel happy because the dearly departed person was actually a real bastard who was always mean to us? We could also feel happy, again without any precedents, because a loved one doesn't need to suffer any longer. Another new situation.

Furthermore, we can also become angry for entirely new reasons, in situations that we have never heard of or encountered before. Despite having no such concepts or memories stored, we will still become annoyed, offended or outraged. Why or how could that be?

Or how did we, respectively our brains, know how to feel **on our first day at school** when we (or our brains) completely lack such an experience? Or even earlier, while entering preschool? On our first date or during our first kiss? There are no such concepts stored in our brains that could be used to construct an emotion. The many emotions we will surely feel during our first bungee jump or sky dive are entirely novel experiences too; we only know it when we do it ourselves. Not a moment before.

And so it is with a great many experiences in life. That is how we learn and progress. It would be futile for me trying to tell you how chocolate ice cream tastes like when you never had any chocolate or ice cream. You'd have to try it yourself and go through the sensations and emotions by yourself.

As we can see from all of these very current cutting-edge examples, there are dozens of theories. And that is all they really are: theories. Not actual knowledge of how things work, where or why. There is simply no scientific evidence that any of the proposed theories are actual fact. None whatsoever. But there are plenty of common sense reasons why they are simply wrong!

*"The scientists of today think deeply instead of clearly. One must be sane to think clearly, but one can think deeply and be quite insane."* Nikola Tesla

We also need to ask a most fundamental question that seems to get ignored. **Why does or should the brain have emotions when it can't even feel pain?** What is the purpose of having feelings? Well, the usual answer is that they are helping us to survive and thrive. And again, that through the long-term process of natural selection, they separate the wheat from the chaff, ensuring that only the best will be able to pass on their genes, and the rest will simply fade away into obscurity. Or the great nothingness that is supposedly awaiting us all.

When you read again over the aforementioned seventy-seven different emotions and feelings, you will notice that some of them may indeed be helpful for us to survive longer and do well in a social setting. Some may also be advantageous in the decision-making or planning process. Or to communicate things more clearly by making facial expressions that correspond to how we feel.

But most of them are simply not rational or make any sense whatsoever. Neither from a personal selfish survival nor a collective evolutionary point of view.

What could possibly be the purpose of the following emotions? Why should the brain come up with them, respectively make the illusory observer – the make-believe creation that is supposedly us – feel them? For example, the feeling of wonder, shyness, regret, frustration, pity, shame, resentment, insecurity, sorrow, awe, envy, loneliness, embarrassment, remorse, horror, despair, and so on.

How does feeling lonely and depressed contribute to us living longer and better? Feeling vengeful and taking violent revenge is hardly conducive to either goal and more likely to result in the premature death of one's own life, to potentially include the early termination of our biological descendants. Feeling insecure is also not exactly a positive or helpful trait. And neither is to have sorrows or feel pity for others.

Perhaps with the exception of psychopaths or sociopaths, *we can all feel and experience an incredible range of complex and complicated emotions, often both simultaneously and instantly.* Some are most pleasant and others rather unpleasant. Our emotions can cause all kinds of mayhem like losing the job we depend on for our survival, say upon telling our boss what we really think of him. Or to stop talking with our parents or siblings, sometimes over decades or forever. That's all neither happy nor healthy.

Someone 'in there' must obviously be very stubborn. *Who is it? Just a make-believe concoction of the brain 'having fun'? A silly brain having a weird sense of humor? Or a fully sentient and conscious being who feels, interacts and responds to other people, its immediate environment and events?*

If our emotions were solely to help us get along better with fellow beings, live in peace and therefore likely longer, cooperate more and live happier, **why would the brain choose to have emotions that doesn't serve it well**, to say the least?

Obviously many of our emotions are very counterproductive to said goals, even damaging to the extreme. Is it just the brain being foolish or stubborn and sabotaging itself? For no reasons other than biochemicals moving around randomly in our skulls, or a bunch of neurons aimlessly firing electrical discharges?

Why would the brain whose main job is to keep us alive allow us to die from broken heart syndrome? Japanese researchers first identified this condition in the 1990s and called it **Takotsubo** (Takotsubo or stress cardiomyopathy); it means octopus pot and symbolizes the disfigurement of a broken heart. It is a direct consequence of severe emotional stress like the death of a loved one, rejection from a partner, a break-up of close relationships or constant anxiety and stress. The heart muscles weaken **suddenly and dramatically** which may lead to acute heart failure, lethal ventricular arrhythmias, and ventricular rupture (a.k.a. death).

**There are simply no benefits for the brain to play such silly, irresponsible or dangerous games.** Besides ensuring our survival, the brain has absolutely no need for complicated or complex feelings. Also, **if our emotions were just part of an elaborate illusion or hoax** controlled by another illusion controlled by the assembly of neurons we have chosen to call our brains, **why do they feel so very real to us? And cause real troubles, pain and even death?** So we have to ask again: **who is us?**

Some of us are more emotionally driven than others. And that often changes over the course of a lifetime. As we grow older, more experienced and wiser, we learn how to better control our feelings. Or to even use them to our advantage. There are many techniques available for us to learn how to deal with our emotions and feelings. And of course, that once again indicates that there must be someone who decides to make these efforts. In other words, **there is a driver who is increasingly in control.**

*Who is that driver?* The illusory sense of conscious self created by the brain that is controlled by another make-believe creation by the brain, the subconscious self of which we are not conscious? But hardcore Machine Man, like the previously mentioned Zombians, say that our brains cause all kinds of behavior – including producing emotions – without any actual conscious intentions. That is supposedly only observed or felt later, again for no discernible reasons.

*Reality however is that we all experience that we are more or less in charge of our feelings.* They come and go, we can focus on some if we want to, or more or less easily dismiss others. Every single moment of our day. Sometimes there are external impulses that we can readily identify, and at other times we may have to contemplate and search for the reasons why we do feel the way we do at that particular moment in time.

So obviously, there must be someone who is in charge. *Someone who feels, controls, desires and decides. And that is likely us, the real us, the who we really are.*

Most people would agree that our emotions and feelings are part and parcel of ourselves. They define and refine our character and personality; they help to turn us into the unique individuals we all are.

Emotions and feelings are important milestones in life by reminding us about our past experiences and the many lessons we have learned already. They help us to make better decisions or plan ahead. They motivate us to keep going in the present, no matter the perhaps difficult situations we may be facing today.

In other words, our many emotions and feelings are essential to who we really are. And yet, since science has not the slightest clue about what they are, where what happens, or where and how they are stored, how could it be possible to simply transfer (as in 'copy and paste') them to our next incarnation inside a computer memory drive (or the like) as suggested by believers in transhumanism?

Well, maybe our many past and present emotions are simply part of our memories? So they must be also stored in our memory banks, right? You know, those parts of the brain where memories are created, stored and retrieved. Where all the knowledge we have accumulated resides, together with all the assorted thoughts we ever had throughout the course of our lifetimes.

After all we can quite easily, even instantly, recall how we felt at any given moment, say at our wedding or a funeral, at school when we got scolded, our first kiss, and so on. Of course, pleasant memories are particularly easy to recall. Some bitter or painful experiences however we may find to be rather unpleasant, and have therefore stored away in more distant or hidden 'little boxes' that could also be accessed if we wanted to, but usually don't.

So it's all in our memory chips, right? Nice and easy. We can just copy and paste it all in one simple transaction! First the sum total of our emotions, feelings, thoughts and knowledge gets downloaded, then uploaded someplace else, and we're good as new. It's just like transferring any and all of the archives from an old computer to the new one. Right?

Well, let's investigate this a bit further and see if it really is that simple!

# Memories

What does contemporary science say about our memories? How are they created and where and how are they stored? How do they get erased or changed? And how can we access them? Whenever we need to use some of our knowledge, remember what we may have said and promised, or when we want to look back to an especially nice moment in the past.

Scientists **believe** that there are many different kinds of memory systems. Unsurprisingly, these are fashionably based on the jargon of computer geeks, including the ascribing of different names to different **assumed** functions. For our purposes, we only need to get a brief overview; the various names by themselves are already quite revealing.

So we are said to have a working memory and a short-term memory. Then there is the explicit memory (or declarative memory) which is one of the two main types of long-term memory; it gets further divided into episodic memory and semantic memory; it also has a subcategory called recognition memory. Implicit memory (or procedural memory) is the other long-term memory.

Autobiographical memory and spatial memory are other **suggested** types of memory. Among others still, like iconic memory and echoic memory (for fast decaying visual, respectively auditory information), or haptic memory (recording our sense of touch).

Let's see a few Wikipedia quotes to help us understand this a bit more. But before we do, allow me a personal observation that is very widely shared by other researchers: Wikipedia has a long history of solely promoting, even glorifying, the Machine Man way of looking at science and medicine. And rigorously deleting all alternative views and explanations. If it occasionally allows any mentioning of an alternative theory or its proponent, it is only to heap plenty of scorn and ridicule.

In short, Wikipedia editors are the Internet's cheerleaders of Machine Man reductionist thinking whereas everything is matter only and that is all there is. So, quoting them is equivalent to giving Machine Man scientists their greatest moments of current glory!

*"The **idea** of the division of memory into short-term and long-term dates back to the 19th century. A **classical model** of memory developed in the 1960s **assumed** that all memories pass from a short-term to a long-term store after a small period of time. This model is **referred to as the "modal model"**... The exact mechanisms by which this transfer takes place, whether all or only some memories are retained permanently, and indeed the existence of a genuine distinction between the two stores, **remain controversial topics** among experts."*

*"The relationship between short-term memory and working memory **is described differently by various theories**, but it is generally acknowledged that the two **concepts** are distinct. **Working memory is a theoretical framework** that refers to structures and processes used for temporarily storing and manipulating information."*

*"Working memory is generally **considered to** have limited capacity."*

*"Working memory is often used synonymously with short-term memory, but **some theorists consider** the two forms of memory distinct, **assuming that** working memory allows for the manipulation of stored information, whereas short-term memory only refers to the short-term storage of information."*

*"In 1974, Baddeley and Hitch introduced the multicomponent **model** of working memory. **The theory proposed** a model containing three components."*

*"Not all researchers agree that short-term and long-term memory are separate systems. Various **researchers have proposed** that stimuli are coded in short-term memory using transmitter depletion... **According to this hypothesis**... **One proposed explanation** of the existence... The relationship between short-*

*term memory and working memory* **is described differently by various theories**...*The decay* **assumption** *is usually paired with the idea of*..."

"*Episodic memory* **is believed to be** *the system that provides the basic support for semantic memory.*"

"*Several neural structures* **are proposed** *to be involved in explicit memory.*"

These are obviously just excerpts from longer articles. Short yet relevant nonetheless. So far, does it look like modern science knows exactly what is going on with the many memory systems that we are said to have? Well, clearly we can glimpse from the above quotes that the answer seems to be a definite No, or not yet. Furthermore, is sure looks like *the many different kind of proposed memories are theoretical constructs only.*

But let's move on and find out about how and where our assorted memories are encoded and stored. *In typical Machine Man fashion, the preordained and only way to research this is trying to find a piece of matter that is responsible for it since matter is all there is.* So there must be something, as in some thing. And that theoretical thing yet to be found was called Engram (by the influential German memory researcher Richard Semon), or a memory trace.

"*Engrams are theorized to be means by which memories are stored as biophysical or biochemical changes in the brain (and other neural tissue) in response to external stimuli.*" Wikipedia

American psychologist and behaviorist Karl Lashley searched for engrams in rats who were previously taught how to get out of a labyrinth. He cut up bits and pieces of their brains to see exactly where the memorized ability to solve maze puzzles were located. *Yet no matter how much brain tissue was cut out in various parts of the brain*, the rats could still remember their way out; *they never lost their memory!*

Many years of failed experiments showed that memory just could not be found anywhere, or otherwise be identified as a physical trace in neurological tissue. Lashley later published a famous paper entitled *In Search Of The Engram* (Society of Experimental Biology Symposium 4: 454–482), that summarized his 33 years of brain research on memory.

To this day, the best answer by the best neurologists still is that *'memory is everywhere in the brain and nowhere.'* Obviously, this conclusion alone will make it rather difficult for our transhumanist friends wanting to **transfer our entire minds** to a computer disk, the cloud, or some kind of cyborg machinery that will preserve who we are, once our physical bodies have turned to ashes and dust.

One issue complicating the search for the nature and location of our elusive memory functions is the neuroplastic character of our brains; its ability to constantly change, from microscopic to larger-scale changes. That happens for many reasons, including our individual lifestyle choices. **This neuroplasticity makes it very unlikely that our brains are the one and only storage place of our memories, if indeed it is the place at all.**

Brain cells themselves are both complex and changeable too. Individual and bundled nerve fibers (axons) constantly rewire themselves in unique patterns, besides changing both the speed and reliability of transmissions. Dendrites (treelike branches of neurons) and synapses (nerve gateways or terminals) are also continually changing and adapting to various electrical or chemical impulses and experiences.

Millions of new neurons are being created every moment of every day. So **anything stored in our old and discarded brain cells would get lost all the time.** Such a system would neither be very energy efficient (a very important and fundamental feature of our brains, as previously discussed) nor make much sense otherwise.

**The failure to locate physical traces of memory should also not be all that surprising upon considering the fundamental reality of Molecular Turnover.** We have discussed this elemental phenomenon at length in chapters *First Conclusions* and *Brain Matters*: **all of the atoms and biomolecules making up our bodies and brains turn over very rapidly and keep getting replaced.**

"Theoretically we still have a small percentage of the same atoms in us that we had when we were born, but actually this percentage must be extremely small. *In a year most of the atoms in us now – at least 98 percent of them – will have been replaced by other atoms* that we take in via air, food, and drink." Dr. Paul Aebersold, eminent American nuclear and biophysicist who discovered Molecular Turnover.

Our brains are never ever the same on an atomic, molecular or full scale level. And every single brain is totally unique. The only thing that really stays constant is that everything keeps changing. *Yet we are always the same personalities with the same memories* of our thoughts, emotions, experiences, and knowledge.

"I have been puzzled by my ability to remember my childhood even though *most of the molecules in my body today are not the same ones I had as a child* – in particular the molecules that make up my brain are constantly being replaced with newly minted molecules – *despite this molecular turnover, I have detailed memories of places where I lived fifty years ago*." Terrence Sejnowski, pioneering computational neuroscientist, Professor at The Salk Institute for Biological Studies, Adjunct Professor Neurobiology at UCSD.

Is there additional evidence that *our memories are not stored in our brains*? Actually, yes there is. Quite a bit indeed.

In chapter *Brain Matters* we have discussed individuals who have only half a brain or no real (detectable) brain, and yet they have no memory deficits or problems in any way. They live normal lives. How could that be possible if our memories were just a function of our brains?

When confronted by such amazing anomalies, such incredible deviations from what is believed to be normal or possible, Machine Man scientists choose to simply ignore it all; they basically bury their collective heads in the sand and hope that the problem, or challenge to their way of thinking, will just go away. By simply not talking about it.

Nevertheless: ***Anomalies essentially prove that the impossible is indeed possible.*** They clearly demonstrate that we need to change our current models and ways of thinking. In other words, we really have to consider any and all other possibilities that were not yet disproved and ruled out. As in, disproved by real factual evidence, not merely by the stubborn (and rather silly) clinging to deeply cherished but obviously erroneous beliefs.

***Terminal lucidity*** is yet another anomaly that points to another location of both our mind and memories, beyond our mere physical brains. And beyond the current reductionist theories of Machine Man scientists.

The term Terminal Lucidity was coined by Dr. Bruce Greyson, Chester F. Carlson Professor Emeritus of Psychiatry and Neurobehavioral Sciences and Professor of Psychiatric Medicine at the University of Virginia, and Michael Nahm, PhD, in a research article that examined 81 case references (published in The Journal of Nervous and Mental Disease, December 2009 in Volume 197, Issue 12).

Throughout history, nurses taking care of patients in hospitals, hospices and nursing homes have reported this (for Machine Man) inexplicable phenomenon. It refers to the sudden return of full mental clarity and memory to patients with heavily deteriorated brains shortly before they actually pass away.

In fact, it is often the most accurate predictor of an impending or imminent death (mostly about a week before, sometimes merely hours). And it happens in almost one hundred percent of the seriously mentally ill, according to innumerable testimonials by veteran nurses who among themselves call it 'the last hurrah,' 'the calm before the storm,' or 'the glow before they go.'

Patients who have suffered sometimes for decades from severe schizophrenia, dementia and other serious psychiatric or neurological disorders like Alzheimer's disease, tumors, strokes or meningitis, suddenly regain all of their mental faculties and full memories before their deaths. ***Their brains were severely dysfunctional, their memories impaired or gone, yet all came back in an instant. Regardless of their still damaged brains.***

Previously missing memories, mental abilities and personality traits were suddenly fully restored. And patients were able to talk again with their loved ones in a normal and coherent way, just like they did before they fell ill. How could that be possible if everything, including our memories, were somehow only a function of our brains?

This reality in itself totally destroys the narrative of Machine Man. *Terminal lucidity or final clarity would be impossible if the brain were indeed necessary for the mind to function, or if the brain created the mind, because these brains were severely damaged* and did not function anymore as shown in both brain scans and actual experience.

Nevertheless the state of their diseased physical brains, people's memories and personalities were still intact. They were still there, somewhere. In hiding, suspension or simply and mostly someplace else, in another dimension of reality.

*Terminal lucidity demonstrates the reality of free will and choice in life, to include the free nature of our memories*, and whether and to what degree we are willing to interact with this world, the current reality, or not. The following is an overview of my thoughts about our memories and emotions, based on empirical research, personal experiences, and a bit of good old common sense logic:

1. There are memories we are currently aware of involving present issues and desires, or anticipated and planned future events.
2. There are recent, past or distant past memories we are very fond of and can therefore easily recall at any time we like.
3. *We decide what we want to remember or not*: there are memories we find to be rather unpleasant, even upsetting, and have therefore decided to compartmentalize, to put away and insulate in distant corners of our minds; these are still ready to be accessed if we wanted to, but usually we prefer not to because they are so unpleasant or outright too painful to remember. It's a bit like having lots of old household items stored away in a storage room. We do have the key to visit, but often don't bother as we are too busy with our present life.

4. Reasons for not wanting to remember certain life events include feelings of regret, guilt and shame, being overwhelmed with grief, and other emotional pains.

5. Sometimes we can become fed up with life or the people in our lives and simply prefer to dwell more within our minds rather than the current unpleasant reality. We may get severely affected by negativity or all kinds of totally unwanted aspects that make life unbearable to the point that we mentally depart and disengage with all the unpleasantness, our emotional hurt or physical pain, feeling unloved, not appreciated or misunderstood.

6. Since we are inherently pleasure seeking beings who generally shun unpleasantness and suffering, *we ourselves (not the brain) determine the strength, durability and availability of our memories by their importance and likeability*, their pleasantness and our fondness for them. Famous among economists are those investors who just love to remember and brag about their winning stock picks, while mysteriously forgetting all about their losses. Strangely, nobody ever hears about them. *Clearly, we can be very good at ignoring or not remembering things, people or events!*

7. When we feel that the end is nigh, that we are about to leave our bodies behind, we may wish to make a last effort to settle things, talk about certain emotional issues and make peace, or to simply express our heretofore unexpressed love for the dearest people in our life. So we fully focus our attention into the here and now again before departing for good.

8. *Where and how strongly we focus our attention is what really matters*: we can be fully focused, be only partially focused, or totally scattered all over the place (e.g. while drunk or otherwise high). Mentally, we can be fully here, partially only, or be totally absent, quite literally floating somewhere up in the clouds. The decision is always up to us, the who we really are. At least if we are aware of this fact.

9. When we are not in charge of our minds, someone else will happily take over and manipulate us to do things we may not want or like to do. People with widely scattered minds are more likely to become victims of hypnosis, brainwashing or other forms of conditioning

(e.g. social engineering by companies, governments or society in general) than those who can stay highly aware and sharply focused.

10. ***We are more or less conscious beings, who are more or less aware of our thoughts, feelings and activities, who notice more or less what is actually happening in our current environments.*** The lesser conscious and not very aware are often creatures of their compulsive habits, automatic behaviors, or semi-automatic routines. Like driving to work on a familiar road while thinking about something else entirely. And of course, the less situational aware we are, the more dangerous life may become!

11. Another paramount principle to what is happening or not happening with our memories is the nature of our beliefs, as we have seen while discussing the Placebo and Nocebo effects: if we believe that our memories deteriorate with age, then they sure will. And if we believe that we do have a fantastic memory, then we will surely remember it all, for as long as we actually wanted to.

In summary, ***all of our memories are always available to us if only we wanted to remember them.*** Sometimes we do want to remember and sometimes we just don't. There are no physical traces of memories or any particular locations where they are stored. Nor are there different kinds of memories. ***All memories are instantly accessible within the energy fields of who we really are.*** These energy fields vibrate and extend to the subatomic space of every single atom making up our bodies and brains.

Most of the thoughts presented here are simply common sense observations of real-life experiences and situations. As such, most people would easily agree. Science may one day prove them right or wrong. In the meantime, it is probably best to be guided by empirical facts. The actual realities of life.

***The many anomalies discussed clearly show that the materialistic paradigm cannot be true.*** Otherwise they were simply not possible and would therefore not happen. The many unproven theories about the nature of our memories and emotions, or how and where they may be stored, are most likely wrong too as they are also based on the faulty premises of physicalism.

What about our thoughts; how and where are thoughts created in the first place? What does science know about it? Well, the short answer is: not much at all, if anything:

"Thought (also called thinking) – the mental process in which beings form psychological associations and models of the world. Thinking is manipulating information, as when we form concepts, engage in problem solving, reason and make decisions. ***Thought, the act of thinking, produces thoughts***." Wikipedia

"Thought (or thinking) can be described as an activity taking place in a:
1. brain – organ that serves as the center of the nervous system in all vertebrate and most invertebrate animals It is the physical structure associated with the mind.
2. mind – abstract entity with the cognitive faculties of consciousness, perception, thinking, judgment, and memory. Having a mind is a characteristic of living creatures. Activities taking place in a mind are called mental processes or cognitive functions." Wikipedia

***"Although thinking is an activity of an existential value for humans, there is no consensus as to how it is defined or understood."*** Wikipedia

Reality is that our brains and minds are essentially a near total mystery. So no matter the fervent desire or exuberant enthusiasm of ***Homo Digitalis – the transhumanist subspecies of Machine Man*** – wanting to live forever, it is obviously not going to be a simple matter of copy and paste, or plug and play.

Yet no matter the lack of required knowledge and proof, respectively the actual presence of solid evidence that completely invalidates their worldview, Machine Man still believes in physicalism, the belief that everything can be reduced to matter, including their own beliefs.

***"It seems to me immensely unlikely that mind is a mere by-product of matter.*** For if my mental processes are determined wholly by the motions of atoms in my brain I have no reason to suppose that my beliefs are true." J.B.S. Haldane, eminent geneticist.

*Machine Man faithfully believes that a conscious intelligent mind came from unconscious dumb matter, by sheer luck and for no reason or purpose.* And that their belief is the only smart and correct one. Adherents of all religions faithfully believe that too!

How close are transhumanists to making their deeply cherished dreams come true? Well, as you can tell, nowhere near at all! My prediction is that for as long as Machine Man scientists insist on researching purely along the lines of physical reductionism, they will not be able to realize even the very beginning of their dreams.

*"The day science begins to study non-physical phenomena, it will make more progress in one decade than in all the previous centuries of its existence."* **Nikola Tesla**

Moreover, if there ever would be a breakthrough in terms of accessing and transferring our memories in a few hundred or thousand years, as unlikely as that is, *it would only be a static situation, a fixed recording of all past thoughts and emotions*, without the ability to think and feel anything new. Simply because there would be *no conscious life* present to have such new thoughts and feelings.

*Somebody must be alive to think and feel, someone must be conscious to live.* Without consciousness there is no life, and therefore no thoughts and feelings either.

But what exactly is consciousness and indeed, what is life itself? In the next two chapters we will find out what the latest insights of Machine Man scientists and philosophers are, before presenting some more evidence that will take us further into the far beyond.

# Living Magic

What is life? Where did it come from and how exactly did that happen? Where does life disappear to when it's seemingly no longer present? And is there any particular value of or purpose to life? Or is life just the result of one big accident plus many little follow-up acts of mere chance, entirely for no reason or purpose?

These are all questions that Machine Man cannot really answer. Of course and as always, they do claim to know yet when we look a bit closer there is no real knowledge. Once again there are only theories, assumptions and beliefs. Lot's of beliefs!

Let's start our investigation with an official definition of what life is, according to Merriam-Webster: "The *quality* that distinguishes a vital and functional being from a dead body."

Wikipedia perhaps more helpfully defines life like this: "Life is a *characteristic* that distinguishes physical entities that have biological processes, such as signaling and self-sustaining processes, from those that do not."

Essentially most of the *officially sanctioned* or employed scientists believe that *Abiogenesis* is the origin of life. Wikipedia defines it as follows:

"Abiogenesis is the natural process by which *life arises from non-living matter*, such as simple organic compounds. While *the details of this process are still unknown*, the *prevailing scientific hypothesis* is that the transition from non-living to living entities was not a single event, but *an evolutionary process* of increasing complexity."

Wikipedia continues, "While the occurrence of abiogenesis is uncontroversial among scientists, its possible mechanisms are poorly understood.

There are *several principles and hypotheses* for how abiogenesis *could have* occurred."

Does that sound like all science is well and truly settled? That those scientists (perhaps more aptly called believers) really know what they are talking about? Or does it somewhat sound like and resemble what we get to hear in various kinds of religious schools the world over?

Here we will not dig deeper into the proposed rather fanciful details of abiogenesis. We could however suitably summarize *the official belief* about the origin of life like this: *Some say that life was created for no reasons by an endless streak of good luck involving dumb and dead matter that nobody made out of nothing.*

Are there any dissenting scientists at all? Yes indeed, there are. More than 1'000 of the world's top scientists (from universities such as Yale, Princeton, Stanford, MIT, UC Berkeley, UCLA, the US National Academy of Sciences, Russian, Hungarian and Czech National Academies) have signed the following statement:

*"We are skeptical of claims for the ability of random mutation and natural selection to account for the complexity of life. Careful examination of the evidence for Darwinian theory should be encouraged."* DissentfromDarwin.org

These eminent professors, doctors and researchers are well versed in the latest scientific discoveries and are experts in a variety of scientific disciplines like cosmology, quantum chemistry, physics, biology, genetics, medicine, and others. Individually and for their own reasoning, they all came to the conclusion that we really don't know how life came about.

Are they all easily dismissed creationists who simply believe in Intelligent Design? Well, not really as their arguments are entirely based upon unquestioned facts and very specific scientific principles in their particular fields of expertise. Furthermore, quite many of these highly accomplished scientists who voiced such deep doubts are actually self-declared atheists who nevertheless remained intellectually curious and honest, without having a particular philosophical or political agenda. Perhaps nowadays, they are a rather rare breed.

They all agree that there are indeed small-scale changes in a population of organisms. These both past and ongoing processes are often called **Microevolution**. However, many of the distinguished but dissenting scientists seriously question the theory of **Universal Common Descent** which suggests that all organisms are related, having descended from a single common ancestor through unguided natural processes.

The above statement of disagreement actually refers to their unanimous doubt in **Darwinian Evolution**, the theory that there was *a blind, unguided process of natural selection acting upon random mutation as the primary mechanism* driving the evolution of life.

Darwinian theory calls for a pattern of gradual evolution. However, many modern paleontologists have pointed out the general lack of finding credible candidates for intermediate, transitional fossils that would confirm the theory. After many centuries of digging nonetheless. Instead, the long-term fossil records show a pattern of a sudden and unexpected emergence of entirely new, complex forms of life.

About 540 million years ago, during a period paleontologists refer to as the **Cambrian explosion**, fossil records show a (geologically speaking) rapid spike (over 13-15 million years) in sophisticated life forms, resulting in *the abrupt appearance of almost all major animal phyla known today*. In the preceding three and a half billion years, most organisms were only very simple, individual cells occasionally organized into colonies.

According to Darwin's theories, there should have been many Precambrian predecessors in the fossil records, but none could ever be found. And neither was any upward branching structure. Charles Darwin himself discussed this inexplicable lack of earlier fossils in his book *On the Origin of Species*, recognizing it as one of the main difficulties for his theory.

*"We are still in the dark about the origin of most major groups of organisms. They appear in the fossil record* as Athena did from the head of Zeus — *full-blown and raring to go*, in contradiction to Darwin's depiction of evolution as resulting from the gradual accumulation of countless infinitesimally minute variations."
Jeffrey H. Schwartz, physical anthropologist and professor of biological anthropology at the University of Pittsburgh.

Professor Schwartz is certainly not alone in his conclusions. Scientific journals and academic literature document many scientific problems and multidisciplinary criticisms about the claim that microevolution also explains macroevolution. The official school curriculum however still forgets to mention such seemingly inconvenient truths.

*"New species usually appear in the fossil record suddenly, not connected with their ancestors by a series of intermediates."* Ernst Mayr, one of the 20th century's leading evolutionary biologists.

Edward Peltzer, an accomplished chemist and researcher, points out that chemistry existed before there was biological life and that all of the original chemical laws still apply today:

"What works (or not) today, worked (or not) back in the beginning. So, our ideas about *what happened* on Earth prior to the emergence of life are eminently testable in the lab. And what we have seen thus far *when the reactions are left unguided* as they would be in the natural world *is not much*."

"Indeed, the *decomposition reactions and competing reactions out distance the synthetic reactions* by far. *It is only when an intelligent agent* (such as a scientist or graduate student) intervenes and *'tweaks' the reactions conditions 'just right' do we see any progress* at all, and even then it is still quite limited and very far from where we need to get."

"Thus, *it is the very chemistry that speaks of a need for something more than just time and chance.* And whether that be simply a highly specified set of initial conditions (fine-tuning) or some form of continual guidance until life ultimately emerges is still unknown."

"But what we do know is the ***random chemical reactions are both woefully insufficient and are often working against the pathways needed to succeed.*** For these reasons I have serious doubts about whether the current Darwinian paradigm will ever make additional progress in this area."

***Geneticists know full well that random genetic mutations don't build more complexity, and that they tend to harm organisms rather than improve them.*** One example of negative mutation is the loss of activity of the gene for L-gulonolactone oxidase (GULO). Over time the human species has lost the ability to internally generate ascorbic acid (Vitamin C) while other primates (and mammals in general) can still produce it inside their bodies.

Vitamin C is is an essential nutrient and antioxidant (crucial for a well-functioning immune system, required for the enzymatic production of neurotransmitters, and involved in the repair of tissue), but we now have to obtain it through our diets. Vitamin C-synthesizing animals don't get heart attacks or have a host of other health problems, like us. That is real random genetic mutation at work.

Another negative genetic mutation caused us to lose the ability to regenerate and regrow sensory organs like our eyes, according to the research findings of Seth Blackshaw, professor of neuroscience, neurology and ophthalmology at the Johns Hopkins University School of Medicine: "Our research overall indicates that the potential for regeneration is there in mammals, including humans, but some evolutionary pressure has turned it off."

***"New mutations don't create new species; they create offspring that are impaired."***
Lynn Margulis, American evolutionary theorist, biologist, science author, and a member of the U.S. National Academy of Sciences.

***"Mutations have a very limited constructive capacity*** because no matter how numerous they may be, ***mutations do not produce any kind of***

*evolution.*" Pierre-Paul Grasse, French zoologist, author of over 300 publications including the influential 52-volume Traité de Zoologie; past president of the French Academy of Sciences.

Speaking of mutations, let me share a funny but true story we could call 'How to really enrage establishment psychologists.' A recent study published in the leading journal *Evolutionary Psychological Science* concluded that **atheists are actually genetic mutants** who owe their very existence to the Industrial Revolution, which led to the relaxation of natural selection, and thereby the accumulation of fitness-damaging genetic mutations.

The study (by British anthropologist Dr Edward Dutton, Swedish psychologist Prof. Guy Madison and Western Illinois University psychologist Prof. Curtis Dunkel) says that compared with religious folks, atheists have more genetic mutations, and as a result are more likely to be left handed or suffer from autism and schizophrenia (and so forth).

Tough stuff. The peer-reviewed study was greeted with some acclaim. But quite naturally, it was mostly greeted with **howls of rage** by today's generally atheistic members of academia who like to fancy themselves as being far more intelligent than Believing Man. Perhaps especially so since they could not really dispute or disprove the paper's findings!

So they resorted to the usual slander and *ad hominem* attacks that are dished out to all scientists who prove the establishment of the day wrong. Never mind. Ad hominem attacks are neither an argument nor a sign of great intelligence.

Professor Sir Fred Hoyle was one of the most distinguished and innovative scientists of the twentieth century, and indeed the man who coined the phrase *The Big Bang* even though he actually didn't think that there ever was one (preferring the *Steady State theory*). He was also the author of dozens of scientific books and quite a few science fiction novels. In *Evolution from Space* he wrote:

"**Life cannot have had a random beginning** ... The trouble is that there are about 2000 enzymes, and the chance of obtaining them all in a random trial is only one part in 10^40,000, an outrageously small probability that could not be faced even if the whole universe consisted of organic soup."

Enzymes are required by almost all metabolic processes in the cell and are therefore absolutely vital to sustaining life. They act as highly specific biochemical catalysts that make the reaction rates (up to) millions of times faster by lowering the activation energy.

So, Machine Man claims that over time thousands of essential enzymes just came about by random luck even though that is *statistically impossible*: 1 to a number with *40'000 zeros* after it, while *the total number of atoms in the known observable universe* is estimated to be only a one followed by *80 zeros*!

"The notion that *not only the biopolymer but the operating program of a living cell could be arrived at by chance* in a primordial organic soup here on the Earth is evidently *nonsense* of a high order." Professor Sir Fred Hoyle

Here is another one of his famous quotes on Darwinian evolution:"The chance that higher life forms might have emerged in this way is comparable with the chance that a tornado sweeping through a junk-yard might assemble a Boeing 747 from the materials therein."

Obviously, *it takes a lot of thinking and planning to build sophisticated machinery*. Every step of the way. It all takes a great deal of intent, knowledge and intelligence, besides sweat, tears and capital. *There simply is no randomness in intelligent achievements, and neither are they just hallucinations of assorted user illusions created by capricious brains.*

And funnily, or rather amazingly, the machines we are able to build are nowhere near as sophisticated or perfect as the ones built by nature, never mind how that came about. Often we take inspiration for new designs and technology by copying the blueprints of nature; it just never happens the other way around. How come if we are the smartest animal around? Is there another level of intelligence that we don't know about or want to acknowledge?

Every human cell is a hugely complex but highly miniaturized factory, complete with a sophisticated network of assembly lines featuring machines with miniature circuits made out of large proteins; cells use molecular engines, apply encoded language, have feedback loops where outputs are routed back as inputs, and run error-checking machinery that can decode and repair DNA. Did forty trillion of these cells just decide to hang out together for some unknown reason, then randomly assembled themselves to build the bodies we inhabit today?

*The second law of thermodynamics* states that the *entropy or disorder* of a physical, chemical or biochemical system and its surroundings will inevitably increase over time. *Left to themselves, as in unattended and neglected, these systems become increasingly random and degraded.* This of course flies in the face of the fantastic claim of a random, simply by chance increase in complexity, or order out of chaos. Obviously, it rather speaks for the actual observable reality of genetic entropy, or deterioration.

Is life just a result of absolute randomness over time for no reasons, or the consequence of a conscious and perhaps all-pervading form of intelligence for some particular purpose? Let's hear the thoughts of two prominent biochemists:

"As a biochemist and software developer who works in genetic and metabolic screening, I am continually amazed by the incredible complexity of life. For example, *each of us has a vast 'computer program' of six billion DNA bases in every cell* that guided our development from a fertilized egg, specifies how to make more than 200 tissue types, and ties all this together in numerous highly functional organ systems."

"Few people outside of genetics or biochemistry realize that evolutionists still can provide *no substantive details* at all *about* the origin of life, and particularly *the origin of genetic information* in the first self-replicating organism. What genes did it require — or did it even have genes? How much DNA and RNA did it have — or did it even have nucleic acids? How did huge information-rich molecules arise before natural selection? Exactly how did the genetic code linking nucleic acids to amino acid sequence

originate? Clearly *the origin of life* — the foundation of evolution – *is still virtually all speculation, and little if no fact."*
Chris Williams, PhD Biochemistry.

"As a biochemist I become most skeptical about Darwinism when I was confronted with *the extreme intricacy of the genetic code and its many most intelligent strategies to code, decode and protect its information*, such as the U x T and ribose x deoxyribose exchanges for the DNA/RNA pair and the translation of its 4-base language to the 20AA language of life that absolutely relies on a diversity of exquisite molecular machines made by the products of such translation *forming a chicken-and-egg dilemma that evolution has no chance at all to answer."* Professor Dr. Marcos Eberlin, a member of the Brazilian Academy of Sciences, founder of the Thomson Mass Spectrometry Laboratory, and the author of *Foresight*, endorsed by three Nobel Prize-winning scientists.

Professor Hoyle was also not a creationist but a prominent proponent of *Panspermia* (from Ancient Greek, meaning *all seeds* or *seeds everywhere*). He suggested that space is filled with huge clouds of bacteria and viruses, and that *comets, asteroids and meteoroids introduced these and perhaps other microorganisms to our planet.* These cosmic carriers may have otherwise been involved in Earth's biochemistry as complex organic molecules are known to exist throughout the solar system and interstellar space.

A true truth-seeking scientist, he couldn't and therefore didn't rule out the potential existence of some kind of higher intelligences, and thought that the real reason why we categorically want to rule out such a possibility has more to do with psychology than science.

His erstwhile PhD student and longtime collaborator (over forty years) is Professor Chandra Wickramasinghe, an eminent astrobiologist, astronomer and mathematician, and the author of more than 30 books and 70 research articles (many co-authored with Prof. Hoyle). Their at first much derided hypothesis about the partly organic nature of interstellar dust was eventually proven to be correct.

In 1973, Francis Crick – a molecular biologist, biophysicist, neuroscientist, and the Nobel Prize-winning co-discoverer of the DNA double helix – and Leslie Orgel, a pioneering biochemist, have gone one step further and postulated the theory of **Directed Panspermia**, the idea that *living organisms were deliberately sent here* by intelligent beings from another planet, for a variety of reasons that are actually still plausible today.

Of course, their premises were at first mocked by the scientific establishment. Despite their impeccable credentials and outstanding achievements. In the meantime however, many other crucial parts of the scientific puzzle have come together, paving the way for today's renewed interest and some serious research into the possibility that life indeed originated somewhere in outer space. Here are some of the latest findings:

- *Astrobiology suggests that where there is water there is also life.* Six scientists from around the world have demonstrated that there was indeed water on Mars; using high-resolution imaging and topographic data, they found clear evidence of a large lake, channels, rivers and sand deltas on the Martian surface (Nature, May 2020).
- ESA's Mars Express spacecraft has discovered underground lakes and ponds of liquid water buried about 1.5 km under the ice in the south polar region of Mars. The largest lake measures about 20 x 30 km (ESA, September 2020).
- The presence of water in all its forms (liquid, ice or vapor) has been found all over our solar system. To just name a few places: warm salty oceans and fresh clean ice on *Enceladus*, the sixth-largest moon of Saturn; ice and liquid underground water on *Ganymede* and *Europa*, both moons of Jupiter.
- Japanese researchers have discovered 4-billion-year-old organic molecules in a meteorite that originated from Mars. It included nitrogen which is a crucial element for all forms of life on Earth, necessary for the building of DNA, RNA, proteins and other vital materials (April 2020).
- Scientists from the highly decorated Russian Academy of Sciences' Space Research Institute have completed a series of simulations and *experiments that prove that life can survive on Mars, Venus,*

*and Europa.* They subjected different types of microorganisms to the exact same atmospheric conditions (such as high heat or radiation levels, extreme cold or rapid changes in temperature) and demonstrated their actual survival (April 2020).

- Researchers have **discovered the first full extraterrestrial protein inside a meteorite** (and named it hemolithin). While it consists of known components (mostly glycine and hydroxyglycine, capped by iron, oxygen and lithium atoms), this particular protein structure has not been found before on our planet. Ever. Previously only individual amino acids or their precursors have been detected, along other organic materials, including sugars (March 2020).

In 2018, Prof. Wickramasinghe, Edward Steele (an Australian molecular immunologist) and 31 other prominent researchers published a peer-reviewed study in the *Progress in Biophysics and Molecular Biology* journal, concluding that the sudden appearance of complex life during the Cambrian Explosion was indeed the result of Panspermia.

This rarely mentioned review article (respectively never ever in the mainstream media) represents "the collective knowledge and wisdom of over 30 scientists and scholars across many disciplines of the Physical and Biological sciences" looking at "key experimental and observational data gathered over the past 60 years."

"Our point of view is that **in the context of an interconnected cosmic bio-sphere involving at least 100 billion habitable exoplanets in our galaxy alone**, and with continuing exchanges of biomaterial, large scale HGT [horizontal gene transfer] including **exchanges of complex genetic packages** in the form of viruses, seeds, bacteria **is unavoidable.**" Prof. Wickramasinghe

Already in 1861, Louis Pasteur (of pasteurized milk etc. fame) famously proved that '**All life comes from life**' (Omne vivum ex vivo) which ultimately means that **life must have originated elsewhere where it was already present** – since there was no life on Earth before, only lifeless bits and pieces of matter in a hostile environment. In other words, life came from somewhere in outer space. Whether it was directed for a purpose or not.

Such conclusions however were considered to be heresy of the worst kind by the secular and scientific powers that be at the time. And ever since until this very day. *What is not allowed to be true, cannot be true, even though it is.* Or, "He who has the gold and pays the scientists makes the rules." If it's not about money, it is the defending of academic positions and professional reputations, all contrary to the fundamental principles of science.

So the only biological truth allowed is that life somehow came about by abiogenesis in a primordial soup of random matter (*"life arises from non-living matter"*), which sounds a bit like Jesus is said to have risen from the dead. Yes, life emanates from dead matter. But no, our story is not superstition or religion, it's purely rational science, you see. Yeah, really.

One of the many reasons why Prof. Wickramasinghe considers panspermia to be far more plausible than abiogenesis, is simply the *"superastronomically improbable transition from non-life to life."* He elaborated, "the choice between life originating on Earth against manifestly insuperable odds, and an origin in the connected volume of a large part of the almost infinite universe is a simple binary choice. We chose the most probable."

*The size of the human brain* is another puzzle that cannot be convincingly explained by mainstream evolutionary doctrines; it *is about six times larger than it should be for a placental mammal of human size*. In chapter *Brain Matters* we have seen that brains are hugely expensive to run in terms of metabolic costs as they burn a lot of calories. All natural processes and organisms however are always extremely energy efficient, way beyond what we can achieve with our most modern machinery.

So why are our brains so exceptionally large? And why have they suddenly tripled in size from Australopithecines to modern humans? The answer is that there are no real answers but again, lots of competing theories.

Some say it's all about social group size, which neglects that many social animals form far larger groups yet have much smaller brains. But to be better able to find and eat bananas and other fruits rather than having to eat leaves or grass is not much of an argument: birds can easily find fruits even though they are said to be birdbrained. What about fruit flies? They too seem to have no problems finding fruits, despite having the brains of a well, fly!

Having to solve ecological stress problems sounds also rather farfetched as climate changes equally affected everybody else with far smaller, more proportionate and higher energy efficient brains; they all seem to have adapted, thrived and survived just as well as we did.

Why does a living brain made up of 1.5 kilograms of warm flesh produce consciousness and the same suddenly freshly deceased brain doesn't any longer? The matter is still the very same; all atoms and molecules are there in the same way as they were before, yet there is no longer any consciousness present. How come if it's all just a derivative of mere matter?

Is it just because the brain is lacking fresh supplies of crucial nutrients and therefore it died? Well, we could always pump blood filled with plenty of glucose and oxygen through the freshly deceased brain. And keep pumping. But of course, that would still not bring back the conscious person we knew and loved. Life. We all know this wonderful quality when we see and feel it. Instinctively and instantly. And we also immediately know when this mysterious quality and elusive characteristic is suddenly absent and gone.

Most of us have seen a dead body. Depending on one's age and circumstances, perhaps not a human dead body, but surely a dead animal body. We recognize even a freshly deceased body that shows no visible signs of injury or decomposition. Somehow we can quickly distinguish a sleeping cat or person from a dead cat or person.

How do we know and why is that so? The body and brain is still composed of the same cells, the same water content, and the same DNA. Yet something is obviously missing. We just know it when we see it, respectively don't see it anymore.

For thousands of years, Asian cultures have taught and lived with the principle of a **life force**, called Qi in China, Ki in Japan, or Prana in India. This vital energy has been described in their respective philosophies, applied in their medical systems, and manipulated in their various forms of martial arts and esoteric practices, like yoga, meditation and feng shui.

We can quite easily recognize life force in the sparkle of people's eyes or the lack thereof.
Eyes instantly reveal a person's subtle energy level, the fortitude of their chi. The adept can clearly see the brightness and intelligence of the mind. Or a person's wisdom and inner strength. Some eyes are literally sparkling with vitality while others seem a bit weak, dull or somewhat dead (colloquially called 'dead fish eyes' or 'no one is home'). Are the eyes really the window to the soul, the conscious living being we are?

Life force is either present or no longer present; it is the energy that distinguishes a living from a dead body. Sounds simple but of course, the concept of life force is both scorned and dismissed by Machine Man as pseudoscience because it cannot be measured with their instruments. *The fact that hundreds of millions of people have successfully applied its principles in real life long before there was even a semblance of civilization in the West is simply ignored* instead of being thoroughly investigated with an open mind.

You have now heard quite a few of the thoughts and theories of highly intelligent and accomplished scientists from different fields. And seen that there really are only open questions about the origin or nature of life. In an upcoming chapter (*Who We Really Are*) I will endeavor to present you my current thoughts about life and other unsolved mysteries.

For now, where does this all leave our dear transhumanist friends? How close are they to actually realize their hopes and dreams? Many highly-paid and promoted peddlers of fantasy keep saying that some kind of at least digital immortality is right around the corner. And many people, both young and old, desperately cling to these promises that may very well screw up their lives. How close is today's state-of-the-art science really?

*Transhumanist proponents of longevity or outright immortality have to first demonstrate that they fully understand what life is*, and second, show their ability to master it in all its shapes and forms. From the most basic forms of life to the very pinnacle of its complexity. Without such knowledge, *life cannot be recreated, extended or transferred to another body*, whether that would be fully or partially biological or a completely artificial construct.

*Scientists cannot create life.* They can somewhat to a very minor degree manipulate existing life, but they can not create it from scratch. We can only measure the vital signs of its presence, but *we can't produce life in the laboratory.* Like take this and that chemical compound, some atoms here and some molecules there, shake and stir it all, or cook and bake it. There simply is no way to manufacture the quality or thing we call life.

What about prolonging already existing life? Forever, or at least a little bit? Well, as a matter of fact, we can't keep any one individual single-celled microorganism – like a nice little bacteria called Jim, the archaea known as Joe, a particular pretty protozoa called Nancy, or Harry, the unicellular algae, and Larry the fungi – alive, neither forever nor beyond the maximum of their natural expiry dates.

Obviously, we cannot *prolong the life of other less complex forms of life* like dogs and cats either. A great many pet owners would surely pay top dollars if they could just spend a few extra years with their beloved pets. Yours truly included. There would definitely be a big market and lots of money to be made, but there is simply no treatment available. Not now or in the foreseeable future. In short, until we can at least meaningfully extend the lives of our little furry friends, our transhumanist friends have rather few reasons to be very optimistic.

The best advice science can currently offer is to reduce our calorie intake without causing malnutrition of essential nutrients. The reasons or underlying mechanisms however are not yet known or understood. Caloric restriction (CR) has shown to somewhat extend the lifespan of yeast, nematode worms (C. elegans), flies and mice in laboratory settings. That of course is not so much a medical treatment or a scientific achievement, but basically an encouragement to lead a healthier life.

And of course, from yeast and worms, or maybe eventually cats and dogs, it is still a very long way to go to keep us alive beyond our general expiration date. The maximum human lifespan is generally accepted to be 125 years, yet only very few people have actually been able to reach this ripe old age, despite making great efforts to live as healthy as possible.

To emphasize scientists' collective ignorance about the nature of life, let me formulate *The Ant Challenge* to Machine Man scientists around the world:

Take your time to analyze everything that makes up an ant, all the atoms and molecules it is made of. You may even copy their DNS but you must assemble the double helix and everything else from scratch. Atom by atom, molecule by molecule.

Now let's see who can first create a living ant, followed by a whole living colony that fully functions just like natural ant colonies. Can't do it? Try to do it by first creating the egg of an ant, also atom by atom, if that is easier for you (hint: it isn't). Success is measured if a living ant emerges, having undergone the usual (for nature) complex metamorphosis from egg to larvae to pupae. Good luck!

And good luck they will need indeed. A great deal of it. Probably over billions of years. Just like the Darwinian Theory postulates. But of course, transhumanists would already be quite happy to somehow or another move in to some kind of cloud computer cyborg organism with both organic and biomechatronic body parts. How likely is that?

We have seen that we don't know what life is and how it really came about. Or where it is located, if indeed it has a specific location. Furthermore, we can't transfer life, like beam it over from one to another body or to a robotic entity of whatever kind. There are no actual or theoretical technologies that could teleport life from one still living mouse to an already dead mouse whereas the first would now be dead and the other one suddenly alive.

***Where and how do we take what and put this what into where?*** Scientists just don't know any of these answers. Not in the slightest. And building some kind of new man-made vessel that could replace our old bodies is not possible either. Synthetic biology or nanotechnology is currently and for the foreseeable future not remotely close to be able to meet *The Ant Challenge*, not to speak of creating an actual human body.

While robotics has made some significant progress in the manufacturing of things or the remote-controlled operation of killing machines, ***ants have far superior abilities and functions than the very best of modern robots.*** By a very large order of magnitude. They are also far smaller. And use only a tiny fraction of energy.

Ants have only about 250'000 neurons in their brains and nervous systems, yet they can instantly process huge amounts of data streaming in from a wide range of sense organs (touch, vibrations, heat, light, smell, taste, temperature, humidity, chemicals).

They communicate with each other using pheromones, sounds and touch, and closely cooperate on many undertakings: from engineering and architecture to logistics or complex problem solving; from interactive teaching, common attack or defense, the cultivating of both crops and livestock, to actual slave-raiding and keeping.

The world's best engineers can't make a robot that comes even remotely close to mimicking a teeny tiny ant that can lift 5'000 times its own body weight! So what exactly are the chances that we will so very soon be capable of creating an artificial robot version of the incredibly complex and actually rather perfect human body?

Likewise, today's top engineering talents cannot replicate a flagellar motor, the rotating wheel *a unicellular bacteria* uses to specifically (randomness or a dispersive nature were ruled out) relocate itself to a friendlier, more suitable environment (e.g. towards more light or oxygen). The engine can change its structure, is made of protein parts, and assembles itself only on demand, exactly wherever and whenever it is needed.

It is a million times smaller than a grain of sand, can rotate up to 100'000 rpm, and almost instantly changes its direction to wherever it wants to go.

Obviously, there is no machinery we can build that comes even remotely close to this kind of miniaturized marvel of biological engineering. Beaten by a single-celled bacteria (without a PhD).

So very little is understood about the absolute biological marvels that are our bodies yet widely ignorant transhumanists feel the need to improve them anyway. They can't build anything that comes even close to a humble bacteria, yet they delude themselves to be smarter than nature itself; masters of the universe. But no robot will ever match or beat the biochemical, electrical or self-replicating abilities of a single human cell. And that includes any and all hypothetical nanorobots or molecular machines. Just consider this example:

The microscopic mitochondrion, an organelle or subunit inside every most tiny human cell, is called the ***powerhouse of the cell*** as it generates most of its supply of chemical energy as adenosine triphosphate (ATP). In addition, it is ***capable of the seemingly magic feat of a biotransformation of elements***, like changing Sodium to Magnesium (Natrium $Na + H = Mg$), Potassium to Calcium ($K + H+ = Ca$), or Magnesium to Iron ($Mn + H = Fe$).

All human cell types contain mitochondria (with the exception of mature red blood cells); one ***muscle cell contains thousands of these tiny biological wonders that are thousands of times smaller the size of the world's smallest computer chips***. They even have their own DNA (called mitochondrial DNA or mtDNA) and synthesize their own proteins. In short, it is most unlikely to need any improvements by transhumanist control freaks fearing death.

So what is a life worth anyway? As with everything, it all depends on whom we ask. Lawyers have answers (and make monetary demands on behalf of their clients). Insurance companies have their answers (they are in the business of taking as much as possible and giving as little as they can get away with). More or less black market dealers in organs come up with at least partial answers too (also using the pay little and charge a lot model).

A murderer would say that a life is worth what it costs to kill it (a bullet costs only a dollar or so, depending on its caliber and where and how many one buys). Governments have answers too and that of course depends on where in the world we live (e.g. U.S. federal government agencies say a human life is worth about $10 million; soldiers don't qualify).

Our individual personal answers will likely differ greatly. Someone who contemplates suicide obviously doesn't value his or her current life very much at that moment in time. The young and strong don't even want to bother thinking about such trivial matters as they focus on enjoying life. While the old and sick billionaire of the Machine Man persuasion would gladly give a million dollars a day to postpone the inevitable.

Of course, the answer of most people is that the life of a loved one is of immeasurable, incalculable and infinite worth. Whereas the same people might answer very differently when they're asked to appraise the dollar value of their nosy or noisy next door neighbors.

Even a hardcore materialistic Machine Man would agree that their truly loved ones are worth a great deal more than any amount of mere money. But what if we took them by the words of their own philosophy?

Purely for argument's sake, we could add up the total costs of the chemicals and water our bodies consists of, at say full retail price. Most likely the grand total would be less than a hundred dollars per body. Now try to imagine the face – and reaction – of a diehard proponent of today's gospel of science upon being offered a crisp and cool one-hundred-dollar bill for his beautiful little baby girl!

That may sound silly and tasteless, and it is both, but it nevertheless represents the pinnacle of physicalism, the notion that everything is physical, and that nothing is over and above it. And if that were really so, it would surely beg the simple but crucial question:

*What is a life worth in a purely random world of mere matter where anything goes and nothing matters?*

Let's conclude our little excursion into the origin and nature of life with a few final thoughts before moving on to talk about another deeply mystifying yet most exciting topic.

- Every cause produces a corresponding effect, so an intelligent effect is likely caused by an intelligent cause.
- It is statistically impossible that every of billions of intelligent effects is caused by dumb luck.
- Even if half of all intelligent effects were caused by dumb luck, **who or what** is the intelligence behind the other half?

# The Conundrum

What is the biggest mystery of all? The puzzle that keeps puzzling? Without a doubt and in one word, it is: consciousness.

So what is consciousness? Why are we conscious? Who or what is creating it? And where is it located? **Machine Man insists** with the usual absolute certainty **that consciousness is caused by our physical brains.** Never mind the fact that once again, no scientist of any kind can say where in the brain it is produced; neither its exact location nor the general area.

They also don't know how it is made (if indeed it is made), by which biochemical processes or electrical activities, in what type of cells, atoms or molecules.

None of the questions about consciousness have been answered or are even close to getting answered. There are only totally vague theories, but no explanations. Not to speak of having actual proof about anything at all. And yet, *those very same still totally ignorant scientists insist with a straight face*, and with the grave voices of people who seemingly know everything, even though they don't, *that consciousness must be the result of some kind of neurological process that happens within our skulls.*

*Any other explanation is ruled out from the very beginning* and considered to be heresy of the worst kind. It's just like saying the Earth is flat or the like. And of course, *they are right about desperately wanting to insist that their non-explanation is the only possible explanation.* Because once they actually conceded that consciousness is not and cannot possibly be made locally within our brains, their entire Machine Man philosophy about who we are would break down. With all the implications that would entail. On many levels.

Regardless, ***proponents of physicalism – the thesis that everything is physical – may very well have reached a dead end***; ***their reductionist approach is unlikely to ever be able to solve the conundrum of consciousness***. Simply because consciousness is likely a form of energy that is beyond the frequency range of this material dimension. And indeed, beyond what we can measure with our current range of instruments.

Therefore the physicalists' understanding of consciousness is perhaps best summed up by the Latin saying ***ignoramus et ignorabimus***: "we do not know and will not know." That of course will never be admitted. So instead, rather than changing their fundamental approach or theories, we will simply get more serves of *spe perpetua*: ***everlasting hope***. A perhaps more candid, well-known and hotly debated premise combines hope with no hope:

David Chalmers, an Australian philosopher and professor, makes the distinction between the 'easy' (cognitive or psychological) and 'hard' (phenomenal) problems of consciousness. He argues that the brain processes that lead to consciousness can ***theoretically*** be explained by physicalism. Because the objective mechanisms involved ***may one day*** be found and proven by scientific methods. The hard part is that we will ***never*** be able to answer the question of: ***why do physical processes lead to subjective conscious experiences?***

We could very well call it a Machine Man theory with a twist. And there are a great many turns too. Theories within theories. ***Strong*** reductionists believe that conscious experience (phenomenal consciousness) exists but that it can nevertheless be fully explained by reducible processes (to ***hopefully*** be found, eventually, sometimes) within the brain.

Then there are ***weak*** reductionists who believe that there is indeed an unsolvable explanatory gap between our individual personal introspection and the underlying observable neurobiology, but that it is nevertheless still part of the same one and only physical reality. They claim that it is a matter of different understandings only, a dualism of concepts rather than a dualism of actual substances.

Yet another branch of scientists and philosophers simply say that consciousness cannot be explained by our puny brains with its limited and fallible cognitive faculties. *We are part of the system that is trying to explain the system and that is simply not going to be possible.*

Perhaps it would be like a conscious little screw in the engine room of a conscious big cruise liner trying to figure out its purpose and function or what the whole ship is all about.

The latter thoughts are at least very honest. And humble. It also shows a truly open mind that is therefore far more likely to find real answers than close-minded skeptics who think they already know it all (in the big picture view anyway).

*"Science cannot solve the ultimate mystery of nature. And that is because, in the last analysis, we ourselves are a part of the mystery that we are trying to solve."* Max Planck

Some current-day thinkers want to ignore the problem altogether by saying that phenomenal consciousness should simply be eliminated from the scientific world (they are known as eliminativists or eliminative materialists). Most of today's neuroscientists and cognitive scientists *believe* that the hard problem *proposed* by Chalmers will eventually also be solved while they are finally finding the solutions to the easy problems.

*The problem with the easy problems is only that they too are actually hard problems since none of them have been solved yet.* Or are even close to being solved. Neither in theory nor in reality. How can mere matter possibly create how we individually experience things? What are the specific mechanisms involved to make such an amazing feat happen?

Professor Chalmers asks, "Why is it that when our cognitive systems engage in visual and auditory information-processing, we have visual or auditory experience: the quality of deep blue, the sensation of middle C?" and more fundamentally, "Why should physical processing give rise to a rich inner life at all?" Good questions indeed.

*"Even a detailed knowledge of the brain's workings and the neural correlates of consciousness may fail to explain how or why human beings have self-aware minds."* David Chalmers

Non-reductive physicalism is the very widespread philosophical view that mind and consciousness cannot be reduced to matter but are still caused by matter; **essentially it is Machine Man believing in magic without admitting it.** They assert that our mental states are created by still unknown (a.k.a. mysterious) physical processes in the brain and yet they can't be reduced to physical states. It's like eating the cake but keeping it too. Wonderful.

Imagine that the connected neurons within our brains somehow corresponded to computer chips. When you put only one into a box of say the size of our skulls, nothing happens. And then you put a whole bunch of these chips in there and randomly connect them all here and there. **What are the chances that this physical construction will eventually bring about a fully conscious, thinking and feeling robot that has a totally individual personality with its own distinctive dreams and desires?**

Would you put any money on the chances of that happening? The bits and pieces of matter **in total** are magically responsible for consciousness to happen, but the **individual** bits and pieces can't do any of it at all: that is the magical thinking of Machine Man that does not dare to say so.

That non-physical mental features are somehow but surely created by our physical brains is the name of the game of most modern-day neuroscientists and philosophers. Put differently, **Machine Man seriously and absolutely claims that consciousness emanates out of a bunch of totally unconscious particles.** Believe in magic but only our kind of magic, you know, the scientific one. Anything else is total nonsense, you see. Yes, sure.

How can we tell whether someone is conscious or not, according to Machine Man? They say that there is no way to tell as we can only observe from the outside. And that even brain surgeons can't know it for sure. Despite looking long, hard and deep, no doubt.

It is an age-old philosophical problem (called the 'other-minds' problem) that goes back thousands of years to the beginning of philosophical debate itself: how can we distinguish between a (theoretical) philosophical zombie, who looks and acts like a conscious person but is not conscious, from a surely conscious being when they have exactly the same physical functions and behavior?

And now we could very well update this problem and ask whether modern-day super computers or top of the line robots already have some kind of subjective inner life experiences of their own. Or will have in the future. If they don't, we have to ask, why not? What is missing in their information processing capabilities that prevents them from having both individual and rich inner perspectives?

We will come back to these questions and the many other unsolved problems we have talked about and present our own answers and theories in chapter *Who We Really Are.*

Talking about theories. One currently (still) celebrated neuroscientist claims that we are all hallucinating all the time. And that what we call reality is merely the result of us all agreeing about our hallucinations. This thinking follows in the footsteps of those philosophers of mind who believe that consciousness is just a form of user illusion.

And that actually brings us further beyond scientific magic, and well into the realms of religion. Even though those thoughts are being expressed by some very hardcore Machine Man theorists. Maya, which literally means illusion or magic, is a very old spiritual concept in Indian Hindu philosophies. Something that appears to be real but is not; the temporary hallucinations or appearances that conceal the true nature of an eternal spiritual reality.

Such Machine Man theorists claim that our experiences of this world are not immediate but time-delayed because all sensations require some processing time. ***So they conclude that our conscious experiences are not reflecting what is actually occurring 'out there' but are merely simulations, or hallucinations, that are produced unconsciously by the brain.***

Reality however tells us differently. *We do experience everything in real time; there is no delay.* That is true even for physical sensations, not to speak of how we feel, for example when we meet someone for the first time, or what we immediately think upon hearing good or bad news. When we touch a hot stove, we'll pull our hands back right away because it burns and hurts right away too; there is no delay as that would only make matters worse.

The only way to feel a time delay is when we had a bit too much wine, or the like. Our senses, nervous systems and brains function *at least at the speed of electricity*, if not much faster. Let me elaborate this a little bit by looking closer at the speed of electricity.

The electrons in a wire that constitute an electric current move (or drift) only very, very slowly yet *the electromagnetic waves generated move at between 50 to 99 percent of the speed of light* (about 300,000 km/s or 300 million meters per second in a vacuum) in everyday electrical and electronic devices.

As previously discussed, we can safely say that nature designs everything far better than humans ever could. In the various fields of engineering and pretty much everywhere else we always try our best to imitate technical features or design aspects of nature; it never happens the other way around (quite likely for very good reasons).

It is not difficult to imagine or conclude that *our most elaborate and highly complex nervous systems are better designed than simple copper wires* that already achieve amazing, almost immediate, transmission speeds. Our nervous systems are far more efficient, and similarly to copper wires, act as conduits or waveguides for the electromagnetic waves coming from and going to the brain.

In other words, *all information is transferred at speeds that are likely to be very close to the speed of light of 300 million meters per second.* Which of course is very fast. Hence it all feels like it's all happening instantaneously (which it really is as we shall see).

But of course, it is perfectly fine with me if Machine Man scientists want to consider themselves to be just slow and hallucinating user illusions, as long as they only speak for themselves.

Upon looking at today's leading research about consciousness, it is fair to conclude that *materialist or physicalist science doesn't know why or how we are conscious*. And yet we all know that we are indeed conscious. *We are not just conscious but we are aware that we are conscious.* That is simply self-evident.

What about animals and plants? Are they conscious too? Or inanimate matter itself? Could atoms or subatomic particles be conscious to some minute degree? Since many proponents of current mainstream science dabble dangerously close to the worlds of wishful magic or outright dogmatic religion, let's first hear the answers of an adept representative of *Homo Mysticum*, or Mystic Man:

*"Consciousness sleeps in minerals, dreams in plants, wakes up in animals, and becomes self-aware in humans."* Rumi, Persian Sufi mystic; 1207 – 1273.

That animals are conscious, and indeed have a very individual character, is very clear to anyone who has ever had a deep relationship with a pet, say a dog, cat or a horse. They all have their own mind on things, desires that go far beyond merely wanting some (or more) food; *essentially, they want to be respected, appreciated and loved. Just like we all do, regardless of our colors, creeds and cultures.*

Some people without personal experiences with pets might object and say that we humans only project our own desires and behaviors onto animals. Or that animals only pretend certain kinds of behavior purely as a mechanism of survival.

Well, it is (or should be) rather obvious that *the very act of pretending already implies a conscious being with a certain intelligence and understanding.* We simply have to be conscious to be able to play the game of pretending.

Other Machine Man objections that claim merely instinctive or reflexive behavior are also wrong, as demonstrated by many scientific studies of even the most unlikely of creatures.

Dr Gregory Berns, a neuroscientist at Emory University in Atlanta and author of *What It's Like to Be a Dog*, scanned the brains of about 90 dogs to find out more about their mental processes. And he demonstrated, among other things, that dogs indeed love their owners for who they are, not for the food they provide.

***Dogs are also highly empathetic***; they feel what their owners feel ***and are naturally highly compassionate***, which of course is a sign of being highly conscious, and indeed, not a characteristic that every human can boast of, to put it nicely. As a matter of fact, to cultivate compassion is one of the main spiritual principles of Buddhism, as the Dalai Lama keeps reminding us. Dogs apparently don't need any such reminders.

Whenever I felt stressed out, a bit down or outright sad (say upon losing my dear father), Ninja, our little chihuahua boy, noticed right away. And came to lovingly comfort me or playfully cheer me up again. When I got a little injury while fixing something in our house or garden, he appeared at once to help, trying to alleviate my pain in his own sweet and affectionate ways. And anytime my wife got bitten by a mosquito, he immediately came to the rescue by licking the exact very spot until it stopped itching. Somehow he just knew.

Also, whenever we argued a little bit about something, Ninja always mediated by going to the room my wife was in, asking her in his funny and cute manners to again get along with me, then came to my office to intensely look at me, telling me likewise. Tirelessly he went back and forth until we both just had to laugh and give each other a big hug and kiss; he would simply not rest until we made up again! Very funny, and very kind.

Of course, one could say that every proud dog (or other pet) owner could entertain us with a great many stories of their own. But neither their nor our interpretations are a mere matter of an overly imaginative mind.

Modern-day science has finally caught up with reality and shown in numerous experiments that pets not only do feel emotions, but actually mirror our mental states, both good and bad. The more stressed out we feel, the more anxious they get and the more it affects their physical health. And of course, the opposite is true as well: the calmer and happier we feel, the calmer, happier and healthier they are too.

*The ability to feel complex emotions and be compassionate are clear signs or byproducts of being aware and conscious. And so is the ability to grieve*, to feel deep distress upon losing a loved one. Mourning is neither necessary for our biological survival nor particularly conducive to make life better in any way.

Elephants are well known to deeply mourn their own kind. And sometimes they also grieve for other species they have befriended. In a wildlife park in Zimbabwe, three elephants displayed obvious grief when they were shown the burial place of their black rhino friends who were killed by poachers. Mundebvu, Makavusi and Toto touched and supported one another just like we do at the funeral of a loved one; they passed sticks to each other while tears were streaming down their faces.

Various research into the lives of elephants revealed that they are highly intelligent, caring and **able to distinguish between good and bad**; they are also very communicative, having their own specific language (in low frequency tones we mostly can't hear). Elephants who had no contact with elephant-hunting humans (like the Masaii people) somehow know that it is best to avoid them, while they are not afraid to be around non-violent people.

There are studies that show how **capuchin monkeys have a strong sense of justice**; they easily recognize a good deal and know full well when they do get cheated in experiments (e.g. while exchanging stones for pieces of cucumber, but suddenly giving a delicious grape to another monkey for the same deal they got, or even for free). They instantly show their displeasure or outright anger in most unmistakable and rather funny ways, including the refusing of their own reward or actually throwing it at researchers.

Similar tests also revealed a host of moral traits like **fairness, reciprocity, cooperation and empathy** among birds, dogs, chimpanzees, and many other animals. They also display **the amazing ability to reconcile and forgive each other** upon having an argument or fight. Which can include hugging and kissing and even having make up sex. Perhaps there is much we can still learn from them, at times.

For the last two hundred years or so, most behavioral scientists dismissed the possibility that animals could have individual personalities. Nowadays however it is generally accepted that all animals have their very own personality and character traits. Just like we do. And indeed, that they come as diverse as human personalities.

They all have personal likes and dislikes; some animals are very curious, affectionate and responsive to commands, while others have a rather rebellious streak. Some are particularly playful (even while alone) or a bit naughty (and knowingly so). There are those who are more easy-going, others are rather stubborn or even vindictive. Sounds a lot like us humans.

**We all have a totally unique personality and character. And that is an inherent part of who we really are.** It's not just a matter of matter, or DNA or brain power.

Hollywood star Barbra Streisand revealed in an interview that her two new pups are actually clones of her beloved dog, Samantha, that passed away. However she said that, "They have different personalities."

What about fish? We say that some people are as cold as a fish, implying that they have no feelings. The latest studies however show that **fish too have a discernible personality and do feel emotions**. The term 'bird-brained' is a word that needs revamping too as research with crows and ravens has demonstrated that they are conscious of their environment, the passage of time, and possess problem-solving and decision-making skills (as always, see chapter *Notes* for details on this and everything else).

Next, let's talk about plants. Is there any evidence that plants are conscious in some way or another? Vegetarians may be surprised and perhaps a bit shocked to hear that even these seemingly lower and unconscious forms of life are also conscious, to some degree. And they too feel a modicum of pain upon being pulled out and uprooted (but of course, not to the same extent as animals being slaughtered).

Dr. Monica Gagliano is a pioneering researcher in the emerging fields of plant bioacoustics and plant cognition; she's the author of numerous peer-reviewed scientific papers and a book with the catchy title *Thus Spoke the Plant*. Her experiments demonstrated that plants can actually learn by association and produce a Pavlov-like response to different kinds of stimuli like wind or light. Other findings include their ability to remember and communicate to neighboring plants (who may respond by modifying their own behavior), and generally, to detect and respond to sounds in their environment.

Dr. Gagliano says, "The **plants** don't have brains. They **don't have neurons and yet they're still performing the exact same task as the dog**. How did they do that? We don't know." She suggests that there may be another system of cognition beyond neurons and brains that we cannot yet fathom as we see the world only from a very limited and subjective human perspective. Well said.

Much research going back over one hundred years has clearly shown that plants react very strongly to music and high-frequency vibrations. For example, their listening to classical music greatly accelerated growth and increased crop yields up to 66 percent, while hard rock or heavy metal produced only negative effects.

A great many both professional and hobby gardeners would also swear that plants strongly respond to love, or the lack thereof. Talking with plants seemed to work wonders too, according to several studies. As long as it is of a positive nature. In one recent small and admittedly not very scientific experiment, a plant that only received compliments for thirty days was flourishing and healthy, but the one that got severely bullied and insulted was wilted and withered.

The proposition that ***inanimate matter is also somewhat conscious to a minuscule degree*** may sound a bit crazy. In the beginning. But when one looks into the mind-boggling insights of quantum physics of the last one hundred years, this seemingly outlandish proposition is not just wishful thinking but actual reality, no matter how microscopic that may be.

Can the principles of quantum mechanics bridge the ancient gap between the seemingly opposing worlds of Machine Man and Mystic Man? Between the increasingly magical theories of materialistic science and the perspectives of perennial philosophy (as opposed to sectarian organized religion)? Could quantum physics bring about a new all-encompassing paradigm that unites us all in a ***post-materialist*** view of the world?

Funnily, old-school materialistic scientists insist that quantum physics only applies to the inner worlds of atoms, and that Newtonian physics still rules our everyday world. On the very opposite side we have enthusiastic New Age authors and others who see the crazy and entirely inexplicable antics of quantum particles in quantum space as proof positive of a united universe where everything including ourselves is not just connected as one but are indeed one. As in, one and the same.

'We are one. We are the world. We are the universe. You is really me. I am you too.' And so on and so forth. One big happy family. Or so we should be. Sounds all nice and sweet in theory, but it sure drives Machine Man nuts, accusing quantum enthusiasts of quackery.
A bit like, "You're a quack," said the quack. Or nowadays, "You're a racist," said the racist.

"Despite the unrivaled empirical success of ***quantum theory, the very suggestion that it may be literally true*** as a description of nature ***is still greeted with cynicism, incomprehension and even anger.***" Tim Folger, Quantum Shmantum, Discover Magazine.

But let's hear what Max Planck has to say, after all he's the discoverer of quantum theory, winning him the Nobel Prize in Physics in 1918:

"As a man who has devoted his whole life to the most clearheaded science, to the study of matter, I can tell you as a result of my research about the atoms this much: *There is no matter as such! All matter originates and exists only by virtue of a force* which brings the particle of an atom to vibration and holds this most minute solar system of the atom together. *We must assume behind this force the existence of a conscious and intelligent mind.* This mind is the matrix of all matter."

Well, that sounds pretty clear and authoritative. So what was his take on consciousness?

*"I regard consciousness as fundamental. I regard matter as derivative from consciousness.* We cannot get behind consciousness. Everything that we talk about, everything that we regard as existing, postulates consciousness."

And what do other luminaries have to say about the nature of matter and consciousness?
Professor Niels Bohr is generally considered to be one of the foremost physicists of the 20th century; he won the Nobel Prize in Physics in 1922 for his foundational contributions to the understanding of quantum physics and the atomic structure (the Bohr atomic model).

He said, *"Everything we call real is made of things that cannot be regarded as real.* If quantum mechanics hasn't profoundly shocked you, you haven't understood it yet."

One of the rather shocking insights of quantum physics is that, in his own words, *"Nothing exists until it is measured."* Essentially, subatomic particles are not actual particles until they are measured or observed; until that happens there are only waves of energy that have the potential to be everywhere and nowhere at the same time.

Once measured or observed, these vibrations of energy turn into short-lived and inherently unstable particles that are mere momentary moments in space and time. This may sound somewhat crazy already, but the most amazing part is yet to come. Niels Bohr explains that: "...naturally, *it still makes no difference whether the observer is a man, an animal, or a piece of apparatus..."*

**So the mere observing and thereby assessing or measuring something actually changes that reality.** And that of course implies that we are indeed not just able to influence what is happening in our immediate private lives, but also in the world in general, simply by our observations and contemplation. This influence may only be to a very minuscule degree and therefore hard to quantify. But it happens. Quite likely, the degree varies depending on the clarity and focus of our individual states of mind and the purity of our consciousness.

Prof. Bohr puts it like this, *"In the great drama of existence we are audience and actors at the same time."* while Prof. Planck said, *"If you change the way you look at things, the things you look at change."*

Perhaps the mystics of ancient times were already right after all. Without being able to see or measure atoms, without knowing anything about the weird worlds of quantum physics. To this very day, scientists cannot understand the totally unpredictable movements of atoms, where protons, electrons and a myriad of subatomic particles appear in the pure void of quantum space, then disappear, sometimes behaving like energy waves, and at other times like particles that occupy always varying positions, here, there, and seemingly everywhere.

*This is the current state of cutting edge science; it is neither mysticism nor religion. Insights of quantum mechanics are just plain and thoroughly proven facts of life.* Even though a great many people are not aware of it yet since this subject is still not being included in the general curriculum of schools, colleges, and universities. The silence is kind of deafening. One can only wonder why.

To this day, most mainstream Machine Man scientists refuse to acknowledge the quantum world or discuss its implications widely just because it totally contradicts their fundamental beliefs about the world and life itself. *Top scientists however do know that consciousness cannot possibly be explained by the materialistic paradigm.* All fathers of quantum physics knew this very well and clearly said so quite a long time ago already!

Experiments that were conducted at the multi-billion dollar facilities of CERN in Geneva (Switzerland) have shown that there is an immediate exchange of information taking place between entangled subatomic particles that were split and sent into opposite directions at incredible speeds. *Even though they were moving away from each other they were somehow able to instantly communicate and exchange information.*

We can certainly say that *the atoms making up our bodies are well and truly entangled too.* Hundred trillion or more human and third-party cells made up of countless molecules, atoms and subatomic particles have come together and act together, mostly in harmony, sometimes less so, depending on our state of mind and a range of external factors.

So, coming back to the discussion about the transmission speeds of information within our bodies, it should certainly not be implausible to suggest *instant communication.* Faster than the speed of electricity or the speed of light. If simple *subatomic particles can immediately change their properties even while thousands of light-years apart*, then it is surely possible to also happen within the cells of our bodies and brains.

Quantum physicist Professor Juan Yin and her colleagues at the University of Science and Technology of China have demonstrated in a sophisticated *real-world* experiment that the minimum speed of entangled particles (photons sent to two detectors 15.3 km apart) is *at least 10'000 times faster than the speed of light.* Considering certain measurement and interpretation issues, it couldn't be ruled out that the 'spooky action at a distance' is indeed instantaneous, as demonstrated numerous times at CERN and in laboratory settings.

A few years later, *constant quantum entanglement and the instant quantum teleportation of encrypted quantum information was successfully demonstrated* for the first time by another team of Chinese scientists. Instead of using customary physical fibers, entangled photon pairs were transmitted from the Micius satellite to two ground stations via laser beams over a record-breaking distance of 2'400 km.

Naturally, perhaps incurable skeptics will still claim (without proof) that the microscopic realm of quantum physics does not apply to the physics of the world we observe and live in, despite the evidence of many widely replicated experiments that show it to be an accurate depiction of reality. They may be surprised to learn that even in our big scale and seemingly rock solid world, essentially instant exchange of information is happening too.

New research by the GFZ German Research Centre for Geosciences has shown that **Prompt Elasto-Gravity Signals** (PEGS) that are emitted by earthquakes actually **travel at the speed of light**, much faster than regular seismic P waves whose speed is only 5 to 8 kilometers per second.

If such signals of "sudden changes in gravity caused by a shift in the earth's internal mass" **can instantly travel through Earth itself**, why should anyone be surprised that there are virtually no time delays within our far smaller besides far less solid bodies – as currently still being suggested by most if not all of the world's top notch neuroscientists?

One thing seems certain: denying the reality and real world implications of the quantum realm will not help them to uncover the nature of consciousness in its endless forms of individual manifestations.

*Consciousness is always a very individual experience no matter how much we will eventually learn about the physical mechanisms of the brain.* This is the mysterious and inexplicable nature of consciousness; everybody experiences their very own personal worlds even though we seemingly share a physical world here on planet Earth. Why seemingly?

Because every single physical location, space or home is also completely different and very personal. That is so within the same country, city or suburb; every single apartment in any particular building looks and feels totally different too. Every view is absolutely unique. And every place is imbued with the particular spirit, the individual energies, tastes and choices (besides smells) of its unique inhabitants. None are the same. Not in the least.

Our individual personal perceptions will always stay individual, personal and private. We can never really walk in someone else's shoes and feel what they feel. No matter how understanding and empathizing we may be. Or how well we can measure and somewhat decode the prevailing brainwaves of others in the distant future.

At best, we will someday be able to measure and discern between someone being a bit agitated and feeling angry or being in a generally upbeat and happy mood. Focused or relaxed. Or depressed and sad. But the full complexities of our myriad of thoughts and feelings that all happen simultaneously at mind speed, and are fully based on our individual levels of knowledge, personal experiences and intimate desires, will remain private.

In summary, Machine Man science still has no clue about the nature of consciousness. The where, what, how and why. Another matter is equally clear. *There is no scientific evidence of any kind that consciousness is somewhere and somehow produced within the spheres of our skulls, within the confines or cells of our brains.*

Which leads us to the question: *is there any evidence that consciousness actually exists outside of our bodies, beyond our brains?*

The following completely inexplicable yet very real occurrences have utterly amazed and greatly confused many adherents of the Machine Man doctrine. To the point where some have come to seriously question the very core of their materialistic belief system, prompting them to investigate further and move beyond into the mysterious worlds of Mystic Man.

# Out There

Research and surveys show that millions of people have had either an out-of-body experience (OBE) or a near-death experience (NDE). Both phenomena are very well documented in a great many books, articles, videos and documentaries. For a wide-ranging and carefully-chosen selection, please consult the *Notes* of this chapter.

In light of all the accumulated evidence and their own first-hand experiences with patients, many initially highly skeptical scientists, brain or heart surgeons of the Machine Man persuasion have completely changed their minds and became convinced that we are indeed spiritual in nature and that there is some kind of continuation of life after death.

But of course and nevertheless, the official world of academia, government and media continues to ignore all proof and stubbornly clings to their reductionist views of the world. For them there is simply too much at stake to ever be able to admit that the insights of quantum physics alone – made over one hundred years ago – have proven their materialistic (reductionist) belief system to be totally wrong. Not to speak of all the other evidence we are discussing in these pages.

Their biggest issue is perhaps not so much that they were wrong all along (and admitting that is hard to do), but that we as a society would slowly but surely have to make some major adjustments to the way we all live together. And those (voluntarily entered into) changes would very likely be to the material detriment of the keepers and main beneficiaries of the status quo.

Reluctant skeptics already admit (or simply have to upon seriously researching the matter) that *these highly mystical experiences lead people to not only dramatically change their lives for the better, but actually do so in a most lasting manner.* Real-life facts like these cannot easily be explained away by talking about the purely temporary effects of a mere hallucination, dream or nightmare.

*Severely depressed people became more positive and happy.* Selfish and greedy folks became more compassionate and charitable. Alcoholics turned and stayed sober. Cruel and aggressive people turned into peaceful and loving people. Previously highly materialistic (and atheistic) achievers started to lead a more simple spiritual life, in tune with nature. Most could quickly let go of previous mental limitations and broaden their mindset, develop previously hidden talents, or otherwise become more intelligent, passionate and creative.

*More than eighty percent of people who went through a near-death experience have fundamentally changed their outlook in life*; they are now very strongly motivated to be the best person they could possibly be. And knowing of their eternal nature, yet being aware about the rather limited time they have available in the here and now, they all share a deep and heartfelt desire to somehow or another help making the world a better place.

In contrast, people rarely if ever change their basic behavior, routines or habits simply because they were hallucinating, for whatever reasons. Not to speak of suddenly making major, lasting and more selfless changes in their lives. *Usually, only a most profound and enlightening experience will induce such changes.* Like matters involving life and death.

Also, *while hallucinations are never really the same, descriptions of OBEs or NDEs always follow the very same patterns*, and have otherwise a great deal in common. Despite such reports coming in from all over the world. No matter people's differences in language, education and social background, or the diversity of their cultures and creeds, *they all became equally aware that they are not their physical bodies but rather spiritual beings temporarily having a human experience.*

What causes these dramatic life-changing experiences? What happens during OBEs or NDEs? And why have they occurred far more frequently over the last few decades?

The growing numbers are generally attributed to the advances in medical science, especially in modern emergency resuscitation techniques that allowed increasingly more people who were already pronounced clinically dead to be revived again during surgery, after a stroke, heart attack or other serious traumas.

Before the 1970s, ambulances were essentially just transportation devices with only very limited facilities and rather poorly trained medics. So patients often arrived dead at the hospital or died soon thereafter. And as they were only seldom revived, they could obviously not come back and tell us what happened.

Mostly but not always (!), near-death experiences follow accidental traumas and other severe medical emergencies that cause a person's physiological death; the cessation of all biological functions. In contrast, out-of-body experiences are usually far less dramatic and yet they are often equally enlightening and life-changing.

There are many different causes that have been identified to trigger more common out-of-body experiences, such as the taking of both legal and illegal drugs, extreme stress, deep meditation, brain stimulation, psychic visions while fasting or during extended prayer, dancing, hypnosis, while dreaming or having an orgasm. Since the 1970s, a great many and still growing number of books and study courses are available to teach us how to voluntarily and consciously experience OBEs (see chapter *Notes* for samples).

Close-minded Machine Man however insists that all these experiences can be explained away as the effects of a dying brain that either releases some chemicals or is just getting starved of oxygen. As usual, they are unable to provide any actual medical or scientific proof. But could their speculations actually be right anyway? Well, the short answer is No. They are clearly very wrong, for a number of reasons.

The first question that immediately comes up is why would a dying brain release any hormones? What would be the purpose? Why would a biological mass of neurons 'decide' to create such most vivid and highly memorable illusions in a Grand Finale kind of style when it is simply shutting down and dying? Is it the mercy of a dying brain that itself cannot feel any pain? Compassion for its really unreal user illusion? Pity for a purely fictitious creation?

And *why do not all revived patients undergo these amazing near-death experiences, but only some?* Or why do so many people also have these transcendental experiences when there is nothing physically or medically wrong with them, when they are all in perfectly good health?

Our brains are only receiving electrical impulses via the nervous system and cannot feel any pain. Simply because there are no pain receptors (or nociceptors – nerve endings that signal the sensation of pain) in the brain. This is why many brain surgeries are performed while the patient is fully awake. Some patients even play the violin or guitar while their brains are being operated upon, getting cut and sliced, with bits and pieces removed here and there.

So *why should there be a sudden act of kindness and empathy of brain cells for themselves when they don't feel any pain anyway?* And why do we not get any such sympathy (like comforting releases of chemicals) from our brains when we actually needed it most, while we are alive and suffer from depressions and all kinds of other agonies?

Now let's look at a brief summary of what exactly was both observed and verified in a great many well-documented medical cases. All of them directly involved highly accomplished and often world-famous doctors from all kinds of countries and cultures. And importantly, originally these medical professionals were all either atheists or agnostics, so they didn't have any bias in favor of religious or spiritual explanations.

And yet, their patients kept reporting totally inexplicable and rather irrefutable evidence of a continuation of life upon being revived. Trusted colleagues from around the world reported equally dramatic stories from their respective operating theaters. And several of the doctors even experienced their very own NDEs or OBEs.

Patients who had their eyes closed with tape and were totally unconscious during surgery, were able to accurately report who was present in the operating room, including previously unknown persons, what they looked like and how they were dressed. Or what they did and how they behaved.

They described in great detail the kind of highly technical procedures they went through, along with what happened during unexpected emergency situations. They also heard what was spoken by doctors and nurses, even in adjacent rooms, or with inserted ears plugs that emitted audible clicks to ensure a non-responsive brain (by measuring a flat or silent EEG).

One elderly man was able to accurately tell a nurse the exact whereabouts of his dentures after she misplaced them in a nearby room and forgot about it. And one lady who was later revived after a cardiac arrest could nevertheless see a blue tennis shoe while she was clinically dead.

The shoe was located on a ledge on a different floor in another part of the hospital, a fact that was not known to her before her operation. It wasn't even her shoe. Subsequently it was found by her nurse who became curious upon hearing her report and went looking for it; this account was witnessed by the respiratory specialist who was involved with the resuscitation.

*Dozens of NDE patients who reported such authentic experiences were actually totally blind since birth; they had never seen light or anything at all and yet they were able to accurately describe people and events in great detail.*

Many patients who have had a near-death experience reported incredible and seemingly impossible things upon being revived. They met and conversed with dead relatives or acquaintances who had actually passed away without them knowing about it beforehand. Some NDE survivors suddenly knew other true facts that they didn't know earlier, or gained scientific insights that later led to the actual filing and granting of new patents.

Other patients who could be revived came back knowing events that would happen in their future. Events that were later confirmed to be true. Like seeing and accurately describing the children they were going to have. Then there were patients who literally died of cancer or other terminal diseases, yet came back completely healed. Some were instantly cured, others a few months after their NDE.

Verified NDE accounts also miraculously recovered from serious injuries. Like being brain dead after car accidents. Or otherwise getting critically injured during wars. And so on.

*Such amazing things did not happen to those patients who could also be revived from clinical death but did not report having made a near-death experience.* If NDEs were merely the result of a dying brain releasing hormones, they would likely all have such experiences too, and also be able to benefit from sudden new knowledge, astounding precognition, spontaneous healing, and other life-changing insights.

And equally so, *none of these astonishing phenomena happened to people who experienced hallucinations for other reasons*, whether they were drug-induced (by both legal and illegal drugs), due to certain medical emergencies, mental illnesses, or as the result of severe sleep deprivation.

But most importantly, *hallucinations can only occur when our brains are actually alive and functioning*. Doctors declare a patient brain dead upon performing three clinical tests:

First, an electroencephalogram (or EEG) measures brain-wave activity, respectively the complete non-function of the entire cerebral cortex. Second, function or non-function of the brain stem is concluded from auditory induced responses, or the complete lack thereof. The third test determines whether there is any blood flow through the brain or not (as without blood flowing, there can be no oxygen or nutrients reaching neurons and other brain cells).

*Some patients experienced intense NDEs even while they were declared brain dead as determined by all three clinical tests.* And they had vivid, life-changing memories that lasted a lifetime, even though a brain dead person cannot possibly have any memories at all.

And yet, despite all of this evidence, there are still those who can never be convinced and insist that it is all just due to oxygen starvation, respectively elevated carbon dioxide levels or the release of hormones, *without being able to explain how a person who was verified whole-brain dead could possibly have hallucinations, plus build and retain lasting and life-changing memories of them.*

Some say that it takes time for cells to die, but won't say how these would all communicate with each other, besides producing and storing memories *and* creating consciousness – all without a heartbeat or ventilation, with absolutely no blood flows in the body or brain, no electrical activity or nerve impulses of any kind. Which is the simple, total and permanent nothing Machine Man calls death.

Medical science says that a lack of oxygen in the brain causes permanent brain damage after three minutes, death becomes immanent after five minutes, and is certain within six to ten minutes. Another medical fact is that a human brain cannot store oxygen or glucose (blood sugar), and that both are absolutely crucial to keep it physiologically alive and functioning.

Nevertheless, numerous doctors independently verified that patients whose brain was not just in the process of dying, but was indeed *certified whole-brain dead,* had these most amazing of experiences anyway. We are not just talking about being dead for a few minutes only, but completely bereft of life for many hours, and sometimes even for several days.

It is also a medical fact that *even mild to moderate brain damage due to a lack of oxygen in the brain will cause a resuscitated patient to suffer from a whole range of very severe health problems.* Like life-long suffering from headaches and confusion, a reduced attention span, poor motor coordination and body movement, seizures, the occasional loss of consciousness, and so on.

And yet, ***none of these problems were observed with or reported by NDE survivors.***

Some recorded survivors were not just brain dead but their corpses were already in the morgue for days before they would suddenly get revived while doctors performed an autopsy. George Rodonaia, a medical doctor and neuropathologist who was also an avowed atheist, was pronounced dead after he was hit by a car; his body was stored for three days in a freezing compartment of the local morgue.

Nevertheless, he was fully conscious throughout his ordeal. His memories were not of being stuck in a dark and narrow freezer, but rather about receiving astonishing insights into his life and detailed events that actually happened in the outside world during the very days his body was in the morgue.

He saw his grieving wife and their two sons, watched her select his exact (later confirmed) burial place, and perceived how the news of his passing was quite distressing to his next-door neighbors. George also noticed that his neighbors were very upset that their newly-born child would simply not stop crying, and that nobody would know the reasons why.

Somehow or another he was able to communicate directly with the baby and was told that his arm hurt badly; he could see that the bone was both twisted and broken. Upon his revival, he told his neighbors all about it. Their doctor later confirmed that the child had indeed a greenstick fracture, probably caused by a twisting motion during childbirth.

All the while, throughout his extraordinary ordeal and while his body and brain were completely dead, George was fully conscious. There were no electrical impulses or activity of any kind throughout his body or brain. He had zero sensory awareness via his physical senses that were not just shut down and dead, but further confined to a cold and dark box in a freezer. And yet he was still able to see and hear events in other locations!

***NDEs demonstrate that we can literally think, feel, see and hear, even smell, without a functioning brain.*** We can function normally upon leaving our bodies and continue to experience things in a non-local way. Which implies that consciousness is not produced locally inside our bodies or brains, but that it continues to exist on the outside too.

Indeed, we could state that ***the verifiable fact of non-local consciousness is proof positive that we are not our brains, but something or somebody else***, an individual being who continues to live and experience, no matter the physical death of our material bodies.

The orthodox neuroscientific view however is that consciousness cannot survive brain death and that it is irrecoverably lost, together with all other mental functions. Because they claim that consciousness can only be created by the brain. Never mind the complete absence of proof, or indeed, even the most basic understanding about the very nature of consciousness.

***Any evidence or logic that goes against absolutist Machine Man doctrine always gets summarily scorned and dismissed,*** with a good dose of ridicule thrown in for good measure. Regardless of its verified truth, profound logic or foundation in acknowledged medical and other sciences. Fundamentalist Machine Man claims to know better anyway; ***they desperately want and need to believe the unbelievable.*** Just like religious fanatics.

The following is a quote by Dr. Peter Fenwick, a neuropsychiatrist and leading authority of NDEs, describing the condition of the brain during a near-death experience:

*"The brain isn't functioning. It's not there. It's destroyed. It's abnormal. But, yet, it can produce these very clear experiences...* an unconscious state is when the brain ceases to function. For example, if you faint, you fall to the floor, you don't know what's happening and the brain isn't working. *The memory systems are particularly sensitive to unconsciousness.* So, you won't remember anything. *But, yet, after one of these experiences* [an NDE], *you come out with clear, lucid memories...* This is a real puzzle for science. I have not yet seen any good scientific explanation which can explain that fact."

Many NDE survivors experience what they describe to be a life review; they could see their entire lives flash in front of their mental eyes, all at once and yet in great detail, everything that has happened, or was thought, felt and said. It was explained to be like an incredibly precise and at the same time very wide-ranging panoramic hologram.

What is even more amazing is that this reviewing process was not just like the linear replaying of a video recording of their entire personal lives, but that *they could also access the memories and both see and feel the perspectives of all the other people they have ever interacted with throughout the course of their lives.* And that is obviously not even remotely possible with a currently living brain, not to speak of an already dead one!

What could a still skeptic do in light of what we have discussed? Well, there is a lot of very specific material that we could present, but it would go beyond the scope of this book. And actually, a great many books have already been written on these subjects. The best way to get started would be to spend some time reviewing the numerous references presented in the chapter *Notes*. With a critical yet open mind, *while strongly desiring to know the truth*.

The more adventurous among my dear readers may even consider to learn about how to have their very own (voluntary) out-of-body experiences, and see for themselves. After all, there is simply nothing that is more convincing than experiencing things for ourselves.

That is actually the background of your author who started his mystical journeys in his late teens; the insights gained and the lessons learned are still relevant for me to this day, four decades later. Indeed, they have motivated the writing of my books about how to be happy, and many other mind and consciousness matters.

Quite simply, there is nothing to lose and much to gain.

One universal benefit practitioners of OBEs (or survivors of NDEs) have reported, is the absolute certainty in the continuation of life after our physiological deaths. It is a very deep inner knowing. As opposed to a mere belief that is usually based on hearsay or doctrine.

"If I lived a billion years more, in my body or yours, there's not a single experience on Earth that could ever be as good as being dead. Nothing." Dr. Dianne Morrissey, NDE survivor.

*Transcending the origin of all fears, the fear of death, is a most worthwhile pursuit; life simply becomes a lot more relaxing and enjoyable!*

Most *mystical travelers* also describe themselves as more confident, positive and optimistic, with a deeper sense of purpose in life. They *are able to easily enjoy the small pleasures in life while remembering the big picture view of things at the same time.*

Another common consequence is the moving away from the stringent limitations of organized religion (that is often or perhaps mostly about social control, submission to hierarchies, and dogmatic beliefs) to the direct personal experiencing of spiritual realities.

# Homo Digitalis

We have now looked at many anomalies that essentially prove that the said to be impossible is nevertheless possible. And discussed all kinds of scientific theses and theories that are more or less just discussion papers that can easily be disproved by practical observations, personal experiences to the contrary, and some common sense logic.

Fact is that much if not most of what is officially claimed to be known is currently still unknown. Or outright wrong. No matter where we look, mysteries abound and real answers are elusive. *For open-minded scientists it's still a wild world out there where not much of anything is really settled.* That of course is in sharp contrast to what mainstream science and its sponsors want us all to **believe**.

Now we are further lead to **believe** that science will very soon be able to extend life, first greatly, then infinitely, and finally eternally.

To live forever has been a continuous dream of mankind to this very day. Day-to-day reality obviously shows that this is still not possible. Our physical bodies continue to decay and die no matter what we try. Nevertheless, a great many of today's super-rich and powerful and their fawning followers have come to believe that they will be able to stay forever young.

Introducing, Digital Man or **Homo Digitalis**, the modern subspecies of Machine Man. Many of them have become **devout disciples of transhumanism** (often symbolized by H+ or humanity+). Most have grown up with computers and other digital devices and are generally considered to be digital natives. They firmly believe that science and technology can solve every problem. Including the problems of aging, disease and death.

The historical quest for immortality will easily be solved by yet another awesome start-up that will be worth gazillions. They believe that neurons are just like the switching elements on a computer chip. And that the brain is just another logic-based digital computer that also works on binary code. And as such its operating system and sundry software merely needs to be hacked or cracked. Then uploaded to a digital drive. And death is no more.

Their enthusiastic beliefs in technological salvation seems to know no bounds, thereby infecting and converting many of the elder and digitally more illiterate generations of Machine Man who are getting ever closer to meeting their maker, or rather, undertaker. And of course, the desperate don't need much prodding and are always quick to grasp at straws.

Homo Digitalis promises us a most blissful digital paradise where the human race will merge with machines to finally become everlasting, living perfect lives in perpetuity.

Such a future however would likely be strictly reserved for the self-proclaimed smartest of the smart: those who are smart enough to be rich and therefore able to afford it all. They will bring along carefully chosen technocrats who will supervise those who do the actual (and dirty) work that robots can't do yet. After that, well, they may not need all too many workers anymore. Robots rock; they just don't complain and never ask for wages either. Or social security and the like. A brave new world order is just around the corner, or so some salivate.

**Transhumanism after all is a project of the elite continuing the ancient occult pursuit of becoming immortal gods and rule happily ever after.**

And it is the still concealed but soon to become obvious continuation of the dark and dubious eugenics movement, where only the best and worthiest will be promoted to live long, healthy and happy lives, to the exclusion of everyone judged to be inferior. You know, the ones deemed to be useless eaters. Of which there are said to be way too many, by a self-professed elite class the world over.

Transhumanists openly talk about wanting to improve or *elevate the human condition*, as if we really needed it, as if there was much wrong with us, as if the biological wonders that are our bodies needed fixing. In their words, they have to first **mitigate the disease of aging**, then completely **eliminate aging** altogether. They also strive to **greatly increase human performance**; our mental and physical faculties; our psychological well-being and intellectual capabilities.

Genetic engineering and gene therapy is believed to lead to immense genetic improvements and the eventual emergence of **a distinct species of radically enhanced humans**. Such **posthumans** are said to emerge after a period of transition (the age of transhumanism) and are expected to excel and be far beyond the abilities of current humans. In every aspect imaginable. Or actually, even beyond what we could possibly imagine with our not yet enhanced 'little' brains of today.

Of course, such superhumans will require to be heavily modified (it's called 'augmented'); specific selections will necessitate the strict elimination of all characteristics and traits that are deemed to be less desirable or outright taboo. To better be able to compete in the transhuman or posthuman world, people will generally desire to augment themselves. Later, it may become compulsory. At least certain parts. The ones that keep the masses docile.

A master race composed of master humans... where have we heard that one before? Will the immortal ruling class all look alike and be equally smart but ruthless? Will kindness become extinct as it is considered to be a weakness, for losers only? Will there be eternal warfare among the quarreling posthuman elite who, as now, will always want more? Time will tell.

Other technologies that are expected to bring about this enlightened new age of bliss are nanotechnology and nanomedicine, or biotechnology to include stem cell, gene and pharmaceutical therapies. Add a dose of artificial intelligence (AI), mix in some robotics and bionics (biologically inspired engineering), a bit of memory transfer, a little brain-computer integration, and if need be, a few artificial or lab-grown body parts.

Some of these technologies will no doubt help to make life better or easier, especially for the disabled or elderly. Like improving hearing, speech or sight. Or assist with mobility problems. And that of course is most welcome. Making progress in medical sciences and technologies will likely continue to mostly be a by-product of space exploration and the quest for military supremacy. Perhaps now, some good will also come from the desperate transhumanist pursuit of eternal life in the physical here and now.

***Immortality, however, is the real core of the transhumanist movement.*** And initially, while pursuing this primary goal, they hope to soon be able to at least prolong their lives by ten to twenty years or so. Here we will focus on these principal aspirations which include the ambition or necessity of mind uploading, merging with conscious machines, and the like.

Will cutting-edge research into our DNA quickly make great progress and soon be able to provide the answers to their problem of dying? Perhaps, yes. But I wouldn't hold my breath. Large scale meta-research has concluded that ninety percent of research on human genes has and still is focused on only ten percent of the human genome (about 2'000 of 19'000 genes).

One reason is that many genes responsible for coding large proteins are just too complicated and difficult to model or study; they are thus neglected in favor of simple genes already well known since the 1980s and 1990s. Competitive pressure to get published in science journals and securing research grants are a factor too (the 'publish or perish' problem). And proteins inside the nucleus of a cell are simply very hard to access and examine.

How about, will the latest genetic engineering techniques like CRISPR-Cas9 help Machine Man to live ever longer? Probably not. A new study published in the journal Science Advances (12 Feb. 2020) has come to the conclusion that the standard gene-editing tool often produces a kind of DNA mutation that gets overlooked by regular genetic analysis.

The technique results in far more errors than previously thought. And worse, it is also more difficult to actually find and eliminate such defective and unwanted outcomes. Which of course is not exactly what transhumanist hopefuls would like to hear.

'Oops, your baby girl will just have to live with a lot of rather long facial hair, besides having only three fingers and four toes. But don't worry, we now know the problem and it will be fixed on your next child.'

A wide range of harmless sounding 'off-target effects' are likely to hinder the widespread adoption of both gene editing and therapies. Besides unintended genetic modifications and mutations, there is the propensity for lasting genetic damage (as in permanently changing our or other species), the initiation of all kinds of tumors and cancers, and you can't make it up, a "significantly increased mortality." Wow, that sure is an off-target effect!

"Even when we think we know something about a gene, we can always be surprised and even startled, like in this case, to find out that a gene we thought was protective may actually be a problem." George Q. Daley, Professor of Biological Chemistry and Molecular Pharmacology, Dean of the Harvard Medical School.

In short, messing around with our genes, upsetting a finely balanced ecosystem, creating genomic instability, and disrupting the functionality of otherwise perfectly normal genes is just not a very smart idea. Machine Man still has to wise up to the basic formula of 'If it ain't broke, don't try to fix it.' Especially so since any damage done cannot be reverted back to normal, and even worse, will affect many future generations to come.

Will the pharmaceutical industry turn out to be the savior of transhumanists worldwide? Well, in chapter *Medical Tales*, we have outlined the many reasons why that is most unlikely to ever happen. Trying to extend biological life is already a huge task by itself, but doing so without also inducing severe dementia that is a most frequent byproduct of pharmaceutical drugs is quite another. Who really wants to live longer but in a demented state?

Pharmaceutical drugs only ever treat symptoms; they never heal anything and all too often lead to greater new problems, like irreversible liver damage (requiring liver transplants) and many other debilitating complications like dramatic weight gains, heart and cardiovascular conditions, chronic pains from bone and joint diseases, assorted types of cancers, severe neurological disorders (affecting over one billion people already and counting), and so on.

Incredibly, and worth repeating, prescription drugs are the third leading cause of death in the United States and Europe, just after heart disease and cancer. That just doesn't sound much like prolonging lifespans.

So at least until the theoretical day comes when Big Pharma will be able to come up with pharmaceuticals that don't lead to our premature deaths and have zero negative side effects (instead of requiring ever more drugs that just treat the additional problems created by previous pills), transhumanists will simply have to look elsewhere for potential solutions to their problem of having to die.

What about blood transfusions already provided by some opportunistic companies to some of the both desperate and wealthy? The medical consensus is that transfusions of human blood from any source, including the very young, are not improving our health beyond a placebo effect, but actually carry some serious risks of blood diseases, adverse immune system reactions, and cancers of many kinds. No fountain of youth here, sorry!

Perhaps some kind of new medical treatment will soon be discovered and beat the curse of death? Maybe; hope springs eternal and everything is at least theoretically possible, so let's take a quick look into the current state of affairs.

In 2007, a large-scale analysis into more than one thousand systematic reviews into medical interventions concluded that only 44% were "likely to be beneficial," 49% were neither beneficial nor harmful, and 7% were likely to be harmful. A 2016 meta-scientific research revealed that only 13.5% of medical interventions were supported by high quality evidence.

And finally, the last meta-research published in 2020 came to the conclusion that *"only one in ten medical treatments are backed by high-quality evidence."* About 37 percent were backed by moderate evidence, 31 percent by low and 22 percent by very low-quality evidence. Well, that sure doesn't sound very promising, but of course, never say never.

Most if not all of **the Digerati**, the multi-billionaire digital elite of Silicon Valley and their followers, **already fervently believe that they will soon be able to upload their minds or their essence** into the cloud and live forever in cyberspace. Many of these digital masters and other hopeful investors have invested countless billions of dollars in start-ups that promise to prolong life and achieve eventual immortality. And quite understandably so.

After all, they have more money than they could ever spend, over many lifetimes. So now they just want to beat the odds of dying before their time is up. And be able to eternally enjoy their immense fortunes. Together with their great-great-great-grandkids. And their selection of forever hot girlfriends. Or boyfriends. Whoever or whatever it may be.

Never mind the fact that **they don't really seem to know what exactly they mean by their minds or their essence.** Is it their past memories and emotions? Or their accumulated knowledge and abilities? Their personality or character traits? Their dreams and desires? Their likes and dislikes? Their intelligence or consciousness? Or is it their hallucinations?

They anticipate and believe that very soon we will all have computers that equal or even surpass the raw processing power of the human brain. And **that such awesome processing power will then magically but inevitably lead to a conscious being** they, respectively their uploaded minds or essence, can come to inhabit upon the physical demise of their bodies, to become some kind of superhuman cyborg that would live happily ever after.

Which of course would raise the hypothetical question of who would **really** be in charge of it all: the magically suddenly conscious machine or the essence of the billionaire whose body (and brain) has died? Well, maybe they would take turns in some kind of futuristic marriage arrangement. Till death do them part. Or rather, something else like the repeated failure to pay their mutual electricity bills or ordering crucial spare parts in time. Oops.

Or maybe it is their endless posthuman squabbling about differing romantic needs, choices of food or political preferences that will lead to a literally messy divorce or some gory domestic violence that may very well prove fatal. Who knows.

Never mind the details, Homo Digitalis hopes to perpetually enjoy highly augmented forms of cybersex and other superlative sensual and intellectual delights. Besides totally awesome physical prowess. To forever lord over the ordinary folks that can't possibly afford any such things. Sorry, but regular folks just have to keep dying. After they've finished a lifetime full of hard work, that is. Doing the things robots can't do yet. Or will refuse to do because it would simply be beneath them.

Back to reality, the biological facts we have discussed in the previous chapters have rather amply demonstrated that the dreams of transhumanist Homo Digitalis are nothing more than happy hallucinations backed by empty promises:

*Machine Man scientists simply don't know anything about the specifics of our thoughts, memories, or emotions.* Like how to take what from where. Current state of the art *science cannot measure or explain consciousness either*; it can neither determine where exactly it is located, how or why it is generated, what it is made of, or how to copy and paste it.

And incredibly, the opposite is true too: *modern neuroscience cannot explain what unconsciousness really is*, what it means to be unconscious. Not even how or why it comes about. Medically speaking. Scientists only know the very basics. The same we all do. Like, if we hit someone over the head hard enough, that person will be knocked out for a while.

We also know that some people more or less voluntarily render themselves unconscious after drinking way too much. Or that we can pass out by taking all sorts of hypnotic or sedative drugs, legal or not. Unconsciousness could also be the result of a severe brain injury or a lack of oxygen in the brain for all sorts of reasons.

We all know that general anesthesia is used to induce unconsciousness in patients before and during surgery. And here it gets interesting: *there are dozens of anesthetic gases and volatile liquids but doctors don't actually know how or why they work.* Which of the many microscopic compounds and molecules that make up ether or any of the other anesthetic agents does what exactly or where? To this very day, it is all a complete mystery.

*"Anesthetics have been used for 160 years, and how they work is one of the great mysteries of neuroscience."* Dr. James Sonner, Professor Emeritus, Anesthesia, University of California San Francisco.

*Everything about consciousness is one giant question mark.* There are only open questions and zero answers.

*Yet consciousness incorporates all that we are*: our individual personalities and preferences, our past and present dreams and desires, all of our memories, our current state of knowledge and individual abilities, our particular feelings and emotions, the specific nature of our characters, our intelligence, and the level of wisdom we have attained in life.

Of course, if we wanted to continue to live forever in this physical dimension of reality, we would have to transfer all past and current aspects of ourselves to a new vessel: *the totality of our individual still living being*. Not just bits and pieces of some past memories (if that were even possible, but we have already seen that it is not either).

Despite their complete lack of knowledge and understanding about the very basics of the mind or consciousness, Machine Man still insists with a religious fervor that is cloaked in the mantle of science that consciousness can only arise out of particles that have no consciousness.

So let's ask them a hypothetical question that may encourage them to look deeper into their actual proposition. *If we really were only a hallucinating user illusion*, a conscious mind that has nothing to say and can only observe the machinations of the subconscious mind, both supposedly being the creations of the brain, *why would we want to transfer the brain's illusions anyway?*

This may sound like an absurd question, yet it reveals the full extent of the rather fantastic theories of Machine Man neuroscientists who well and truly believe this to be true; it is their currently leading explanation. Literally, state-of-the-art.

If that were all true, we may have to ask who would really want to record and relisten to the incoherent ramblings of a fantasizing mirage or a delusional idiot? Probably nobody unless you were a shrink and got paid to do so. So if we believed that we are just the illusions of a brain made up over a lifetime, what exactly would be the point to transfer these illusions?

What would be the value of recovering and preserving all of our past hallucinations, if that were even possible? *It would be like a digital photo album nobody ever watches*. Who would really care to see or feel every mental and emotional mirage the mere illusions of aunt Margaret or uncle Bill ever had over the course of their lifetimes?

Presumably, even a supercomputer that were to magically become conscious would get bored replaying somebody else's recordings of their now dead brain's past hallucinations. Such computers-to-be are most unlikely to develop the habit of just perusing the data we have stored in their memory drives; to pass some time while in sleep mode, for curiosity's sake, entertainment purposes, or to exchange a bit of gossip with other computers.

Homo Digitalis believes that they are the most rational people ever. They claim to only believe in what science says. Yet amazingly, most actually *don't seem to know what neuroscience really says* about who they are. Otherwise they would not want to upload their past hallucinations, the verdict of today's science; they would simply realize that their past memories are not worth much at all and cannot remake them again into who they used to be.

The very fact that Homo Digitalis wants to transfer his or her personal *essence* to another kind of body means that *somehow or another they feel that they are something more* than just their brains' past hallucinations, something of more value and purpose, a somebody, a person with a unique individual personality who wants to stay alive and keep having a good time, *a conscious presence that feels timeless, somewhat like an eternal being.*

Regardless of their feelings, like all Machine Man, **Homo Digitalis** fully subscribes to the physicalist worldview they were taught, and frowns upon or ridicules any notion of psychic phenomena or paranormal occurrences. Or the possibility of an afterlife, or even *an always-life, one that has no real beginning or end.*

Ultimately, *the transhumanist's desire to achieve immortality is simply a spiritual longing*, the craving to feel spiritually connected, the wanting to know who we really are, the desire to remember it all once again, and to just live happily ever after, without fears and worries.

The problem is only that they go about it the wrong way. And that is most understandable. Since kindergarten they were told that there is nothing but matter and that they are all gonna die. And be dead for good. For real.

*These deeply-held and rather depressing beliefs* combined with the day-to-day realities of physical life *are in sharp contrast and conflict with their inner knowing*, creating a kind of discord, a cognitive dissonance that is often diagnosed as a mental disease to be duly treated with assorted psycho-pills. Essentially turning spiritual seekers into lifelong clients (and victims) of pharmaceutical companies.

*Transhumanists are really spiritually starved atheists who look outside for what can only be found inside.* Truly advanced scientists will eventually find external proof for what they already know within, while the confused will only encounter more confusion. The principles of quantum physics have amply shown this to be true. The observer influences the observed.

For now, transhumanists are simply stuck with their fundamental belief that precludes them from making any real progress. To them, only physicalism matters.

So to hopefully eventually upload their minds, their idea is to scan the brain and its structure in ever greater detail, trying to get an ever better resolution of the image of a particular brain. Then somehow or another, they hope to create a software model of the image that is as close as possible to the real fleshy thing. After that, they hope and believe that once this software is run on a powerful-enough computer, the whole works will simply behave like the original. And that somehow the person will be back alive and living, just like before.

Currently, the necessary technology to even just do the scanning part is nowhere near the level required. Nor is it clear what those levels actually are. Eventual far higher resolutions of brain imaging however, will still not enable mind uploading because the approach itself is faulty. It is based on the fundamentally wrong physicalist theory of atoms and molecules producing thoughts and feelings, or creating minds and consciousness.

And that belief, by the way, raises an interesting question for Machine Man scientists. Why should or how could any of our thoughts be real or beliefs be true if they really were the mere product of inexplicable and mostly random movements of atoms in our brains?

*But even if their physicalist approach were right, they would still be wrong.* The sliced and scanned digital map of a brain including an eventual complete diagram of its neural wiring throughout tens of billions of neurons and roughly 200 trillion synaptic connections would be *just one particular moment in time of the brain of one particular person*, yet all brains are different and all are plastic and all keep evolving like uniquely individual pieces of art in constant progress, sculpted by the thoughts, feelings and actions of its proprietor.

*Even a most detailed temporary snapshot of our brains will not magically make us alive again when it is run as a software version on a computer that operates an artificial robot body.* To make an exact X-ray of a car engine, then run a software model of it on the computer will not create its driver or transport anyone anywhere either.

And likewise, cryogenically frozen brains, with or without their bodies still attached, a favorite insurance policy play of the very wealthy and desperately hopeful, are still dead too. Just like the frozen steaks in your freezer department (or frozen tofu, for vegans). They will never ever turn into a living and grazing cow again (or sprouting soybean), no matter the hyped and hoped for technology to be.

***Dead and frozen brain cells will simply not spring to life again and produce new hallucinations***, once defrosted sometimes in the future, maybe by our distant descendants. Besides, they may have very different priorities in life or just other living costs to worry about. Sorry, great-great-great-grandpa, maybe some other time, when I'm a little bit more cashed up!

For a little more morbid fun, let's formulate ***The I'm my Brain Challenge*** to all enthusiastic transhumanists, asking them to prove Machine Man right that we are just creations of our brains, that consciousness is created by mere unconscious matter.

A perfect candidate would surely be Elon Musk, the flamboyant multi-billionaire, founder and chief executive of many high tech companies, including Neuralink Corporation that develops implantable brain–machine interfaces (BMIs). His transhumanist credentials are impeccable: he invested a cool $100 million into this venture, believes that we live in a computer simulation (more on that to come!), and so on and so forth.

He could always have the very latest model of his company's devices implanted into his brain, one that could somehow or another help him communicate with the world, at least by spelling words using Morse code that get displayed on a computer screen for us to read.

Then, upon his eventual but definite physical death, remove his brain. Connect the main blood vessels to a machine that keeps pumping his own blood through the brain. Ensure that it is sufficiently oxygenated, filtered, and supplied with enough glucose to keep everything running smoothly. If need be, jump start the brain with an electric jolt or two.

Liberally inject neurotransmitters (like serotonin, noradrenaline, dopamine etc.) a bit here and there, as needed. And to keep Elon in high spirits, add a good dose of ethanol and THC once in a while. Or anytime upon demand. He could keep busy listening to music, hearing or reading books, maybe even watching movies, depending on the implant's features available at the time of his demise.

Elon would become **the first immortal in the history of the world**, sales of his products would simply skyrocket, and we could all stay entertained and enlightened reading his Tweets live streamed directly from his genius brain.

And should he ever have enough of it and said so, we can always pull the plugs and power down everything. But hopefully, he would allow us to send his brain to Mars on one of his rockets and become our roving reporter, so to speak, tweeting his latest insights and observations literally from the last frontier that separates humble humans from becoming posthuman gods.

Another great contender would of course be Mark Zuckerberg, the multi-billionaire founder and CEO of Facebook who also likes to dabble in transhumanist endeavors. He is widely rumored to be a cyborg already anyway, so he might as well prove us all right by becoming the world's first full-fledged cyborg. The real deal.

Anyway, let's see who will take up the challenge first, if anyone. If not, why not? There's nothing to lose and much to gain! Or maybe, not so much...

Let's hear what Dr. Peter Breggin MD thinks about poking and probing the brain. Widely known as "the conscience of psychiatry," he's an eminent psychiatrist and the author of over 20 important books exposing the dangers of psycho-pharmaceuticals and electroconvulsive therapy (ECT).

For over fifty years, Dr. Breggin strongly campaigned against psychiatry's harmful practices like lobotomies and other experimental psychosurgeries, coercive involuntary treatments, and biological theories of psychiatry. Instead, he advocates "psychotherapy, education, empathy, love, and broader human services."

In an interview with Dr. Joseph Mercola, an osteopathic physician, best-selling author, and the founder of Mercola.com, Dr. Breggin said:

"He wants to put in multiple threadlike electrodes into the brain, into webs of neurons, and put in low voltage stimulation. This is insane. The brain can't tolerate this. He hopes to [be able to] communicate but there's not going to be any communication. *The brain isn't going to talk to these electrodes. That's not how the brain works. The brain talks to itself.* It's not going to talk to Elon Musk [or anyone else] and he's going to disrupt the brain talking to itself. It's a terrible thing to do."

Meanwhile, Dr. Jeff Lichtman (a neuroscientist and Professor of Molecular and Cellular Biology at Harvard University, who currently works with a team of experts to create a complete map of the brain's neural connections called "connectomes") likens what we need to know about the brain as having to walk one mile, and what we actually do know now as "about three inches."

In an interview in Inverse Magazine, Noam Chomsky, a world-renowned linguist, philosopher, cognitive scientist, Institute Professor Emeritus at the Massachusetts Institute of Technology (MIT) and the author of more than 100 books, concluded that, *"Trying to find out what I'm thinking... there's no way of developing technology because we don't understand how to proceed."*

Dr. Henry Marsh is a top English neurosurgeon who has pioneered neurosurgical advances over his 40 years of practice. He had a lot of very interesting things to say in a TV interview on SophieCo with Sophie Shevardnadze. First, let's note that he well and truly believes that we are the brain and that there is no such thing as a human soul or an afterlife.

On a quick funny note, he actually compared his job as a neurosurgeon to be a bit like a plumber, even though he is fully aware about "the incredible complexity of the brain" where just one cubic millimeter of the surface of the brain contains up to 100'000 neurons making one billion electrical connections.

He said, "I believe everything you and I are thinking and feeling at the moment is generated by the activity of our brains. But we really don't know how. I mean, yes, we understand a certain amount about vision and movement, but *how consciousness arises, how pain arises – we haven't a clue*," and continues, "The fact of the matter is that contemporary science even at the level of quantum mechanics cannot explain it."

When Sophie asked Dr. Marsh about the idea of downloading our brains into computers or enhancing our brains with computer chips, he said: "That's fairy-tales. Transhumanists, yes. It's fairy-tales. It's the old fear of death written in another form."

Sophie then asked, "We do understand how memory is stored in a brain, don't we?" and got the quick reply, "Not really, no." He later added. *"Nobody can locate a memory in the brain."*

No matter how we look at it or wish it to become true, mind uploading is just not possible. At the very least it is not going to happen for a very, very long time. If ever. And neither is the transfer of our consciousness. Or the relocation of our essence. Or the transmission of life itself, the very life we are, but don't really understand.

Let's hear some more thoughts of another distinguished scientist. Kenneth D. Miller is Professor of Neuroscience and Professor of Physiology & Cellular Biophysics at Columbia University. The following quote is from an article Dr. Miller wrote for the New York Times (Oct. 10, 2015) titled *Will You Ever Be Able to Upload Your Brain?*

"Neuroscience is progressing rapidly, but *the distance to go in understanding brain function is enormous.* It will almost certainly be a very long time before we can hope to preserve a brain in sufficient detail and for sufficient time that *some civilization much farther in the future, perhaps thousands or even millions of years from now*, might have the technological capacity to 'upload' and recreate that individual's mind."

The good professor freely admits his "fears of annihilation" and generously shares his personal insights. Knowing that he didn't exist for the 13.8 billion years that the universe existed before his birth, he expects the same will be true again after his death. He takes comfort in the realization that "the universe is not about me or any other individual; we come and we go as part of a much larger process."

And he concludes that he feels increasingly content with this awareness, and **suggests that we all need to find our own solutions to the problem of death.**

His well-meaning advice however is likely ice-cold comfort to a Silicon Valley billionaire who lords over a global digital empire that has well and truly extended its tentacles into the real world, now telling us what we are allowed to think and say, read and know, believe and do. Or who we should love and hate, respectively vote for.

*Not knowing any of the basic answers to all of the crucial questions however is certainly no obstacle to diehard disciples of transhumanism and their newly-found religion for atheists.*

And a religion it sure is; it is featuring all the required hallmarks and dogmatic beliefs. One Californian engineer has already founded a new religion called "Way to the Future" with the mission to "develop and promote the realization of a Godhead based on Artificial Intelligence."

Oh, the irony: **Homo Digitalis hates the very idea of a God, but loves to play God by creating algorithms they hope will turn into a God to first serve then rule us all.** Yes, you heard it right, as crazy as it may sound: algorithms are programmed to initially serve us and eventually just rule us. But that would be perfectly alright. After all, it would be *their* God.

And maybe, if they behave well, they would even get to keep some special administrator privileges, giving them the accustomed edge over regular folks. The *Brave New World* of technocrats and plutocrats where everyone is equal, but some a bit more than others.

**Is transhumanism a happy philosophy?** Much can be said about happiness, and I have done so in my first two books. But in short, it is not. All Machine Man philosophies are entirely fear-based. And there is no joy in that. No matter how you look at it.

Popping hundreds of vitamin pills and other supplements a day trying to stave off the inevitable, ***desperately trying to add years to your life until the fabled singularity finally happens***, like a leading prophet who has made many glorious promises that keep getting postponed, is unlikely to be a particularly happy affair. And neither is living in the future.

Also, we can't live a happy life thinking that we are really imperfect and fallible beings who screw things up all the time and be happy at the same time. It shows low self-esteem. And it is a kind of complaining; it means not being happy with who or what they are right now. Or indeed, who or what we all are, once such self-hating beliefs have been duly projected toward the rest of us, thereby ***creating a human-hating attitude and agenda*** altogether.

In essence, transhumanists make a rather pessimistic assessment of humanity in general, but always couch it in optimistic tones that are ultimately just despondent yet wishful thoughts expressed with religious fervor. Ironically, they place their faith in machines made by man.

***Transhumanists believe and preach sermons*** like this: "The computer knows best. Or better than us. Artificial Intelligence (AI) will save us from ourselves, from making mistakes, from the many human errors that lead to the destruction of our world. We dumb humans need to be saved by smart machines; we are fallible and can't trust ourselves so we have to trust infallible machines; we imperfect beings have to merge with perfect machines, and all will be well."

They can hardly wait until human intelligence is expected to be far surpassed by an artificial superintelligence. Computers are hoped to become so powerful that at some point they will simply have to become conscious. Like us, just better. Smarter. Wiser. And never mind that nobody knows what consciousness really is or how it comes about.

But computers will not become conscious just because they have ever higher processing power. And it doesn't really make sense to compare our living brains with silicon-based digital computers. Nevertheless, many have tried to do it anyway. Our brains likely operate on sophisticated biological quantum computing principles (superposition) that are higher by many orders of magnitude, while even the most powerful computers are just simple binary systems that switch between two states only; bits of 1s and 0s that are either on or off.

Even in basic binary attempts to calculate the difference in performance, our brains have shown to be far more powerful and efficient than supercomputers that need to operate many separate parts (see more in chapter *Beyond Machine Man* and *Notes*). Computers are always static while a human brain is neuroplastic; it constantly changes and rewires itself as needed. In other words, it is alive. Brain to computer comparisons would be not so much apples to oranges but more futuristic supercomputers to archaic pocket calculators (if at all).

Robert Epstein, an American psychologist, professor and author says, "We are not born with: information, data, rules, software, knowledge, lexicons, representations, algorithms, programs, models, memories, images, processors, subroutines, encoders, decoders, symbols, or buffers – design elements that allow digital computers to behave somewhat intelligently. Not only are we not born with such things, we also don't develop them – ever."

On a little ecological side note. The human brain runs on a very modest 12 to 20 Watts (depending on our resting metabolic rate) while a top super-computer needs 30 million Watts (megawatts) of power and a lot of space. Besides enormous cooling capacities. Our brains just need a hamburger or tofu sandwich here and there, use a tiny little space, require no maintenance or supervision, and get cooled by the occasional cold beer or tofu ice cream.

So, will robots eventually come to the rescue of transhumanists? They sure help us manufacture things quicker, better and cheaper. And take over all kinds of dangerous or otherwise unpleasant and therefore unwanted work. Nevertheless the merits or hype, robots are mere machines made by man running software that is entirely programmed by people.

**Computers** and robots (including humanoid robots) run by computers have memories but they ***will never be sentient*** the way we are; they can do what they have been programmed to do, but they cannot feel and desire, or create and be conscious like us.

Software that is generally referred to as Artificial Intelligence (AI) will never come even close to natural intelligence (NI) which we still don't understand at all. AI should really be called 'machine intelligence' but of course that sounds a lot less dramatic and would stimulate far less investment or grant money. So AI it is. While the term inspires great awe and even fear among people, it is mostly all hype.

***Today's AI is not much more than pattern-recognition software*** performed by computers that can execute such boring tasks faster than we humans can. Algorithms only specify the nature of number crunching (data processing, calculations) to be performed. There is no mysterious monster lurking below the surface, waiting to be unleashed and destroy us humble humans. Or save us from physical death, for that matter.

Software always follows the simple rule of GIGO: garbage in – garbage out. Computers follow the orders of more or less well written code by more or less intelligent programmers. Algorithms usually process input of nonsensical data without questioning it first, which will produce output of equally useless data.

Artificial Intelligence is often classed in three categories. The first is weak or narrow AI (or ANI, highlighting the *narrow* part) which narrowly focuses on one specialized field. Like an email spam filter that determines what should be put in the trash box or not. Or computers in the car that fine-tune the best performance of the engine and regulate many other little tasks.

Search engines or social media platforms use ANI (a.k.a. pattern-recognition software) to serve us information that is deemed to be acceptable or desirable, and filters out (a.k.a. censors) what is considered to be bad or dangerous news and information – as determined by the level of knowledge, commercial interests, and political or cognitive biases (a.k.a. low IQs) of its coders, their bosses and owners.

Narrow AI is also good at playing chess and other games, performs a variety of tasks on our mobile phones, executes algorithmic high-frequency trades on Wall Street, and automates jobs in manufacturing or military applications. It can also do predictive or rudimentary creative auto-completing of sentences, which is essentially the pattern-recognition and probability calculation of already existing writing. As written by humans.

In the end, current AI is all about *'when this than that'* (or multiples thereof, 'when this this this this and this, then that or that' and so on) which is great, but not particularly impressive. There is **not much real intelligence** in software besides the intellect of its coders. As in, truly autonomous intelligence. **AI is basically just automated information processing.**

The two other proposed versions, Artificial general intelligence (AGI) and Artificial superintelligence (ASI) are still purely hypothetical. Pie in the sky, the stuff of science fiction movies. AGI is the dream that machines will eventually be capable of understanding the world as we humans do, and to generally operate at our intellectual levels, with our very wide range of cognitive abilities.

ASI is the kind of stuff that makes transhumanists drivel and causes alarmists to tremble with fear even though that is even further 'out there' in the realm of pure fantasy. Or religion.

But past performance is simply never a guarantee of future results. And algorithms don't write themselves. At best, they will write short specific algorithms as we humans have instructed them to write, to do what we want to be done. No more, no less.

Computers running software that is termed to be artificially intelligent have:

- no actual consciousness; there is no living being there and never will be
- no inherent independent intelligence
- no free will; they execute programmed code looking for patterns
- no common sense or the ability to synthesize conclusions

- no built-in knowing of right and wrong; they do as they were told
- no unique or evolving personality or character
- no inherent personal wants or individual desires
- no objectives, motives or intentions of their own
- no independent decision making other than following parameters
- no sentience or sensuality
- no emotions or feelings
- no wisdom
- no intuition
- no instincts
- no imagination
- no deducing what people might think or believe
- no ability to adapt to the totally unplanned, unpredictable or modified
- no intelligence to answer hypothetical 'what if' questions
- no expectations of a reward like we have: treats, foods, alcohol, drugs, sexual favors or some extra electricity ("Give me more Watts, please.")
- no ability to understand jokes

Human intelligence naturally incorporates all of the above and more. In contrast, machine intelligence is not much more than the total of their data crunching abilities expressed in floating-point operations per second (FLOPS). All very useful in many ways. But only as dangerous as destructive humans make it to be. In other words, psychopaths or sociopaths should simply not be (left) in charge anywhere about anything!

Which includes programming. Or running software companies. Any companies really. Or politicians and government departments, military forces, police commands, and last but not least, intelligence services. Imagine the day we started to thoroughly test leaders for psychopathy, narcissism and Machiavellianism...

*"Your brain does not process information, retrieve knowledge or store memories. In short: your brain is not a computer."* Robert Epstein

Jack Ma, the multi-billionaire co-founder and former executive chairman of Alibaba.com, certainly knows a great deal about state-of-the-art computing. He said, "Most of the projections about AI are wrong... people who are street smart about AI are not scared by it." And, "Computers may be clever, but human beings are much smarter. We invented the computer – I've never seen a computer invent a human being."

So the idea that we really have to merge with machines in order to keep up with AI, another splendid idea of Elon Musk, is simply nonsense. Or fearmongering. Most likely it is all about self promotion. Nowadays it's called 'shockvertising' (shock advertising). It sells well.

One very new theory about consciousness says that it is the result of electromagnetic fields that were created by neurons. As usual, transhumanists prematurely rejoice as the hypothesis is somehow supposed to pave the way for computers to become conscious and think and feel like us. However, it is just another Machine Man theory that focuses on electromagnetic waves and their fields instead of unconscious physical particles.

There are literally millions of huge data centers around the world spanning up to 630'000 square meters (6.3 million sq. ft.) where thousands of powerful servers are connected in networks running the IP protocol suite. The National Security Agency (NSA), Amazon, Google and many others including telephone companies operate closely interconnected digital machinery in huge clouds; there is plenty of firing of sophisticated computer chips going on, all emanating huge amounts of electromagnetic (besides thermal) energy.

And yet, in all these places, there is no consciousness to be found anywhere. Not even an inkling of any kind. Nobody has ever reported some strange or creepy stuff going on, not to speak of encountering even a rudimentary form of a conscious being. Like the proverbial ghost in the machine. Just waiting to take over...

But the brain doesn't produce consciousness and neither will a supercomputer or quantum computer. As we have seen already in chapter *Out There,* there is absolutely no physical basis to consciousness; people with completely dead brains, without even a hint of electrical or magnetic activities for hours and days on end, remained fully conscious, making new memories. In short, virtual consciousness will have to remain the works of science fiction.

Ironically, the promised land of technological bliss is often promoted by people who profess a deep belief in science yet suffer from a serious lack of knowledge about current state-of-the-art science. It is odd but true. ***Transhumanism is a bit of a cult for the scientifically challenged and spiritually starved.*** As such it sure deserves to be buried. For good. Along the myriad of other cults that lead people astray, misguiding us to control us.

Transhumanist Homo Digitalis reveal themselves through their actions; they display the same kind of fanaticism as any of the religious zealots that end up hurting the innocent; they ban people with different viewpoints or knowledge; they don't engage in arguments but emotionally tackle people, shouting them down or worse; they have a cultist attitude believing that only they are right and look down on people with different experiences; they see non-believers as enemies to be ostracized, ridiculed, shadowbanned or outright shut down in the most vicious ways possible. That in short are the elitist high priests of high tech, the masters of Silicon Valley, aided and abetted by their silly sycophants.

And like every cult, transhumanists desperately cling to false hopes and empty promises. On many dedicated websites and discussion boards, they celebrate new technological progress that is supposed to bring their nirvana closer, and finally prove them right. Well, the only problem is that whenever you actually look deeper into the latest science or technology, it is all just dressed up hot air, to put it nicely. Catchy headlines without substance.

For example, the supposed ability to read our thoughts and be able to surf the internet with our mind is being hailed as a transhumanist triumph. Yet it is not reading our thoughts at all.
Most of us silently speak words in our heads while we are reading. This is called internal verbalization or subvocalization.

Electrodes on the face and jaw can pick up otherwise undetectable neuromuscular signals, which are fed to a computer that recognizes patterns to compare and tie in particular signals with particular words. It works with a very limited vocabulary only, for that person only. And only while internally reading and verbalizing recognized words. So, there is no reading of our minds, or getting closer to being able to copy and paste our essence to another device.

"You would have to have some kind of technology, which doesn't at all exist, to tap what the brain is doing when it's constructing thoughts. *We're nowhere near even imagining what kind of technology* that would be, even for much simpler things like how do you remember what you saw five minutes ago." Noam Chomsky

In summary, never mind the latest advances in science and technology or what our personal beliefs or fantasies may be, it sure looks like biological death will remain the great equalizer. Immortality within our current physical or eventually physically enhanced bodies is just not going to happen anytime soon. Certainly not in this century, or the next one. And most likely, not in this millennium. Or actually, ever.

*Ultimately, transhumanism is just an empty promise by people who are mortally afraid of dying.* As unwelcome as the thought may be for ardent or desperate believers in H+, they too will have to eventually accept the fact that they will have to leave their mortal coils behind just like everyone else.

Some people realize this early on in their lives. Others a bit later, maybe upon falling seriously ill. But we all have to come to grips with this reality. Sooner or later. At the very latest upon lying on our death beds, or thereabouts.

One day, perhaps upon reading this book, Homo Digitalis will come to realize that it is a good idea to make sincere philosophical inquiries. And do some spiritual exploring and experiencing that will bring them real peace of mind. The earlier in life, the better.

It sure beats being more or less often to almost constantly drunk or drugged out of their minds, sometimes to the point of oblivion. Desperately trying not to think about the looming big black void that is said to last forever.

So finally, let's say goodbye to Homo Digitalis. May they live long and prosper. Until everything goes black. Or rather, they see the blue screen of death (a.k.a. fatal system error).

Just kidding, because it won't happen. Not to them or anyone else. Never mind our beliefs!

# Who We Really Are

At first, let's briefly review *who we are said to be*. Then ponder on the many philosophical questions and rather chilling implications of the very latest Machine Man theory, brought to us courtesy of Homo Digitalis. All, as usual, seasoned with the occasional dark sense of humor. And last but not least, we will talk some more about *who we really are*.

(By the way, according to the latest research findings, those who really enjoy black humor have both higher intelligence and education levels, while being the least aggressive or suffering from mood disorders. So don't feel bad while laughing a bit here and there!)

*Machine Man* (or *Homo Machina*) *believes* that we are our bodies with a more or less intelligent brain. We are an animal that is smarter than all the other animals, but we are still just another animal. To be rational or enlightened means to not believe in any religious folklore or other superstitions. And to be dead means to be, well, dead. Forever.

*Believing Man* (or *Homo Credo*) is for the most part another subspecies of Machine Man, because both *believe* that they *are* their physical bodies made of flesh and bones, atoms and molecules. The only or main philosophical difference is that Believing Man believes to *have* a soul that continues to live in some kind of an afterlife (no matter whether that is more heavenly or not).

Homo Credo believe to be their bodies made of meat and muscles and that when they die, they, who were the now dead body composed of unconscious particles of matter, suddenly and mysteriously turn into something or somebody else, and raise as an eternal soul.

Dead and already decomposing matter changes into something suddenly alive again and forever so. That is an equally fantastic feat as Machine Man scientist who turn nothing into something, where all of a sudden, dead and unconscious particles appear out of nowhere, and by sheer luck turn into living and conscious beings, all for no purpose or reason.

**Digital Man** (or *Homo Digitalis*) generally **believes** in *Homo Machina* philosophy, however there are growing numbers who also seriously believe that we are not made of matter but digits; that we are merely simulated players like the characters or avatars used in a computer game. They believe that our entire reality here on planet Earth and indeed, the universe itself, is one giant holographic computer simulation.

*There are actually university professors who are among the believers*. But of course, you can't call them that. Because they also believe to be fully rational people without a scintilla of superstitious or silly beliefs.

Is it possible that proponents of this philosophy could be right and we all just lived an artificial life a bit like a three-dimensional computer avatar? And how did Homo Digitalis come to believe ideas like this?

Well, to the second question, perhaps it is the mere fact that they grew up playing ever more sophisticated computer games. It all looks and feels so very real. While playing, we also get sad or mad, excited and happy. Just like in real life. And our minds keep playing the game even after we have already switched off the computer screens and gone to bed.

*It is not particularly surprising that video gamers who like to waste their real lives in fake worlds have a hard time to distinguish between what is real and what is not.* They simply extrapolate from their favorite pastime to believing that we all, not just them, live in a computer simulation.

Growing up reading or watching the fairy tales of Harry Potter and his friends is surely also helpful to believe in the premises and promises of transhumanism. And so is an affinity for science fiction movies. Add a bit of seemingly miraculous computer technology to such magical thinking, mix it with scant knowledge of science, and everything seems possible.

The aforementioned Elon Musk thinks that the amazing progress made over 40 years of video games, from the original Pong to the highly realistic 3D games of today will continue, and even if the growth rate of that progress would somewhat slow down a bit, future games will become indistinguishable from reality. And he hypothesizes that the odds that we live in the real reality (called 'base reality') is only one in billions.

He basically believes in the simulation hypothesis postulated by widely recognized Nick Bostrom, a professor at University of Oxford, the founding director of the Future of Humanity Institute, and the author of *Human Enhancement* and *Superintelligence*. The theory is essentially a trilemma where we have to either choose one of three unfavorable options, or where only two out of three favorable options are possible at the same time.

**The reasoning of the we-live-in-a-simulation-crowd** goes along these lines: If it's true that humanity will not kill itself off before reaching a posthuman civilization that could have the sophisticated computer technology to run simulations of its ancestors, and if many of these posthumans would be interested to play such games and actually do so, then we are statistically likely to live in a simulation right now ("almost certainly").

How likely are the three propositions made in the original paper (see chapter *Notes*)? And have all these luminaries reached the right conclusion? For the record and enthusiasts of this trilemma (I'm not one them), we will argue that the first two of Prof. Nick's propositions are possible, and that the third and final one is impossible. We really do live in a real world of real matter and real energy. While we are here, this reality is certainly our base reality.

The simulation hypothesis is not just implausible and irrational, but also highly dangerous as it turns real life into a real video game: *everything goes because nothing is real anyway.*

Presumably, proponents of the simulation theory wouldn't mind too much if someone came to delete them (kill is such a quaint word and unbefitting a video game, isn't it) and their families. After all, they are only a simulation and the owner of the simulation can always just reboot the game, if they wanted to, that is. Nothing of value is lost, right?

We could all just go back to the old days where everything goes because nothing matters. Got a dispute with the neighbors? Just do what you gotta do, whatever, it doesn't matter. If the whole world believed this philosophy, we would see lots and lots of mayhem and misery. Constantly and continuously.

And why should we actually care about anything? Like the environment, climate change, pollution, peace, justice, cruelty to animals or anyone else. It's all just a big video game, don't you know? Keep playing, do what you want and have fun before they pull the plug!

We have already widely discussed the current rather bizarre beliefs of neuroscientists and other scientists, and concluded that nevertheless their theories, ***we do have free will.***

Hence it is highly doubtful that a hypothetical future user running this particular reality as a simulation would be particularly pleased or feel greatly amused with eight billion human characters, including dozens or hundreds of their personal ancestors, plus countless trillions of animals doing their thing, all constantly messing up his or her twisted game.

All doing whatever they want whenever they want. Total chaos and anarchy pure. The bane of any control freak who has reached the God level and obtained full system administrator privileges. Not too much fun, especially after paying top dollars to buy and run the game!

***The fact that we do have free will proves that we don't live in a simulation; free will cannot be simulated otherwise it wouldn't be free.*** And by the way, setting our decision-making to random mode is not free will. Anyone who says so should agree to have any and all decisions in life decided by a random choice generator for ten years or so, then come back and tell us whether things turned out to their liking. And if they wanted to continue!

To program us to always follow our best self-interests is not free will either; sometimes we do what is best for us and sometimes we don't, even though we know it better. Doing silly or not so smart things is quite common among Homo Sapiens. Acts of altruism or heroism too frequently go against our best personal self-interests. But we do them anyway.

Furthermore, to have free will also means to have *free feelings* and erratic emotions: *we are free to feel the way we feel about things and we can change that at anytime we feel like; this too cannot be simulated.* There simply is not much logic or great predictability to our most personal feelings and emotions; much of it is based on our characters, our experiences in life, and more, including the exertion of our free will.

Like many others, I have no children, and therefore I have no descendants who could possibly be interested in running a computer simulation of me. So, since someone must have created the simulation character that is me by accident, *I hereby challenge any assumed future super intelligent being* (human or otherwise) running this video game to simply delete me now. As in today. Just remove all traces of my existence.

"Can't do it? Well, maybe you're not so smart or powerful after all. Or perhaps you just don't exist!" And neither do any other future super intelligent beings that are said to run this simulation on their hard drives.

(For those smarty pants in the here and now who say that since I have no descendants, I don't actually exist and merely think I do, and therefore nobody hears my demands to delete me, please come and visit me. I would happily punch you on the nose and send you to the imaginary doctor to fix it. Oh, and the pain you'd feel is not real, so don't be mad at the nonexistent me, or your distant descendant who just wanted to see his ancestor's reactions, purely for his or her amusement.

And by the way, I will not pay the doctor's bill since you say that I don't exist. But surely you would not mind paying it yourself as you are also just a simulation. And your distant relative will surely not mind either as he, she or it plays only with fake computer money, not the currency of their exalted posthuman future.)

Now let me ask the supposedly super smart system administrator of the simulation: "Do you really enjoy seeing the simulations of your ancestors die terrible deaths in wars, get brutally raped and murdered, suffer horrible pains while being sick and injured. Living their lives in abject poverty, distress and terror? Are you a total psycho or what? You have no decency, compassion, love or appreciation for the (underlying actual) ancestors that made it possible for you piece of garbage to exist?"

"As an apology and gesture of goodwill, I expect you to transfer one billion dollars into my bank account forthwith. Or better, make it two. One never knows. For you it's just play money anyway, right? You owe me, buddy, even if I'm just a simulation. Do it. Now!"

Of course, the guy running the simulation may choose not to answer my insults, pleadings or challenges, and stay hidden. Which is cowardly, but fine. That may all sound a bit crazy, and it is. Yet to find out the truth we have to investigate this further, in all the juicy details!

Who is hearing our prayers, the ones billions of simulations fervently pray to get a pretty girlfriend, a handsome husband, more money, and so on? Is anyone running the show reading our every of gazillions of thoughts straight from our simulated minds? Is there anybody out there listening to every word we say? Or feeling what we feel day in, day out?

Well, that is obviously highly unlikely. But if nobody is noticing any of it, why not? So why do we think, talk and feel? Or, why should we (purported simulations) have to do it?

Are all our many trials and tribulations in life just sick fantasies of demented descendants? And how would they know it all anyway? What is the basis of the eight billion simulated minds? Where did all the thoughts, articulations and feelings come from? Is everything just an assumption by some twisted minds in the future? Or did they somehow extract it all from our dug up bones? The ones they could still find, that haven't turned to dust yet?

And if someone did indeed pay attention, what exactly would be the purpose of us virtual reality characters experiencing our many daily aches and pains? A sore throat here, some aching bones there, arthritis in the knees and joints, diminishing faculties as we grow older, broken hearts, feeling lonely, being desperate or depressed...

Is that all for our descendants to feel and experience too? If so, why would they want to go through all that themselves? Are they some kind of masochists? And, don't they have enough of their own stuff to go through, in their own time and reality? Also, would they experience all of it of eight billion people or just the pains of their immediate forebears?

And who writes the books, composes the music, creates the art, all that is constantly ongoing as in what I write right now? You are reading it in the coming months and years exactly as I write it at this very moment. Neither you nor anybody else in the future can affect this live process as it happens in (for example my current) real time.

Of any work of art, countless versions keep getting redacted and changed. Some end up in the literal or digital trash bin, other versions will be kept, but only the one final version gets published, featured or displayed. Are future game players reading, watching or listening to all that is being constantly created and frequently modified by everyone in their game? Are they always looking over our shoulders? That would be so creepy, besides incredibly boring.

Fact is that ***our distant offspring could not live, feel and experience our lives and theirs at the same time in such minute moment-to-moment details***. We simply can't live our lives and the lives of any other at the same time. And, presumably, the day will still only have 24 hours per day in the future. So what exactly would be the point of us (supposed) avatars having all these most personal feelings and uniquely individual experiences?

Why would anyone bother to program us like that? It only takes time and costs money. And likewise, why go through the extra expense and additional trouble to make us said to be digital characters sleep for eight hours or so and thus be unavailable? (Imagine your favorite avatar suddenly deciding to take a nap while you want to play!) Or why should virtual players have to dream? Having dreams within a dream seems to be rather pointless.

(Actually, scientists don't really know why we humans have dreams or why we need to sleep. It goes against a core principle of evolution: when we sleep we are most vulnerable to attack. There are as usual many theories, but also as usual, there is no real understanding or conclusive evidence for any of them since we don't understand the brain or consciousness.)

*Most if not all people are primarily and inherently interested in themselves*, their own lives, desires and ambitions. We expand from there to first include our dearest, the ones we feel closest to, whether they may be family, friends or partners in life. Next, perhaps, come our colleagues at work (probably minus the horrible bosses). And the more kind, loving and caring we may become in life, the more we can also afford to be cordial, generous and altruistic with other people, including strangers.

*It is most unlikely that our distant descendants would be less selfish than we currently are.* And be suddenly very interested to spend their own base reality time worrying about distant digital forebears whom they have never met or care about.

Maybe it is because they are so far ahead of us still selfish and rather primitive ancestors? Being more enlightened and therefore kinder posthumans, or something like that? Again, that would be most unlikely to the point of totally impossible. To program us all to suffer needlessly, go through heartaches, have all kind of sorrows, and experience plenty of pain in life, does not exactly display a very kind, loving and caring heart or mind. To put it mildly.

To anyone ever contemplating to code and run their own ancestor simulation, trying to prove that we actually already live in a simulation, let's formulate another little challenge to highlight the actual complexities involved. Introducing, ***The Simulation Challenge*** to all current and coming generations of Homo Digitalis:

'I will believe that we live in a computer simulation if you can design a computer game where all players are fully aware of their environment, make fully autonomous and totally individual decisions about anything at anytime; they can affect and change the environment of the game itself, as they wish – all without any input of the video game designer.'

'Furthermore, all of billions of human simulations can procreate and produce new baby players that grow up, are also fully conscious, with free will and the capacity to change whatever they like in their virtual world, including permanently deleting its parents, or anyone else in whatever manner they see fit.'

'Speaking of terminating, all players must be able to get injured or permanently crippled while playing, bleed real blood, and when they die or get killed they really are dead. In other words, there are no extra lives that can be earned or the like.'

'We must be able to collect and analyze all blood that gets spilled and it has to have all the different blood types with totally individual blood profiles. Oh, and did I mention that every of the billions of players must have a totally unique DNA besides all different finger and voice prints? Of course, the irises of every individual's eyes too must be as unique as they are here, in our proposed present simulation.'

'Moreover, gravity must fully apply in this simulated universe world to be created, along all of the other laws of physics and thermodynamics, to include quantum physics and facts. There must be irreversible time that progresses from the past, through the present, into the future. Yet time and space has to be relative too.'

'And that simulated world needs to exist in an equally endless and expanding universe, like the one we inhabit, filled with countless trillions of synchronized galaxies, stars and planets.

Show me a computer game like that and I will become a true believer too. Otherwise, keep dreaming, or rather, playing!'

All this is required to prove that we live in a computer simulation. Making hypothetical claims is easy. But the burden of proof always lies with the ones making the assertions. To say that there can or ever will be posthumans is a mere assumption (a.k.a. belief). And so is that they *might* have the technology to run authentic and autonomous ancestor simulations that are fully conscious.

And to say that such hypothetical posthumans *might* be interested to run a simulation of their early ancestors is yet another assumption. To say that there *might* be countless such simulations (to increase the statistical likelihood) adds one more to the tally.

The moon *might* also crash onto the earth, the sky *might* fall on our heads, and the hens of the world *might* unite and decide to stop laying eggs until we treated them much better. Oh, and the world's politicians *might* stop being corrupt and lying sacks of you know what and all *might* suddenly become honest and nice.

***The piling of two might happen on top of two assumptions to make an assertion of truth puts the simulation theory well and truly in the realm of science fiction, not science fact.***

In summary, the we-live-in-a-simulation story is based on multi-layered and incredible assumptions, goes against the reality of free will and free feelings, fails logic and common sense, serves no practical purpose, is entirely pointless and incredibly cruel, is unnecessarily complex, and likely, very expensive, besides potentially highly dangerous.

Furthermore, AI (a.k.a. automated idiots) will not exceed HI (human intelligence). And computers will never become conscious (as consciousness is not made by matter, or bits and bytes, or electromagnetic fields), or God-like (as in eventually turning into some kind of super intelligent, all-knowing and all-powerful sentient force or being).

It all makes for interesting conversation, creates great headlines, and perhaps sells many books and speaking engagements. The really interesting part however is the fact that it is not an entirely new theory; the simulation hypothesis is merely the most modern incarnation of philosophical skepticism, an age-old concept that goes back at least five thousand years.

Hinduism considers the entire universe to be an illusion or magic show (Maya) and we are all players in a divine play (God's Lila). Buddhism too says that all physical manifestations are a mere illusion. Things appear to be real but are not really real. That includes all of us too. Ancient Greek, Chinese (*Butterfly Dream* of Zhuangzi) and Western philosophers proposed very similar ideas.

*"It is possible that I am dreaming right now and that all of my perceptions are false."*
René Descartes, French philosopher, mathematician and scientist; 1596–1650.

It is truly amazing how little things fundamentally change over the course of thousands of years. Machine Man and its modern subspecies, Digital Man, all try to reinvent the wheel, and being both atheists and physicalists, they do their utmost to avoid any semblance of religion. And yet, here they are, ***essentially repeating old philosophies and believing in magic***, upon repackaging everything in for them more palatable modern terms.

How does Mystic Man see it all? Do we really live in some kind of illusory world that appears to be real but is not? What are the insights of the perennial philosophers and enlightened sages throughout time? Or, what are the beliefs of Homo Mysticum?

***Mystic Man*** (or *Homo Mysticum*) ***does not really believe anything***; ultimately there is no dogma of any kind. Yet as a child, like everybody else, most Mystic Man were exposed to the predominant belief system of the society and family they grew up in. Whether that was Hinduism, Confucianism, Buddhism, Judaism, Christianity, or Islam, and so on. Nowadays, Atheism is most widespread, and so is New Age philosophy, Paganism or Pantheism.

*Amazingly, no matter their original background or the particular time they lived in, Mystic Man all came to the same final conclusions. And they all had to give up all doctrine to become enlightened.*

One simply has to overcome any and all unnecessary mental conditioning that is part and parcel of every organized form of religion. Doctrines and hierarchies are only meant to distinguish between us and them, to disconnect and mentally enslave us, and thus control our lives and earthly possessions. *Club consciousness of any kind is always dividing us while enlightenment is eternally uniting.*

What exactly is enlightenment? It may sound very mysterious and complicated but it really is quite simple. Furthermore, it is an ever ongoing process and not a destination by itself. There are a great many dimensions to it, a bit like the different achievement levels we can attain in a computer game. *The beginning of enlightenment is making the deep personal experience that we are not our physical bodies but an eternal spiritual spark of energy.*

'Making the deep personal experience' is the key sentence; *it is not about believing anything but solely about experiencing everything.* We have either experienced such realities, or not yet, respectively, we don't remember it at this moment. For a variety of reasons, but mostly, because we don't want to remember it right now.

We can come to mentally understand who we really are by learning about anomalies (like NDEs and OBEs) that prove that the impossible is nevertheless possible. Or by studying and analyzing the huge trove of multi-disciplinary evidence that has accrued over millennia. We can also listen to testimonials by people we respect and trust. But knowledge, logic and common sense can only bring us to *the point of neutrality*, where we are once again open to perceive all realities. *Becoming open-minded skeptics rather than close-minded ones who will not want to see the light even when it shines straight into their very eyes.*

Really knowing this amazing truth to be true however is only possible when we have gained firsthand experience. That is how we really learn. Or remember once again what we have purposely forgotten. Millions of people around the world have independently come to this conclusion. All in their own ways. In their own time. Whenever they were ready.

What is the easiest way to become thus enlightened? All we need is to really want to make such wonderful experiences. Really wanting to know who we really are. To well and truly have the intense desire to learn and know the truth is the key to success. Together with generally loving and living the truth. In all aspects and situations. Both within and without. Internally and externally.

"Knowledge gained through experience is far superior and many times more useful than bookish knowledge." Mahatma Gandhi

*Homo Mysticum are united in the personal knowledge that we are eternal spiritual beings who are temporarily experiencing this particular physical world embodied in a mortal vessel made of matter.*

"Thou art a little soul bearing about a corpse, as Epictetus used to say." Marcus Aurelius

We don't *have* a soul but *are* the conscious spiritual spark of life who experiences different dimensions of the universe at different times in different bodies, or incarnations. Without end. It is not something that needs to be earned. *Everybody makes it out alive because we are always alive.* Regardless of whether we lived a moral or immoral life. However, we can only experience dimensions that correspond and thereby match our own vibration levels.

And we are responsible for our actions. Or sometimes, non-actions. Therefore we have to restore the balance and reestablish harmony. Work out what needs to be worked out. Heal what needs to be healed. One way or the other. We all decide to do so. Voluntarily. Upon realizing once again who we really are.

"We are not human beings having a spiritual experience. We are spiritual beings having a human experience." Pierre Teilhard de Chardin

***This world of material vibrations is really real***. Although it is temporary and always changing its forms and appearances. And the universe as a whole really is a multiverse. Not at all in the purely physicalist way like some scientists believe it to be. But rather in terms of energy, oscillations, pulse and rhythm, strength, purity and spin.

In the same way as many frequencies of radio and countless other electromagnetic waves occur and occupy the same space at the same time, different more or less dense dimensions also simultaneously exist vibrating at different frequencies and rhythms.

Nikola Tesla, one of history's truly great scientists, concurs by stating: ***"If you want to find the secrets of the universe, think in terms of energy, frequency and vibration."***

***Mystic Man has come to the realization that spirit is a form of pure primary energy that is also present in this world, but not of this world***; it influences and partly even animates the physical dimension but ***it is not produced by the material world of atoms or parts thereof.***
Actually, it is quite the opposite. Totally pure energy gets ever more diluted to the point of eventually turning into physical waves of energy, and finally, more or less dense matter.

It is a bit like the gradual diminishing of the electric potential or electric pressure and tension between different points, flowing from a higher to a lower voltage. At the end point of primary transmission of power, the voltage of secondary transmission decreases from 1000kV to 132kV. Step down transformers decrease it further to 33kV and 11kV, then much lower to the 415V of line transmission.

Large factories get a higher voltage than private homes do. And batteries again use ever lower voltages. From truck (24V) and car batteries (12V) to mobile phone (3V) and watch batteries (1.5V).

The voltage across the membrane of a single neuron is about 70 millivolts (or 0.07 volts). With an average membrane thickness of 5 nanometers that translates to 14 million volts per meter, producing an electrostatic force that is four times higher than required to produce a lightning during thunderstorms (Source: knowingneurons.com).

Not a bad performance for a tiny little neuron of which we have about eighty six billion, each with about seven thousand synaptic connections to other neurons, for an estimated total of 500 trillion synapses.

Everything is oscillating energy. Spirit is the highest form of energy, the ultimate reality that exists beyond the lower forms of vibrating energy waves that make up the many kinds of physical dimensions, the more or less material worlds of differing densities.

*Spirit is the essence of who we really are; it is the primal energy of the multiverse at large. There is no beginning to it nor is there an end. It just is. Always.* There are permanent and all-pervading spiritual dimensions in the universe and there are temporary and constantly changing material dimensions consisting of both already manifested and not yet manifested physical forms (as material particles and fleeting sparks of energies).

*The material universe is the quantum manifestation of the spiritual field,* the spiritual dimension, the permanent part of the universe consisting of primary spiritual energy.

Both the predominantly material and the purely spiritual worlds are real. And so are the various dimensions in between, above and below. So it is not either this is true or that is true. *Both realities exist at the same time and are therefore equally true.*

*"The atoms or elementary particles themselves are not real; they form a world of potentialities or possibilities rather than one of things or facts."* Werner Heisenberg

Currently, we live in a time-delayed, momentum-driven, and more dense material dimension where everything has slowed down and manifestations require a lot more focus and effort (a.k.a. work) than in the more refined dimensions that are our regular real homes. Having said that, where we normally live all depends on the state of awareness or the purity grade of our consciousness. Like always attracts like.

"I do not believe...I know. I have had the experience of being gripped by something that is far stronger than myself, something that people call God." Carl Jung

Spiritual dimensions need to be experienced. There is nothing to prove or argue about, nor is there any need to convince anyone about anything. Or to preach and evangelize. There are no hierarchical organizations to join, no money needs to be contributed or things to be done in order to qualify. *We all qualify naturally as we are already eternal parts of this reality.* There is no rush as we will all know it again. At the latest when we leave our bodies behind.

"Meditation is the dissolution of thoughts in Eternal awareness or Pure consciousness without objectification, *knowing without thinking*, merging finitude in infinity." Voltaire

# Beyond Machine Man

Making the distinction between *different degrees of purity and thereby strength of a primary energy*, all the way from the totally pure spiritual to the ever less pure, more diluted material dimensions, may sound like yet another theory. And as far as mainstream science goes, that may indeed be so. To put it mildly.

But likewise, to be fair, we also have to acknowledge the fact that all Machine Man theories about the universe, besides much else as we have seen in our discussions, are equally just theories. Not more, not less. *A closer look always reveals that there is no proof of anything at all.* And that includes beautiful mathematical calculations of any kind; these are all based on a myriad of assumptions, and as such are quite meaningless. Even if they are made to look pretty on paper. It's all houses built of cards. On a beach.

For example, the mathematical equations that are said to rule quantum mechanics and the general theory of relativity are completely at odds with each other. Many decades of trying to unify the theories by creating a quantum version of general relativity have (so far) failed to bridge the fundamental gap between the two primary pillars of twentieth century physics.

*"The existing scientific concepts cover always only a very limited part of reality, and the other part that has not yet been understood is infinite."*
Werner Heisenberg

The predominant Lambda-CDM model is both the standard model of Big Bang cosmology and particle physics itself. *It is suggested and widely believed, not proven*, that the known visible universe consists of five percent ordinary matter and energy. And that dark matter and dark energy together account for 95% of the total mass-energy content in the universe.

*Dark matter and dark energy however are not scientific facts.* Both are *only thought to* exist, yet are nonetheless included in mathematical formulas, to make them work, true or not. All too often, theoretical constructs or placeholders simply needed to be invented. They always start with pretty equations, then try to match them up with reality later on. And when real-world observations prove the theories totally wrong, as they already do, they just invent another particle or some mysterious force to keep the erroneous but beloved models going.

*"Today's scientists have substituted mathematics for experiments,* and they wander off through equation after equation, and eventually build a structure which has no relation to reality." Nikola Tesla

Who knows, perhaps one day it will indeed be possible to measure and prove the existence of pure spirit with physical devices, although it is likely to remain elusive until we have changed our attitude and thereby our approach. Maybe future scientists will call dark energy (said to be 68% of the total energy of the known universe) the spiritual force that shapes and forms all unmanifested dark matter (thought to be 27% of mass-energy) which subsequently turns into the manifested physical matter that we can already measure, observe and influence in the here and now.

In the meantime, another great unsolved problem in today's cosmology and physics is the asymmetry of matter and antimatter (not to be confused with dark matter) in the observable universe. *According to the Big Bang theory, models and mathematics, there are supposed to be equal amounts of matter and antimatter.*

All particles are said to have an equivalent antiparticle, one being positively charged and the opposite one negatively charged. They are supposed to have canceled or destroyed each other and converted back to energy. So the matter making up our universe or the bodies we inhabit shouldn't really exist, according to theory. Funnily, Machine Man science seriously says that we shouldn't exist. But obviously, we do exist. No matter what the models say.

The theory cannot account for the fact that there is way too much matter and not enough antimatter; it looks like the visible universe is almost entirely composed of ordinary baryonic matter. The assumed five percent part of it, that is. The part that includes our Milky Way, all that we can currently measure and see with our still limited devices.

Have you noticed that the Lambda-CDM model always refers to the observable, visible or known universe? That obviously means that it is not all of it. Only a part of it. And most of it is still unknown. *We could say that the known is actually unknown, and the unknown is equally unknown.* To top it all off, the universe is generally thought to expand very rapidly. Also for entirely unknown reasons. Into what exactly it expands, is equally unknown.

It may be a highly unpalatable truth for Machine Man, yet ultimately, today's top theory of physical cosmology has to be summarized like this: *Some say that somehow something came out of nothing and acted upon the nothing to produce everything, all for no reason.*

So how does *Homo Mysticum* explain consciousness? Or life itself? We have looked into the absolutist views of Homo Machina and seen that there are no actual answers available. Just theories that seem to be rather farfetched: the closer and deeper we look into the details, the more implausible they all become.

The perspective of Mystic Man is that consciousness derives from life, and indeed, is life. In other words, *consciousness is an inherent attribute of life* just like water in its liquid state feels wet. And vice versa: *life is a fundamental characteristics of consciousness.*

Consciousness just is; it is not the result of an electrical, electromagnetic, chemical, biological or otherwise physical action. Physical processes in the brain cannot and do not give rise to consciousness; *only life can give rise to consciousness because consciousness itself is life.* That is the secret. To be individually experienced. To date it is solely proven by personal empirical evidence. Which is part of the scientific method.

***Consciousness and life are attributes of the autonomous fundamental energy that is spirit.*** The pure primary energy that underlies *All That Is*, of which we are a part. ***Sparks of spirit is who we really are.*** It is the principal vital force that exists throughout all physical and non-physical dimensions at all times since ***it has no beginning or end.***

This primal and constant spiritual energy exists beyond the physics of the Standard Model, and beyond spacetime; it is timeless yet its effects can be observed and measured at different times in different ways; it is nonlocal but can nevertheless express itself locally.

A bit like entangled particles, the primary force operates outside of time and space while affecting both the space and time, power and velocity, rhythm and spin of physical particles that are essentially just temporary flashes or waves of energy.

The inexplicable, seemingly random and mostly unpredictable movements of atoms that puzzle Machine Man scientists are ultimately controlled by spirit; the intentions, desires and expressions of various spiritual energies are collapsing and thereby influencing the energy waves of the quantum realm, its quantum fields and the subsequent appearances and movements of subatomic particles.

This is not to say that everything is determined in advance. Not at all. There is no spacetime in this ultimate dimension anyway. But more importantly, we live in a universe where there are infinite possibilities, where we all have free will and we all accept the responsibility that comes with it, even though some of us are currently not (wanting to be) aware of this reality.

The freedom to choose what we want to experience or desire to do applies throughout all dimensions, the more or less material, the more or less spiritual. Ultimately, we are the masters of our destiny wherever we are, here, there and everywhere. The only thing that binds or limit us are the consequences of our choices. Cause and effect too knows no boundaries, neither in time nor in space or location.

The spiritual dimensions are individually realized to various degrees of reality, strength and purity, and experienced in different states of awareness and clarity, all wholly depending on our own personal attitudes, intentions and desires.

If we categorically deny the very existence of primary spirit, we cannot consciously realize its reality; if we are open to its possibility, we are likely to experience it from time to time; if we strongly desire to experience this reality, we surely will, eventually to the point of being able to tune in at will, anytime and anywhere.

*Where there is no spirit there is neither life nor consciousness, and therefore no thoughts and feelings, intentions and desires, or intelligence and creativity.*

It is that simple. And in this simplicity lies also the solution to the philosophical problem of zombies that are postulated to be indistinguishable from normal human beings but are said to lack sentience or qualia, a personal conscious experience. Many a smart philosopher believes that they are actually conceivable. Some say that they are entirely possible.

Or actually, that zombies already are a reality. As in, our reality right now. As we have seen, the Zombie Argument is the foremost explanation of today's top notch neuroscientists; we are said and believed to be merely observing conscious automatons, self-operating machines whose brains cause all sorts of behavior, all solely directed by the mythical unconscious.

My take on this is likely to be far too simple for modern-day academics to accept: *If a zombie lacks life, it is just a dead body, devoid of spirit and consciousness.* If it moves, it is obviously both alive and conscious, infused with the primary energy that is us. So it's not a zombie. They can't and don't exist. Or rather, they do exist but only in our imagination. And in works of art like books and movies or a host of computer games and animations.

*Spirit equals life and consciousness*, which includes all of our intentions and desires, hopes and dreams, thoughts and feelings, knowledge and abilities. It's all about having the right perspective that comes from posteriori knowledge: empirical evidence based on personal experience.

Furthermore, Occam's razor or the law of parsimony (attributed to Franciscan friar William of Ockham; 1285–1347) suggests that simpler solutions are more likely to be correct than complex ones; while evaluating competing theories to solve a problem, ***the solution that actually makes the fewest assumptions is most probably the right one.***

We have discussed many aspects about who we really are, discovered amazing anomalies, and seen the many deficiencies of the materialistic models of explanation. None of the big questions in life can be answered by Machine Man, yet everything makes perfect sense once we have personally experienced the timeless insights of Homo Mysticum. Suddenly, it all just comes together like one giant puzzle that gets assembled in a flash.

As a matter of fact, besides introducing some lesser-known information, much of what we have done throughout this book is attempting to find the truth by the systematic elimination of other factors. We could very well call it the Sherlock Holmes model:

*"How often have I said to you that when you have eliminated the impossible, whatever remains, however improbable, must be the truth?* We know that he did not come through the door, the window, or the chimney. We also know that he could not have been concealed in the room, as there is no concealment possible. When, then, did he come?"
Sir Arthur Conan Doyle, in a Sherlock Holmes quote in *The Sign of the Four*, 1890.

We could adapt the quote a little bit like this: We know that matter did not come out of nothing, for no reason, that every cause has an effect, that life must come from life, that nothing can ever disappear or cease to exist, that we are alive, exist now, and therefore will continue to exist. Why, then, the irrational fear of death that only spoils life?

To bring it all together, let's summarize the main points of the previously discussed thoughts and theses. For better clarity, we will keep it as short as possible, without going into all of the details or the many reasons why. So please refer again to the respective chapters for the full train of thoughts. We will also expand on several insights, present new information, make additional observations, and come to some perhaps surprising conclusions.

One: **We are not our bodies.** The travails of Paul Schmitz, the most unfortunate racist, have shown us that he was still the very same person despite having only about 50% of his original body parts.

Our bodies are biological avatars that we inhabit while we live in the physical world. It allows us – the who we really are – to experience things that can only be experienced in this ever-changing and temporary material world of polarities. Where there is simultaneously good and bad, up and down, big and small, hot and cold, dark and light, and so on. Where we have physical senses that can experience physical sensations. Where things can happen that otherwise would not possibly happen. Or things don't happen that are normal to happen.

Only here can we experience things like being born, growing up, to keep loving despite going through difficult situations, getting older and eventually confronting the biggest fear and illusion of all; death, believed to be the final and endless end of our lives. On 'the other side' we simply cannot hurt or get hurt, kill or be killed, as there is no such concept over there. There is no need to struggle or work either, or experiencing a lack of this or that.

Hardships like being too hot or cold, real dangers of any kind, or emotional pains inflicted by human relationships do not occur in other dimensions. But here they sure do, for us to experience and learn. There are lots of ways we can amuse ourselves too. We play all kinds of games in this world, including the game of playing the supreme master of all, the richest, most famous or powerful. Or simply trying to become immortal and forever-ruling gods.

Two: **We are not our DNA.** Our DNA is a blue print of potentials that contains personal biological information to build and renew our particular bodies.

DNA gets activated and controlled via epigenetic factors; it is influenced by our core beliefs which in turn control our thoughts, and consequently what we do or don't do. Our behavior, habits and lifestyles further control these epigenetic switches. And so does the environment we live in, for better and worse.

Physical characteristics are originally part of the DNA's genetic blueprint that codes the proteins of our bodies. However, while DNA can physically change a little bit over the course of a lifetime, our bodies' physical appearances and developments often change in most dramatic ways, even though our DNA is still mostly the same we were born with.

Just see how many young children look very pretty or really handsome well into their teens, but somehow or another they manage to turn their physical bodies and overall appearances into quite the opposite.

Suddenly or gradually, they have become mere shadows of their former natural beauty and brilliance. Sometimes it's outright distressing to behold; originally totally amazing people now looking ever more sad, mad or bad. Or depressed, angry and mean. Sadly, some have quite literally turned into empty shells; somewhat they are not quite present any longer.

It is not because of their DNA which is still the same. ***We are simply not our DNA.*** And ***epigenetic factors are only part of the reason***s why this happens to some of us. Or not at all to others who throughout their lives simply continue to look mostly the same, albeit with a few more wrinkles and perhaps less hair, besides other natural signs of aging.

Our more or less healthy states of mind and the vibration or energy levels of our general consciousness are the main drivers behind it all, whether we succumb and wither away prematurely, or cope and thrive regardless of our external circumstances.

Some of us keep sparkling our entire lives despite going through many adverse moments and suffering from plenty of hardships. Others simply fade away rather rapidly, often despite growing up in total comfort and amazing luxury, eating healthy foods, and so on. But their lights have quite visibly dimmed as they failed to renew their energy levels; the high energy vibration of who we really are has slowed down to a mere fraction of its original brilliant state, its normal healthy condition.

*We either influence matter and the general environment more than it influences us, or vice versa.* It is our choice. If we are aware of it. Some of us are, others not yet.

And, we either know how to re-charge our spiritual batteries, or don't. Because we don't want to, respectively don't bother because we believe that spiritual stuff is all just nonsense anyway. And that there is only matter. But simply eating more matter (a.k.a. calories) will obviously not do the trick as a world aplenty of the overweight and obese clearly shows.

Technically, besides working on biochemical signals, the double helix structure of our DNA acts like an antenna on electromagnetic principles between who we really are, our brains and bodies. Transfer of information is essentially happening in real-time. There is a quasi instant exchange of information within the quantum energy fields of our cells, between individual cells, organs and throughout our bodies.

Ether or Aether is the underlying energy field that contains and transmits all information received from who we really are via our minds. This intentional and therefore energized, dynamic and moving information then causes particles like protons, neutrons and electrons to come and go, getting assembled or disassembled, becoming excited or de-excited (fall from an excited energy level to a lower energy level).

The existence of aether, quintessence, or the fifth element was known throughout the ages, including among the ancient Greeks, but the phenomenon was discarded by Machine Man science in 1887, based on a single, albeit repeated, experiment during a time when most astrophysicists (including Einstein) erroneously thought that the universe is of a fixed size.

Unknown to many, there were actually two possible conclusions to the Michelson–Morley experiment, one that supported the reality of aether, and the other, the chosen one, that dismissed it outright (see *Notes*). Observational evidence however still supports this elusive medium that serves as a conduit of information and connects entire galaxies in real-time.

A 2019 study published in The Astrophysical Journal revealed a mysterious instantaneous coherence between galaxy rotation and neighbor motion on a several-megaparsec scale; one megaparsec equals a distance of 3.26 million light years. The team of Korean scientists then ask simple but hard questions: "How can the dynamical coherence be established over such large scales? Undoubtedly, direct interactions are impossible between galaxies separated by several megaparsecs. Then what caused this mysterious coherence in large scales?"

Dr. Sid Deutsch, a professor of electrical and biomedical engineering, asks in his final book (*Einstein's Greatest Mistake: Abandonment of the Aether*) another pertinent question: "How can light, or any electromagnetic wave, travel for billions of years across the vastness of the Universe, without losing any energy?"

Good questions indeed. The likely answer is aether, the energy field that is the universal yet ***locally more or less concentrated and dense*** glue that literally holds together the universe, assembling or disassembling all matter. Currently there is a revival of interest; new research and theories cautiously proclaim that the discredited aether really could exist; it simply and elegantly explains anomalies and solves a lot of real-life observed problems in physics.

"The modern concept of the vacuum of space, confirmed every day by experiment, is a ***relativistic ether***. But we do not call it this because it is taboo." Robert B. Laughlin, Nobel Laureate in Physics 1998, Professor of Physics and Applied Physics at Stanford University.

There just is no nothingness. There is always something (that, for example, creates a wave form). Modern-day proponents however like to call it the new aether even though it is not. Now aether is potentially called the fifth fundamental force, vacuum energy ("an underlying background energy that exists in space throughout the entire universe"), dark matter, quintessence (same old same old), virtual particles, the Higgs Field, and so on.

"All perceptible matter comes from a primary substance, or tenuity beyond conception, filling all space, the akasha, or luminiferous ether, which is acted upon by the life-giving Prana or creative force, calling into existence, in never-ending cycles all things and phenomena." Nikola Tesla, in Man's Greatest Achievement; 1907.

Three: **We are not our brains**. The brain and the central nervous system is constantly steering the body's various muscle movements, simultaneously translating the input from as many as twenty-one senses, and continually looking after all of the many life-sustaining physical functions, including (for example) the balancing of ideal chemical conditions, body temperature and fluid levels of our bodies. Luckily, this homeostasis happens automatically, independent of our mental approval or conscious decision-making.

Perhaps most people are not particularly aware of these physical processes, yet we can all learn to observe and influence them to a certain degree. Some of us have learned to outright control and master some homeostatic processes. Like Yogis who don't eat or drink for extended periods of time. Or Wim Hof, the Dutch fellow who sits essentially naked and for extended hours in icy cold water, snow or ice without even catching a cold. Martial artists too are known to master their bodily functions to amazing levels of proficiency.

An advanced meditation technique called g-Tummo, the meditation of inner fire, has been practiced by Tibetan monks for thousands of years. Harvard Medical School professor Herbert Benson has thoroughly researched and documented this phenomenon for over twenty years; it was replicated in numerous clinical experiments. Adepts are able to dry wet sheets wrapped around their naked bodies while sitting or walking in the freezing cold conditions of the Himalayas; they could quickly raise their body temperature, dramatically decrease their metabolism or intake of oxygen, and control the nature of their brainwaves.

Many studies have shown that the practice of regular meditation actually changes the physical structure of our brains. So the mind makes a real-life impact on the brain while it is not the brain or a part thereof. Furthermore, we meditate because we decide to meditate out of free will; it is our desire and deliberate choice that comes first. The brain changes thereafter only, over a period of time.

It is not the brain that made the original decision. We did. Maybe because a good friend recommended us to meditate and we decided to give it a try too. It is not the brain's non-existent unconscious or a mythical user illusion that caused us to meditate and thereby change itself. It was our decision and the subsequent action we took that caused the brain's structure to change.

*We can live with half a brain or without a brain and we can willfully influence and change our brains with our choices and indeed, our minds alone; we are simply not our brains.*

Our brain – together with the central and peripheral nervous systems – is a fully integrated, harmonious and flexible ecosystem that operates on multiple levels of realities, in various frequencies of brainwaves and according to numerous principles, some known and others yet to be discovered.

The brain acts as a multidimensional interface for the mind that is operated by us, the who we really are; it translates and transmits information, and it transforms subtle energies in both directions, spiralling simultaneously upwards and downwards. The mind's positive or negative energies (thoughts and patterns) pervade the physical brain to control the operation of the body's cells and muscles or to perceive the translated information transmitted from our senses. This energetic fusion and the subsequent communication of information likely happens via the underlying energy fields of aether that pervade all space, including the quantum realm.

Perhaps one day, quantum physics will be able to show that *we, the who we really are, cause constant quantum collapses with our thoughts and deliberations, with our observations and desires.* Thus creating the physical situations and circumstances we may falsely perceive to be the one and only reality – once we are fully immersed in the purely physicalist belief system of Machine Man, thereby denying all other possibilities, despite the many anomalies that nevertheless prove them to exist. But ignoring something will not make it go away.

"My brain is only a receiver, in the Universe there is a core from which we obtain knowledge, strength and inspiration. I have not penetrated into the secrets of this core, but I know that it exists." Nikola Tesla

On another little technical note, within the brain and our bodies there is no tangible time delay for energy waves to travel, for the exchange of electromagnetic signals of information.

What scientists measure with their still crude machinery, and what does indeed take some time, are the various constantly ongoing biochemical processes that reenergize the action potentials within individual cells, respectively the regeneration of electric and magnetic fields, besides general repairs and maintenance work needed to upkeep homeostasis, the movements of muscles, and the operation of our physical senses.

Biochemical actions are far too slow to account for what we think, feel and experience immediately; *the purpose of molecular biological activities is to regenerate, maintain and reenergize the various systems, organs, muscles and cells making up our bodies.* That is my theory anyway. To be proven right or wrong.

The interfacing mind operates at mind speed which means it is far faster than the speed of light; it enables instant communication over any distance and indeed, the instant relocation of who we really are to any place at any time. Think of a place you have been and you are there, faster than any airplane or the speed of light. Think of many places at the same time and you can be there all at once.

Some might object and say that this only works thanks to the recollection of our memories. Well, first of all, science does not acknowledge this reality by still insisting on non-existent time delays within our brains, and secondly, they also claim that memories can deteriorate and become faulty which is not really so (see below and chapter *Memories*).

Fact is that we can also fantasize, imagine and create all kinds of entirely new thoughts at the speed of mind too; there are no preexisting memories involved whenever we instantly come up with something completely original, some outrageous new thoughts, seemingly crazy concepts, amazing inventions and great ideas that pop up out of nowhere. Instantly.

Another fact is that the mind can operate independently of the brain as we have seen while discussing NDEs and OBEs. Where people who were born blind could mentally see and describe unknown persons and environments, or their entirely unfamiliar activities, all while being certified clinically dead. *It proves that the brain is not necessary for the mind to function, and that it is a separate form of energy, outside the realm of any form of matter.*

Further proof of this is provided by people that are generally called savants. The savant syndrome is not at all understood by science, neither how or why it comes about (yes, there are some theories, and no, they don't make any sense). In *congenital* savant syndrome, most extraordinary skills and amazing abilities usually surface in early childhood; sometimes but not always it may be associated with a form of autism (1 in 10 to 1 in 200).

In *acquired* savant syndrome, ordinary people suddenly possess totally astonishing new skills upon recovering from a severe concussion, a stroke, even a lightning strike, or any other kind of incident involving the central nervous system. *Previously, they had no such capabilities, qualifications or even interests in their newfound exceptional talents.*

To the utter surprise of their families and friends, they have become prodigies in playing the piano or other instruments at master levels or beyond, compose incredibly complex music, turn into absolute mathematical geniuses, and create all kinds of awesome pieces of art.

Then there are also **sudden savants** who as the name implies suddenly turn into geniuses without any external cause or discernible reason. It just happens. Unexpectedly. Instantly.
And quite often, such people are at least initially hesitant to talk about it or even mention it.

Another for Machine Man most inexplicable anomaly is the well-documented but mostly unknown (a.k.a. ignored) phenomenon of Xenoglossy: people who just woke up one day and fluently talked in another completely new language, one that they have never learned or even heard before. Often they spoke very exotic languages, frequently in local dialects or accents, and according to the respective foreign customs. Some could read and write as well.

It is (or should be) very obvious that the brain could not and **did not have any of the required genius memories** or sudden expert foreign language abilities stored beforehand as these skills were not previously available or possible. This further demonstrates that at least **our sophisticated memories are a mental function of our minds**, not a physical feature of the neurons in our brains.

How could something be recalled that wasn't even there in the first place?

**The brain has never learned and memorized any of these amazing new skills and talents.** Therefore they can't be explained away by one part of the brain somehow compensating for a problem someplace else, but some Machine Man scientists try to do that anyway. You can't compensate someone by giving something that doesn't exist. Besides, sudden savants never had health issues of any kind so there were no problems to begin with.

Furthermore, **all these extraordinary abilities require really refined motor skills**, which are learned abilities based on the continuous practice and honing of specific gross or fine motor skills, going through the cognitive phase, the associative phase, and the autonomous phase. How could someone suddenly play like a master pianist when they have never even played the piano before?

So the key question that begs to be answered is: where did all of these most amazing memories and motor skills come from? Moreover, ***where does the original creativity and incredible artistic inspiration originate from?*** Since the origin can't possibly be the brain as nothing was previously there, there are only three possible explanations, even if they sounded totally impossible or outright insane to Machine Man.

The person, ***the who we really are***, had acquired and mastered these skills before even being born in the current body and the mind suddenly expanded once again to reveal these abilities inherent in the mind. Or the person got partially infused, inspired or possessed by another person, a different currently disembodied spirit, coming through his or her mind and hence their bodies. Or the person, the who we really are, was suddenly able to again tune into the perfect creative stream, the absolute knowledge and total intelligence of primal spirit energy.

But let's hear from one of these prodigies. Derek Amato became a sudden musical genius after suffering from a concussion that resulted in a 35% hearing loss; he can't read music or perform a simple children's song and yet he composes extraordinary music and plays it perfectly on the piano. Without any prior knowledge or ability. He says, "***It's almost like the ghost of Beethoven jumped into my body***, right, and took over and I just kinda went crazy."

He continues, "Since I woke up with the immediate ability to play the piano, I see these nonstop geometrical squares that go left to right in my mind's eye. And it's not repetitive music going in a circle just like one song. Each one of these squares maybe have a lot of notes to each square rather than just one note. ***It's almost as if someone basically plugged a super intense musical stream into my brain. It's twenty-four hours, nonstop composition*** even when I'm sleeping."

There are many other kind of anomalies and real-life indications that ***the mind perceives energy*** like sound or light waves and communicates with the body before the brain even gets involved. Some of these occurrences have been demonstrated in replicated experiments.

Skin conductance measurements by Dean Radin showed stress or calmness already before the computer would show participants the next calming or upsetting image, indicating our ability to sense and know what is coming next. The body also reacted to impending future events by increasing or decreasing heart rates before pleasant or unpleasant sounds could be heard and processed by the brain, ahead of any and all corresponding activity in the brain.

WiFi, radio or TV and any other of the waves of the electromagnetic spectrum fly seemingly unnoticeable through space (although it is really through aether since space is pervaded by aether), carrying information and producing an effect once decoded and modulated.

Why should or could there be no other kinds of even higher oscillating waves of energy that were likewise doing that too? And similarly, why should such far more refined and powerful primary energies not be able to also produce a real-world physical effect in this more or less dense material world of ours? Ultimately, everything and all is energy.

Four: **We are not our minds.** Thoughts come and go, floating by like clouds in the sky. Some are white and bright, others more dark and gloomy. We can let the thoughts drift by and simply observe them. We can focus on one or observe several thoughts at the same time, sometimes really getting into a specific one, then choose another one, dismiss what we don't want to pursue, or keep thinking about what we like or need to think about.

Without a doubt, we can control our minds, what we think, whether we think more or less positively, and so on. Some of us are already very good at this while others have yet to learn more about it. Through various techniques like meditation, contemplation of nature, the arts or martial arts, yoga or sports, fishing or a myriad of other ways, according to our personal temperaments and interests.

Practitioners of lucid dreaming – when the dreamer is aware about being in the dream state and has some control over what happens or where and with whom – or those skilled in voluntary out-of-body experiences (OBE) demonstrate that *we can actually control our thoughts even while our bodies and brains are asleep.*

Our mind is a bit like a television, and our thoughts, perceptions and memories are like the TV programs; we can tune in, tune out, watch intently or not, change the channel often or only rarely, pay close attention to a particular actor or actress, carefully listen to the script or not, notice the beautiful screenplay or not so much, and so on.

It is us, the who we really are, who decides it all. Or could do so, if we are aware of it!

*In the meantime*, in sharp contrast and not at all surprising, *Machine Man psychologists are literally afraid of their brains*. They say that our brains have a neural bias for negativity and will release stressful hormones and neurotransmitters whenever we think or say negative words of any kind, like 'no' or 'disease' and 'poverty' or 'death.' Even worse, for them, they believe that their brains only barely respond to positive thoughts and words.

This affliction, they say, is not only affecting the person whose brain and therefore mind is expressing itself negatively, but it is also shared with everybody else who happens to merely hear it. In other words, it is said to be bad. To counteract such dire negative effects, we must consciously think as many positive thoughts as we can. Repeatedly. Or better, all the time.

They say that every negative word has to be counteracted by a minimum of five positive messages. Whenever somebody says 'no' we have to counterbalance the negative effects on our brains by quickly saying at least five life-affirming words. Or else. Be afraid, be very afraid. Of your own brain. Ah, the joys of living a Machine Man life...

Five: *We are not our emotions.* We have seen that over time or with increasing age we can and do learn to control our emotions. And actually, the better we know ourselves and the transient nature of emotions, the more we will be able to experience true feelings.

In my first book (Yes I Am Happy Now!) I have talked at length about how and why we live in a multidimensional universe of vibrations; that it's all more or less powerful energies vibrating at different wave lengths or frequencies. And that includes also *our emotions; every type of emotion operates in a different wave band of energy*, oscillating in a specific range of Hertz, or parts and magnitudes thereof, under the laws of resonance and induction.

Moreover, I have made the distinction between emotions and feelings. Emotions are a reactive sensation that are based on something that has happened in the past. Or something that we anticipate to happen in the future. Emotions like anger, fear, sadness, worries, guilt and so on. Every moment we allow our mind to be overtaken by emotions, we start to live either in the past or in the future. Immediately. We are simply not fully present any longer.

I've further described many strategies of how we can reduce the negative effects of emotions within ourselves, thus giving far less resonance to the negativity of others. As our sensitivity increases, we will still notice negative vibrations, but will simply not get affected anymore.

*All emotions are ultimately founded on fear and the not being aware of who we really are.* Feelings however are a totally different story; by default they are all most positive and totally natural. *The feeling of happiness is an integral part of who we really are.* And so is feeling passionate, seeking pleasure and joy. Being naturally relaxed, calm and confident. Feeling true love. Experiencing real friendships as equals, without a hint of envy or jealousy (both are fear-based emotions). Having fun. Laughing, joking and smiling.

*Once we fully realize again who we really are, we will automatically experience more of our true inherent positive feelings and less negative emotions.* And as we do, we will become ever happier again. Happiness really is our natural heritage!

<u>Six</u>: *We do have free will.* With our willpower we control and direct our minds and our emotions. Or choose what we want to experience in our lives. From small and trivial things to matters of great importance.

With our free will we also create new realities according to our intentions, desires and abilities. Or solve problems in our daily lives by deciding the best course of action. Adepts can even steer the contents of their dreams or the direction of their out-of-body experiences.

<u>Seven:</u> **We are not the unconscious.** We are neither a mythical subconsciousness nor otherwise an only observing conscious user illusion that has no influence over what is being decided by a capricious brain; **there simply is no subconscious or unconscious mind with any power or greater influence over us.**

Since we do have free will, **nothing or nobody has any or total control over our minds**, unless we ourselves have ceded our sovereignty for some reason or another. Or less likely, if we were detained at Guantanamo Bay (or a similar facility someplace else) and got severely sleep deprived, or were otherwise physically and mentally tortured and traumatized.

With the right motivations we can believe all kinds of things, fooling ourselves in endless ways, limiting ourselves to a fraction of our abilities, which includes forgetting or locking away memories for all sorts of reasons. Or giving in to do what others want us to do. Like buying a certain product or service at a certain time.

But even repeated or subliminal advertising will never be able to make me buy anything from a Fa(s)t Food chain, or a sugar and additive laden soda drink company. No matter how often I had to listen to their song and dance. Or how popular their products may be. None of that matters as I'm freely deciding on my choices. Others may seemingly relinquish their freedom just to be cool, fit in better, and so on. But still, their choices are not made by their absolutely non-existent unconscious that got supposedly manipulated because it is said to be so feeble-minded, but nevertheless in charge of you. Wanting to fit in is a free choice too.

*We all have the power to decide what we think and believe or how we feel and act at any given moment in our lives; it is probably best to never ever give away this power to anyone, for any reasons.*

There are many techniques that people, companies or governments try to influence us. They only succeed with the lesser conscious, aware or educated who come to believe their endless marketing messages and propaganda ploys. All aim at our core values and beliefs. And once we have changed our beliefs, we are easy prey. That's why it's called a con game, confidence trick or simply, a scam. Relieving us of our dollars, time and energy. Or worse, our health.

Again, the non-existent unconscious (or subconscious) has nothing to do with it. It is always the changed belief that matters. And even upon eventually learning the actual truths or real facts about a matter at hand, many of us are too afraid (or cowardly) to admit to ourselves and others that we were wrong, that we got bamboozled, deceived and conned. So we may prefer to stick with the fake story, perhaps defending it all the way. Rarely to good results.

Besides the power of our beliefs, what really matters is our self-confidence. Confidence trickster rely on weak victims, people with a low self-esteem, inferior self-assurance, and therefore, subpar energy levels. Con artists exploit these people in many different ways, often by deliberately weakening their targets even further, to perpetuate their profiteering.

***People who know who they really are naturally have a strong self-confidence.*** Nothing can easily sway or persuade them. And nobody can take away their free will or stop them from freely choosing what they want or like best. They are literally independent free spirits. The flip side of the coin is that the less we know who we really are, the less confident we are likely to be. And the easier we can be manipulated or persuaded.

Ever changing given or chosen external labels simply don't give much real strength and genuine confidence. Yes, there are many outwardly successful people who seem to be very confident at first sight, to the point of being rather arrogant. But once you dig deeper you will see that it is not really real. Money, power or fame after all does not bring about real inner strength or peace of mind. Or happiness, for that matter.

And of course, arrogance is not at all the same as self-confidence. Quite the opposite. ***Arrogance is a sign of insecurity yet the insecure like to call the confident arrogant.***

The truly confident, that is. In my many years of traveling the globe, doing high end marketing (of Swiss luxury watches) and management consulting, I've met many highly successful entrepreneurs from all walks of life. And noticed how humble and gentle yet confident and courageous these self-made billionaires and centimillionaires really were.

Many famous self-help or personal development authors and speakers, and essentially all New Age gurus and leaders, preach that the number one reason people fail in their lives is because of the negative influences of their subconsciousness. They offer the desperate but trusting 'highly effective tools' to communicate with their sub-or unconscious mind in order to reprogram it for success.

Since ***the sub-or unconscious doesn't actually exist,*** the only reality is that these tools are highly expensive rather than highly effective. The intentions of these teachers and coaches may be all benevolent and good, and there is certainly nothing wrong with making some money while helping others. They are also likely to well and truly believe what they are telling and selling.

Nevertheless, their methods cannot and therefore do not work as there is no subconscious or unconscious mind; ***believing this fallacy actually does a lot of harm as it deprives people of their inherent power,*** needlessly giving it away to a fantasy.

***The current consciousness of Machine Man is actually already the unconscious,*** or subconscious if you prefer, as they are simply not aware of who we really are. Therefore they are less conscious than we normally are in our more elevated and enlightened natural state of consciousness.

They already do live in a kind of unconscious, subconscious or subpar condition in the current here and now, so there is really no need to artificially introduce another even lower level. ***Sadly, the schizophrenic*** *belief in a non-existent unconscious has turned many people into confused schizophrenics, and will likely continue to do so.*

Believing in a non-existent unconscious simply reveals the not knowing about how the mind and our memory fundamentally works or who we really are.

By believing Machine Man and therefore denying and not knowing who we really are, we literally dim our lights, diminish our awareness, and throttle our energy to sometimes barely sustainable levels. Further ***believing the erroneous belief of a fictitious unconscious only weakens us more, creates a great deal of confusion and much unhappiness.*** Or worse, a kind of split mind or outright multiple personality disorder ('dissociative identity disorder').

The same mental health experts also say that we should ***"fake it until you make it."*** It is one of their attempts to reprogram what does not exist, ***to foolishly fool a supposedly foolish unconscious or subconscious mind.***

However, pretending no matter what will not make any of it come true. Pretending to be happy will not make it so. Sure, we can stand every day in front of the mirror for months on end and tell ourselves that we are so very happy, but every time we say so, we also know that it is a lie and we only get more depressed.

***Fake it until you make it only works if you can convincingly lie to yourself.*** And that is simply not possible; we all essentially know when we try to fool ourselves. We may do it anyway for a little while, but since it actually feels rather silly, a bit sad or outright bad, we will stop it sooner or later.

It is far better to stay real and be honest with ourselves, learn to deal with our problems, get to know who we really are, and thus become well and truly happy once again!

<u>Eight:</u> ***We are not our egos.*** And there is no such thing. The concept of an ego is just that, a concept. It is an artificial construct for which there is zero

scientific evidence. Like there is zero evidence for an unconscious mind or a user illusion created by the brain. And again, it is interesting to note how neuroscience copied this idea from ancient religious cultures.

Regardless of all absence of real proof, many psychologists or adherents of Eastern philosophies, perhaps all New Age gurus and probably most of their followers, love to believe in the mythical ego; they are endlessly writing, breathlessly warning and fervently whining about its highly negative activities and consequences.

They preach that the "Ego" really needs to be subdued, or better still, totally exterminated, in order to become "self-realized" or "enlightened" and thus be able to merge into the endless *Oneness*. The great *One-and-All*. Or the *Big Nothing*. These are rather big subjects that really require a book of its own. Therefore allow me to just make two brief comments on this: Partially right but incomplete knowledge usually leads to very wrong conclusions. And: *We are eternally one yet forever individual.*

Mostly though, people use the term 'ego' in everyday conversations to criticize, insult or condemn others. Yet what they really talk about is someone with a particularly high pride. Sometimes that is somewhat justified and at other times not at all. Most big achievers in life were and are rather humble people; the more we do know about a subject, the more we are also aware how little we truly know. And vice versa. The less we know, the more we may think that we know. It's a funny world!

Philosophically speaking, the original meaning of the ego concept has been forgotten. Instead, over time, it was turned into a religious dogma that is more often than not used to control people. The perennial wisdom got lost: we need to free ourselves from a mistaken identity before we can become enlightened once again. It did not mean permanent self-annihilation which is not possible anyway, even if someone likes to think so.

Ego simply means the mistaken self-identification with our given and chosen labels. In other words, ego is Machine Man erroneously thinking that they are their bodies that come with a plethora of labels. We are male or female, or nowadays a seemingly endless choice of genders. We are black, brown, white, yellow or anything in between. We also identify with our countries, cultures, and cities. Our professions. Even our favorite sports team.

Believing Man believes all this too. Mostly, they self-identify with all of the standard labels plus the one bestowed upon them by their particular religious faith. Which is usually the one assigned by being born in a particular part of the world. They further believe to have a soul somewhere inside their bodies. The one they hope to turn into after they (the body) died.

But no matter how many labels we may have or assign to ourselves, we are still not our purely descriptive labels; they can and do change over time anyway. And once we leave this particular dimension behind, none of them matter all that much anymore either. Just like none of the clothes we were wearing some twenty odd years ago really matter today; they are simply history, gone for good.

*We are not our given or chosen labels no matter how much we may think so.*

There is nothing inherently wrong with being a little bit proud of our countries, cultures or creeds. Or our professional status and the like. However, we need to realize that many labels are entirely artificial constructs, made by us humans. And most of them have nothing at all to do with who we really are as eternal individuals. That sure includes whatever history says about our country. Or what our distant ancestors achieved; what they did do, or didn't do.

*We can neither take credit for our ancestors' achievements nor are we to blame for their mistakes – no matter what those who divide and rule us with ego (identity) politics say.*

To solely and fully associate our identities with our external and merely temporary labels is a mistake that often, even mostly, leads to great unhappiness. Or bad decisions that may cause much mayhem and big upheavals, followed by sorrows, tears and pain.

The idea of an ego to be fought and conquered is a great excuse and tool for con artists and cult leaders of all kinds to exert control over their followers. It is sad but true. People who keep criticizing or talking about how big and bad your ego (never theirs) supposedly is are best avoided. They are not much fun to be with anyway. To put it mildly.

And by the way: **Why do fanatical ego-bashers always have the biggest egos?**

Incidentally, more often than not, we can easily recognize these folks by their talking or writing about us *having* a soul rather *being* the soul. Or *having* a higher self rather than actually *being* it. Additionally, they just love to talk about the subconsciousness (or lower self) that really needs to be pandered to. Before offering their usually costly solutions.

As always, it is good to be aware of the name of the game. And therefore to be able to just walk away. Simply ignoring incredibly insane ideas is sometimes the best course of action!

<u>Nine:</u> **We are not our memories.** Yet they have become part and parcel of our personalities, knowledge and abilities. Our memories help us to learn from past experiences; to better focus on what we find enjoyable; to avoid repeating mistakes; to feel great today cherishing special moments; to appreciate and love special people; to treasure wonderful places, and to be easily able to do things we have already mastered in the past.

Our memories are like a story book recording the stories of our lives; we are both authors and actors. Thoughts, emotions and memories are very subtle energy waves vibrating at different frequencies and harmonies that get woven into our eternal spiritual energy bodies, a bit like a complex carpet that contains fibers of all kinds, in colors of all shades.

There are memories we remember simply because we do want to remember them, and memories we don't remember just because we don't want to remember them; we ban some of our memories for all kinds of reasons.

These memories are still available to us at any time, but we simply choose not to access them.

That choice is always a conscious choice whether we like to recognize that fact later or not. Sometimes we consciously decide to forget some small things simply because we deem them to be totally insignificant for us. But it was still a choice. Truly important experiences however we simply cannot forget (for a more detailed summary, please read again the eleven bullet points in chapter *Memories*).

The only time memory problems may not seem to be direct voluntary choices, is the onset of serious medical problems. But as we have seen while discussing terminal lucidity ('the last hurrah'), even patients who have suffered for decades from severe disorders like Alzheimer's disease, tumors, strokes or meningitis could become fully lucid again and remember it all shortly before passing away. Despite their still existing physical problems.

Unfortunately, some people have to experience very severe physical and mental abuse, and subsequently don't remember what has happened to them. Or only vaguely. That too was a conscious decision made at the time in order to be able to continue with their lives, with their sanity still or mostly intact. In hindsight however, that may not appear to be so.

Memory lapses can also be the result of a lifestyle choice. We may have had way too much to drink and therefore lost all awareness of what has happened at the end of the night. Our senses and brains have become so numb that we, the conscious person, has literally gone someplace else; we have spaced out into a different dimensional reality. And therefore we simply don't remember what has happened in this one.

Then there is the issue of supposedly having fake or faulty memories. *Selective memories are also a matter of choice*, whether we are honest enough to admit it to ourselves, or not.

Most of us want to believe that we are highly moral people. Even if we may have done something that was actually a bit immoral, or not quite right.

So we may simply adjust what we do remember accordingly to benefit us wanting to feel righteous. We internally come up with fake excuses or false justifications that we actually know to be wrong, yet **want to believe to be true** anyway. So we blame others for our mistakes. It is the easier way out.

But it has really nothing to do with having a faulty memory. **It is simply us wanting to feel innocent.** It is harder to fully enjoy life while feeling guilty. We all have an internal compass about what is right and wrong. An inborn moral sense. Conscience is part and parcel of being conscious; we can do our best to ignore it but only psychopaths or sociopaths actually succeed. Yet even they know that they have done something others consider to be wrong.

We can somewhat numb our conscience by regularly drinking copious amounts of alcohol. Or take other mind-numbing drugs, pharmaceutical or otherwise. But still, we usually remember that we did wrong, and why we may need sleeping pills just to fall asleep. The real memories are still there, and therefore may continue to haunt us even in our dreams.

Facts simply don't change just because we may not want to remember them. And there will always be repercussions to more or less subtly remind us of what has happened. Selective or seemingly faulty memories cannot erase the consequences of our actions. **We really are the masters of our destiny.** As such we are solely and fully responsible for what we do and don't do; for our choices, words and deeds.

Throughout the ages this universal law has been expressed differently by differing cultures, yet it always means the same thing. Like attracts like. Birds of feather flock together. What goes around, comes around. The law of attraction. Christianity says: "A man reaps what he sows." Eastern philosophies like Hinduism or Buddhism call it *Karma*.

Issac Newton formulated it in his third law of motion as 'actio est reactio', Latin for 'action is reaction'. Every force or action on one object is followed by a reaction on another. The energy is always of equal magnitude, but going in the opposite direction, going back to its origin. Or, every action causes a counteraction. Nothing and nobody can escape this mechanism. Even if we may think so, or don't want to remember the facts of a matter.

*"Chance is a word void of sense; nothing can exist without a cause."* Voltaire

Quite likely there are no time limits either; sooner or later the balance of energy will be restored. Somewhere, somehow or another. The law of conservation of energy in both physics and chemistry stipulates that energy cannot be created or destroyed, but only transformed or transferred from one form to another.

Transhumanists wanting to live forever in this realm should really take notice about these universal principles of energy that seek to always restore balance and harmony. Some people do die young despite doing everything right, and others get to live to a very old age despite doing a great deal wrong.

Our life expectancy is not all about whether we have good genes or not, or even whether we have good gene expressions or not. We can live a healthy lifestyle eating nutritious food, drinking clean water, popping lots of daily supplements, and still pass away at a young age from say, lung cancer. While others do none of the above, smoke to a ripe old age and have no problems at all.

Besides our state of heart and mind, much seems to have to do with our personal eternal history, our individual intentions of why we came here at this particular time and in this particular body or circumstances. Much depends on what we personally want or need to experience and achieve. And since we are all totally unique and thus very different, there a literally endless ways we live our lives and express ourselves, including the way we leave.

Then, naturally or not, there are also other unplanned circumstances that may cut our time on planet Earth shorter than we currently may want it to be. Transhumanists too die of all sorts of incidents and accidents or become the victims of targeted or seemingly random violence. No matter how sheltered or careful they may be.

All that of course should not prevent us from wanting to live a healthy and happy lifestyle while we can. But living healthy is not necessarily about living longer since many of the very health-conscious pass away at an early age anyway. It is really about living better in the sense of **being able to fully use and enjoy all of our mental and physical faculties** until the time has come to move on.

Trying to live forever in the here and now, anxiously or fearfully trying to literally run (or jog) away from the eventually approaching clutches of physical death, will always remain a futile exercise, but living life to the fullest and happiest brings about both instant and ongoing benefits. When we are happy now, we sow the seeds of future happy moments. That too is an expression of the law of karma; actio est reactio.

"Happiness is not a reward – it is a consequence. Suffering is not a punishment – it is a result." Robert Green Ingersoll

<u>Ten:</u> **We are sparks of spirit, the primary energy of the universe,** the original force behind all forces and manifestations, the superior intelligence that underlies all information which in turn underlies, pervades and instructs all matter. As such we are always alive, naturally conscious, and inherently intelligent.

**We are already immortals,** so there is really no need having to pursue this age-old dream by Machine Man who claims to be illuminated even though they live their lives in the dark. We are timeless spiritual individuals, not mortal material bodies made out of mere matter.

We all are eternal souls rather than pieces of meat and bones who have a soul stashed away somewhere, as Believing Man likes to believe. This is so whether we believe this to be true or not, whether we believe we deserve it to be true or not.

**We are multidimensional beings** who simultaneously exist in multiple dimensions or oscillating realities at differing frequencies. If simple subatomic particles can be in quantum superposition, existing in several separate quantum states or places at the same time, we energy beings, operating at far more complex and refined vibrations, can surely do that too.

For those who say that quantum principles only apply to the subatomic space, very recently a team of European scientists demonstrated that even larger molecules with masses beyond 25,000 Daltons and consisting up to 2'000 atoms can be in quantum superposition, by far the heaviest objects shown to exhibit matter-wave interference (published September 23, 2019 in the research journal *Nature Physics*).

Similarly, scientists believed that entangled particles would lose their most confusing link upon exposure to outside factors. However, very recently, physicists were able to produce super hot energetic clouds of up to 15 trillion highly entangled atoms that, upon measuring (observing) one, instantly changed the properties of the other particles in the group or pair, regardless of how far apart they were (May 15, 2020 in Nature Communications).

To some or perhaps many, the reality of our everlasting multidimensional existence may be temporarily hidden while we roam the material worlds of space and time, yet we can regain our sensitivity and memory at any time, whenever we are truly ready and strongly desire to once again remember who we really are.

The philosophical concept of 'Maya' or illusion is simply us falsely identifying ourselves as being our current physical bodies. This is the original meaning that got mistaken over time by Homo Credo to mean that we live in a not really real, fake world. Or a computer simulation, as imagined by Homo Digitalis (when they are not playing computer games).

The more polluted our minds have become with heavy Machine Man philosophy, the more we believe to be just mortal machines made of mere matter, the heavier and denser, the darker and less enlightened, the more serious and less light-hearted, and often more depressed, our existence, our life likely becomes. In other words, the less happy.

*By choice we are more or less conscious spiritual beings who are more or less aware* about our surroundings and our thoughts, feelings and memories; it all depends on our individual goals, dreams and desires.

As energy beings, we are automatically able to both transmit and read energy, whether we are currently aware of it or not. We constantly send out different forms of energies and at the same time we also receive all kinds of energy waves emanating from our environment, both animate and inanimate. Energy that is more or less subtle, denser or not, pervading deeper or less deep, expanding further or not very far, depending on its strength and power.

The more sensitive we remember or want to be and therefore are, the more we feel these energies. We can decide to tune in and notice, or tune out and be oblivious to all. Be aware to different degrees, or blank out most or all of it. It is always our choice. Because we throttle and diminish ourselves. Or not. Respectively, not any longer.

*Ultimately, in our original primary state, we are all inherently full of knowledge and wisdom, radiating love, peace and happiness, including those who don't know it anymore, simply because they currently refuse to remember this reality, for all kinds of reasons.*

They don't want to be aware of it. Therefore they don't tune in to this reality. And that is perfectly alright. After all, we are all on our own individual timetables. With our very own personal dreams and desires. Currently doing what we like and love to do. Which includes playing our games. Until we get tired of them, and are ready to move on once again. To a different dimension. Going back to the individual reality we came from. Home, sweet home.

Is that all just a fantasy? Well, most survivors of NDEs *didn't want to come back* to their physical bodies in the here and now, but rather, were kind of sent back as their time had not yet come and they still had certain things to do or complete. The reality they've experienced on their excursions 'to the other side' were so wonderful and blissful in comparison, they would have happily 'traded in' their bodies and simply stayed.

Applying the Sherlock Holmes model, we can summarize the ten *Theses Beyond Machine Man* like this: We can't possibly be our bodies, DNA or brains, we can not be our minds or our emotions as we control and direct both with our free will, we can't conceivably be the unconscious or an ego as there are no such things, we sure have memories but can't be our past, therefore we must be something else altogether: we are evidently living, conscious and intelligent beings whose energies exist now and, since nothing can ever cease to exist, will always continue to exist.

*"Science has found that nothing can disappear without a trace. Nature does not know extinction. All it knows is transformation."* Werner von Braun, pioneering aerospace engineer and space architect.

The discussion about whether we are products of nature or nurture has occupied the minds of a great many people from a great many different disciplines. The respective conclusions hardened into beliefs have spawned all kinds of political schools and various social politics, becoming by itself a determining factor in many people's lives.

*So what is it, nature or nurture? In short, it is both and neither.* We, the spiritual sparks of energy, do get strongly influenced by matter – via our minds and both our subtle and dense material bodies – as we also strongly influence matter itself via our minds, through ethereal forces and direct physical interactions (e.g. eating, breathing, working). Even by the mere act of observing, and thereby measuring, we influence our personal realities to various degrees, from the mostly minute to the sometimes noticeable.

Matter is not just matter. The material dimensions including its myriad of subatomic particles are essentially all just forms of energy too.

There are all kinds of energy vibrations like gravitational or magnetic fields, electric currents, and light, sound or radio waves. Or still theoretical and entirely unproven dark matter and dark energy. Besides neutron stars and black holes. *Everything that exists in the universe consists of constantly interacting quanta* (the plural of quantum), including atoms and parts thereof. Everything is infused with a degree of intelligence, fields of information that contain all of the blueprints required. Nothing more, or less.

From **bit to it** (information to matter) however is only partially true. *It really is spirit over mind, and mind over body.* The spiritual force is the **intelligence** that directs and controls the informational fields that control and create what we inside our bodies and with the help of our physical senses finally perceive to be matter composed of atoms and molecules.

*"The field is the sole governing agency of the particle."* Albert Einstein

Nature, or physical particles, thought to be controlled by the DNA and epigenetic factors our bodies inherit from our physical ancestors, sure determines a lot of things in our lives. But as we have seen, these all change over time, depending on our lifestyle, thoughts and so on. *So nature sure is a factor, and increasingly so the more we believe that to be true.*

And **nurture, or energy fields**, the way we were brought up, the vibrations we have been exposed to since we were born and the beliefs we have been instilled with, the education and experience levels we have attained so far, and other factors, also have a great influence over us as we have seen while discussing the power of the Placebo or Nocebo effects. *The power of our beliefs matter greatly too.* Even though they are just an intangible form of energy we can't measure yet. They still determine our thoughts and actions in life.

*While both nature and nurture are important factors, it is what we make of what we have been given, that matters most.* We, as eternal energetic beings, can make the best out of both, if we are aware of it. We can overcome and move beyond much, most or even all of the negative aspects of both nature and nurture – once we are again fully aware of who we really are. In that sense, both don't count for all that much any longer. Or not as much as it used to matter. We can feel again totally unlimited while still being somewhat limited.

Upon making this realization, Homo Mysticum has become once again, and quite literally so, a free spirit. And as such *we can now make good use of the positive aspects of nature and nurture while transcending the negative parts.* Therefore, both nature and nurture matter, but knowing who we really are matters a great deal more. That is the primary insight of the enlightened mystics since time immemorial.

Quite a few of the discussed subjects are likely to raise additional questions. And that is great and as it should be for science to make progress and for people and societies to grow.

However, we could and should notice that **the big picture view of the thoughts presented here can quite easily integrate all of the real-life anomalies and genuine mysteries in life**, and thereby explain how things fundamentally are – while making the least number of assumptions. Or perhaps none at all since every fundamental insight is based on the personal experiences and observations of a great many and most diverse people over a very long period of time. Their individual accounts may somewhat differ, yet in essence they all agree.

*"There are two ways to be fooled. One is to believe what isn't true; the other is to refuse to believe what is true."* Søren Kierkegaard

The existence of spiritual dimensions has also been confirmed by many afterlife researchers; it simply is science fact rather than religious fiction. Below the surface of officialdom, there is an enormous wealth of objective information, fully replicated scientific studies and other carefully documented evidence about the existence of a plethora of psychic phenomena available to the sincere scientist or student of life (see chapter *Notes* for information).

Real paranormal occurrences really are happening. A long list of highly distinguished and accomplished scientists with extraordinary intellectual abilities have recorded them for over one hundred years. And all have independently come to the very same conclusions upon following the scientific method. Which includes **controlled laboratory experiments that have exceeded the probability of chance by trillions to one**. Essentially, they all confirm what the mystics of the ages have known all along.

In sharp contrast, the physicalist worldview of **Machine Man is simply and totally unable to explain even a single one of these verifiable facts without breaking its very foundation**. Therefore, the only option available to them is having to deny that these things are actually happening. They simply declare all evidence to be fake, even though that is not so if one were to investigate honestly and thoroughly. Yet they are absolutely unwilling to have or keep an open mind and do some real research. For reasons both material and immaterial.

*"I know that most men, including those at ease with problems of the greatest complexity, can seldom accept even the simplest and most obvious truth if it be such as would oblige them to admit the falsity of conclusions which they have delighted in explaining to colleagues, which they have proudly taught to others, and which they have woven, thread by thread, into the fabric of their lives."* Leo Tolstoy

# Why It Really Matters

Nowadays, atheism has largely replaced the narratives of religions, and indeed itself become the predominant religion of officialdom; governments, bureaucracies and academia, aided and abetted by the corporate mainstream media. The nominal (s)elected rulers mostly still play being pious in public even though they usually aren't. Their financial backers sure aren't. Hence their fondness for the premises and promises of transhumanism.

The materialistic philosophy of Machine Man is now firmly entrenched in the said to be enlightened West, even among a great many kinds of *Homo Credo* (or Believing Man). Among the younger generations, we can easily notice an ever-growing enthusiastic belief in the seemingly endless fantasies of transhumanism and the much touted eventual coming of the technical singularity that promise to save us from all suffering and even death.

*However, to have such absolute faith in the modern high tech version of high priests is simply a rather bad idea*; outsourcing our worldly and spiritual curiosity, well-being and development to salary-dependent, profit-driven or power-hungry technocrats is likely to end in tears. Collectively. And individually. At least in the last stages of one's life.

We people are quite a funny bunch: death in its supposed finality is the key ingredient that we find so very entertaining in our books and movies, computer games and so on. Since time immemorial, fictional death is portrayed in almost infinite shapes and forms, often the crueler or more 'colorful' the better. Yet in real life conversations it is usually a totally taboo subject. No one dares to openly talk about it. Even though we really should as it would put everything in perspective, allowing us to focus on what really matters in life.

*Fear of death is the origin of all fears.* Every possible fear we can think of or be scared about is related to our potential and eventual dying. The fear that someday we will simply cease to exist. We try not to think about it personally but nevertheless watch a great deal of digital dying on our screens. Every day. We are clearly fascinated, afraid and sometimes terrified by death, the great equalizer that potentially gives more meaning to our lives.

*There is nothing that can truly allay this ultimate of fears for diehard believers in Machine Man philosophy who as a consequence often do die needlessly hard.* Believing Man has hope to keep living someplace else but this hope is only as deep as their underlying faith. And that can get thoroughly shaken by the daily treadmill of materialistic life, while they are constantly exposed to the currently predominant narrative promoted by officialdom.

And Mystic Man, well, they just know. For sure. There is no dying of the spiritual force, the boundless spirit or eternal soul we really are. Physical death is only the shedding of our mortal coils. By well and truly knowing this reality, they have removed the ultimate obstacle to living a happy life, for good, along all of the other accompanying fears and anxieties.

*"Nothing can come out of nothing, any more than a thing can go back to nothing."*
Marcus Aurelius, Roman emperor and a Stoic philosopher.

*Homo Mysticum* is also better able to cope with grief, the immense pain that comes from losing loved ones. Missing the physical presence of dearly departed still hurts, but Mystic Man is absolutely sure to meet them once again relatively soon. And in the meantime, they do know how to stay connected (as described in my second book in the second-last chapter).

*Religion is about experiencing, not believing;* spiritual realities are either personally experienced, or not (yet). The word religion says it very well in its Latin roots: *religare, or 'to reconnect'* – i.e. re (again) + ligare (connect, unite, tie together).

In the preceding chapters we have seen how much of today's cutting-edge science about our brain, mind or consciousness is pure speculation only;

that most if not all of the celebrated theories are merely mind-boggling mental constructs and usually quite indistinguishable from the weirdest of religious beliefs out there.

***Beliefs matter a great deal.*** A bit like a master plan of life, they greatly influence what we think and do, or don't do. Ultimately they are far more influential and important than the small individual parts or combinations of our DNA. Beliefs can literally make or break us.

The wrong beliefs may cause us to harm (or worse) others and totally ruin our lives (even if we don't get caught). Or to simply turn into a mindless and rarely happy consumer robot who ultimately achieved nothing of value and wasted countless opportunities to advance in life. Or to otherwise easily give up without even trying. Or to support the very wrong causes and leaders. Or to live a life filled with sadness and stress, insecurities and fears. Or to eat unhealthy food and otherwise have bad habits that only make us sick and frail.

***Bad beliefs lead to bad thoughts; bad thoughts lead to bad actions; bad actions lead to bad results; bad results lead to bad feelings.***

Beliefs that are aligned with truths usually bring happiness, and vice versa. Beliefs that are based on falsehoods will ultimately lead to despair and depression. Life can be quite simple. Unless or until we make it complicated. Always keeping the big picture in mind will help us make the right decisions in all matters of life. ***Knowing who we really are means to know the big picture, and to act accordingly.***

Once we have fully realized that we are an immortal spiritual being we have again become a whole (holy) person. And therefore we just can't possibly 'misbehave' in this, that or another way. To be fully self-realized and at the same time still be unloving, uncaring or worse towards others is simply but surely unlikely, to the point of impossible.

Imagine the kind of world we could live in if we all just knew who we really are. There would be less fear and more kindness. Less division (of any kind) and more unity. More cooperation and less competition. More long-term thinking and less short-sighted selfishness. And we'd all be way too busy living lives full of love, peace and happiness to even think about waging wars that benefit only the few to the detriment of many.

Today's reality however is rather different. Religion and spirituality is frowned upon to the point of ridicule. Mostly atheistic psychiatrists, psychologists and psycho-analysts have usurped the role of priests and (w) holistic healers in society. All is said to be relative. Almost anything goes. And morality is whatever feels good.

While there are many good practitioners with only the best of intentions, the general problem with modern-day mind doctors is their predominant yet erroneous beliefs which can do great harm to their patients. Their own personal and professional confusions will inevitably lead to our mental and emotional confusions too. Or worse.

We have talked about *the schizophrenic beliefs of their split mind concept where an imaginary unconscious is believed to greatly influence or outright dictate a person's life.* Or seen how many of today's psychologists now calling themselves neuroscientists totally believe in the physical reductionist stories of Machine Man (sadly, even more so than many other still open-minded scientists). And that has certain consequences, as all beliefs have.

The big question is why would they want to treat the rambling illusions of the brain in the first place? Most really believe that we are just a user illusion that hallucinates all kinds of rubbish, that constantly makes up false realities, and is not really real. Why do they take all that seriously then? It must be kind of hard to pretend to actually care for your patient if you are really totally convinced that it is all just a confused brain that fantasizes about things.

So how do contemporary mind 'doctors' treat user illusions, confusions and delusions? A brain's hallucinations, nightmares and fantasies? People that are not really people per se, but merely large accumulations of biological cells harboring hallucinating brains (that perhaps do outrageous things like voting for the wrong president or otherwise behave in selfish, silly or outright stupid ways, besides thinking totally unapproved thoughts).

What is their magic cure? Well, just give them some pills. And that is what they actually do. Simply give people tranquilizing pills that keep them calm, dreaming and obedient. Taking the psychoactive medications they prescribe only makes us mentally and emotionally number and otherwise adversely affects our cognitive abilities. Besides causing weight gains, impotence or worse, like a dramatic shortening of our lives (e.g. by suicide, an admitted potential side effect).

So many people are already taking psychoactive drugs yet strangely or perhaps suspiciously there are ever more patients supposedly suffering from depression, anxiety and so on.

We are told to believe the peddlers of unproven unscientific theories about make-believe yet permanent chemical imbalances in our brains that condemn us to buy and take pills for the rest of our lives. Pills that turn lives into dull affairs where we don't feel depressed anymore but neither feel any real excitement either. The big Zombification of society, courtesy of Big Pharma and the best scientists and doctors money can buy.

**Machine Man philosophy comes at a price.** There are many profound consequences, both on a personal individual level as well as for society – and science – as a whole.

We have discussed quite many examples of the current cutting-edge explanations about everything: about the brain, memories and emotions, the make-believe mind split into unconscious and conscious parts, life and consciousness. The theories have one thing in common: all seem to be a bit far-fetched. All are based upon rather illogical, inconsistent and improbable assumptions or course of events.

Any and all other potential explanations were and still are excluded from the very beginning as being borderline insane, besides totally impossible. As a consequence, **real science has suffered greatly**. Limiting our minds literally means to have a small mind. And small minds are unlikely to be able to go beyond their self-imposed limits.

Probably for a long time to come, the fundamental problem of Machine Man scientists remains that they just have to **squeeze everything into their overall rigid belief system of physical reductionism.** Otherwise it all crumbles into nothingness. Therefore they cannot follow the true scientific method which stipulates that one has to go wherever the evidence may lead us, and discard all the theories that are disproved by any such new information.

Real science is never really settled even though nowadays it is claimed to be by basically corrupt politicians controlled by selfish billionaires for nefarious political and economic purposes; they just love to parade their personal selection of questionable scientists in public while completely ignoring or outright censoring the many real experts who say otherwise.

**"Scientific knowledge is a body of statements of varying degrees of certainty – some most unsure, some nearly sure, but none absolutely certain."** Richard Feynman, Nobel Prize winning theoretical physicist known for his pioneering work in quantum mechanics and quantum electrodynamics.

Another result of their rather unscientific and dogmatic worldview is the current wave of moral relativity and the widespread lack of personal responsibility that is engulfing our societies. Small wonder. Their socalled science has turned us all into some kind of barely conscious non-players. Entirely innocent observers who cannot be responsible for their actions, criminal or otherwise.

**By the verdict of today's science we are said to be uninvolved virtuous victims who are pushed and shoved around by the mysterious spasms of our brains, respectively the unknowable intentions and machinations of the unconscious.**

They proclaim that there is no free will and things just happen for no reasons, by mere chance or coincidence, or for reasons that are well, not for us to know. We are therefore all completely innocent and totally blameless, no matter what. Now we are free to always just blame the most perfect of scapegoats, one that will never ever be able to talk back!

Very convenient perhaps for us personally if we've committed a crime and actually did get caught. However, the ultimate conclusion of this folly may and perhaps will be the eventual complete dissolution of our justice systems. Why should we – or how could we! – punish people and put them in prisons if they are just innocent victims of their brains creating some unconscious user illusions that may occasionally cause some misbehavior or worse?

*Why should I have to pay my speeding tickets when the culprits were unknown twitches of my brain and its hallucinating user illusion that made the car go faster than some other user illusions deemed to be the maximum speed limit?*

Racism is another direct consequence of us erroneously identifying ourselves purely as our material bodies, as suggested by Machine Man science and philosophy. Strictly speaking, racism is defined as members of one race feeling superior to people of other races. Nowadays, the term is being far more liberally used for all sorts of thought crimes. Racists are said to even include those who don't take our particular sexual urges all too seriously.

Other current absurdities include us being racists for what complete strangers yet fellow members of our race did or didn't do hundreds or thousands of years ago. It is simply the age old guilt and blame game being played for political purposes and personal gains.

*Materialism, atheism and label or club consciousness all go hand in hand.* We live in a world of labels where many actually believe to be what merely describes their bodies and beliefs, their thoughts and feelings, their dreams and desires, their preferences and choices.

*Machine Man people have quite literally become their country, culture, color, club and creed.* Some labels are given, others are chosen. Some descriptions stay the same while others keep changing over the course of our lives.

For (too) many, these descriptive and comforting labels have actually become life and death issues that need to be defended and fought over – sometimes literally at all costs. They also provide a convenient excuse to feel like a victim who needs to be coddled and compensated. Poor me forever and it's all your fault kind of thing. Yes, sure. And yes, there are some real victims but they actually tend to be quiet.

Essentially, we are allowing ourselves to become ever more divided along an ever-growing number of labels. Divide and rule (*divide et impera*) is still the name of the game of the ruling classes. Along with might is right. Or survival of the fittest. In other words, Machine Man philosophy at its finest.

***Ultimately, racism is ignorance about our real identity.*** Not knowing who we really are.
Fully identifying ourselves with our given or chosen labels. It's a bit like self-identifying as the clothes we wear – a seemingly rather silly idea, and yet that kind of happens too, albeit on a different level: "Kleider machen Leute" – "fine feathers make fine birds," wrote Gottfried Keller, a classical Swiss poet and writer.

Another both direct and ugly consequence is the historic eugenics movement – the promoting of supposedly superior people and traits, respectively the reduction of those deemed to be undesirable. Eugenics is now being revived under the auspices of gene editing, at first for seemingly harmless or even beneficial reasons only.

Transhumanists openly desire to breed a superior class of designer babies. Super strong and ultra intelligent. But where will they draw the line? And who will do it? The armchair general needing totally obedient killer soldiers? Fanatical racists desiring racial supremacy?Billionaires wanting to live and rule forever? Factory owners demanding work slaves that never tire? People wishing to have a perfectly beautiful and always willing sex mate?

It still is selective breeding by another name and technology. Furthermore, bio-weapons that only target specific genetic groups (or genotypes) for warfare and equally nefarious purposes (e.g. ethnic cleansing) have already been developed by lunatics the world over and potentially pose a danger to all of us: if we can do it to them, they can also do it to us!

**Racists really thrive in the current Machine Man environment,** no matter how strongly that would be denied by our secular leaders in academia, governments and so on.

Accordingly and not surprisingly, the latest generations (and future leaders) who were thoroughly exposed to a most relentless indoctrination campaign of atheistic materialism have adopted widely popular memes and acronyms like YOLO: "you only live once" or DILLIGAF, which means "do I look like I give a f**k?"

**It makes perfect sense to solely or at least mostly focus on material aspects of life if we are convinced that the physical death of our bodies is the end of everything.** The big black nothing that lasts forever awaits. So it's much smarter to profit now. Enjoy it all while you can! "Après moi le déluge" – "After me, the flood."

Have as much sex with whoever or whatever as possible. "Love is just a chemical release in the brain as part of the breeding process anyway, so it is a bit overrated." Long time couples who have been married for decades and whose love only gets deeper and stronger as they grow older are conveniently ignored by such silly science and its uncritical adherents. And so are many other forms of loving relationships that have absolutely nothing to do with either breeding or sex. Or food and the like.

Is there any real – as opposed to feigned – need for moral or ethical behavior? Apart from getting along better with other people, respectively easier getting what we want from them? But what if no one is watching and we were absolutely sure that we would never ever get caught? Why should or would we really care and behave morally then?

The primordial soup that has supposedly produced us wouldn't know the difference between good or bad anyway. And there is no such thing as a God too. Or moral rights and wrongs; it's all relative. Right? So why bother to behave or be good, generous and kind? Why should moral conduct or fairness truly matter for the 'enlightened' atheist who wants to enjoy it all?

After all, conscious life is only a random yet lucky combination of unconscious dead matter. Or a fantasy that is nevertheless somehow preoccupied with self-preservation. And the brain that created the particular user illusion that is me will soon turn to worm fodder anyway, along with the rest of my body. So, just do it. Whatever it is you want doing, anything that feels good. Who cares? YOLO.

*"If there is no God, everything is permitted."* Fyodor Dostoevsky

Some members of today's politicized academia already propose the adoption of cannibalism to reduce the Earth's population and thereby our carbon footprints. Initially at least, the idea is not to kill humans for our daily food, but rather to eat the already-dead. Perhaps starting with our loved ones to quite literally show them our love? Finger-licking good...

Turning the remains of our dearly departed into compost to fertilize gardens and crops is already legal and being done in Washington State (USA) as an eco-friendly alternative to burials or cremations. 'Smell the roses, honey; they smell a bit like aunt Sophie.'

Should that and more of the same, like eating meat grown from your own body's cells, be very surprising? After all we are just a sophisticated animal, albeit supposedly the smartest one. Or so they say. And we already eat animals of all kinds, so why should it matter in the least? Especially if it easily and elegantly solves our assorted environmental problems... culinary delights await; who said that progress has to be dull and boring, right?

***Sadly, a human-hating attitude is widely shared among equally self-hating elitists who mistake their ruthlessness for intelligence.*** There are literally hundreds of their often most appalling quotes in the public domain going back over more than fifty years, all advocating a massive culling of the herd, so to speak. Of course they only ever talk about the common people, workers and such. It's never about themselves and their exalted families. Because, you know, they are very important. Or so they believe.

*"In the event that I am reincarnated, I would like to return as a deadly virus, in order to contribute something to solve overpopulation."* Prince Phillip, husband of Queen Elizabeth II and co-founder of the World Wildlife Fund. His Royal Highness helpfully suggested that, *"Cannibalism is a radical but realistic solution to the problem of overpopulation."*

*"A total population of 250-300 million people, **a 95% decline from present levels**, would be ideal."* Ted Turner, multi-billionaire founder of CNN.

*"We must speak more clearly about sexuality, contraception, about abortion, about values that control population, because the ecological crisis, in short, is the population crisis. **Cut the population by 90%** and there aren't enough people left to do a great deal of ecological damage."* Mikhail Gorbachev, the eighth and last leader of the Soviet Union.

What can one say to such sentiments and possibly intentions? Well, allow me to contribute a little semiserious and perhaps helpful suggestion: *Population control is a great idea once its proponents have lead by example and duly disposed of themselves.*

Enthusiastic believers in transhumanist promises should carefully consider whether these very powerful and super rich proponents of drastic reductions in the world's population would actually let them know if there suddenly were a magic potion (or technology of any kind) that really could prolong life. Would fervent believers in eugenics and their innate superiority be inclined to freely share it with those they consider to be inferiors?

Would the existence of such a hypothetical miracle drug or procedure become known to all and made widely available to the very commoners and people the elitists have declared to be so excessive and expendable, slated to be eliminated for the greater good (of themselves)?

Whether there really are too many people on our planet or not is a rather long subject by itself. What we can say for sure is that history shows that with increasing wealth and the accompanying sense of material security and comfort, people always opt for having smaller families. Or none at all. Actually leading to today's graying and shrinking of essentially all Western societies, including Japan and even China.

What is equally clear is that we humans produce a lot of totally unnecessary pollution. We heavily pollute our land, water and air. And indeed, the very food we eat. All far beyond the unavoidable. Much if not all could be managed far better with a bit more thought and care, with less greed and corruption, with more forward-thinking innovation and less defending of a rapidly decaying status quo built on unsustainable practices.

In short, environmental degradation and all forms of exploitation are just some of the dire consequences of an overly materialistic world view. *Selfish and silly short-term thinking is simply inherent in Machine Man philosophy.*

So, having said all of the above, is Machine Man intrinsically immoral? And, can a total materialist be very decent and good, striving to always do the right thing? The first answer is a resounding No and the second a clear Yes.

Homo Mysticum is fully aware of the fact that every eternal spirit (or spiritual soul) is inherently good. We all have a natural moral sense and know perfectly well what is right and wrong. Even psychopaths or sociopaths have an inkling of a conscience in the sense that they know when they do something that is generally considered to be wrong, although they themselves don't feel any regrets or empathy, and always have plenty of excuses.

Fact is that we humans have an inborn strong reluctance to kill as every military leader in the world can attest, to their utter displeasure one might add. People have a deep-seated desire to wanting to get along. We have to be heavily manipulated with continuous propaganda and incessant fearmongering for quite some time before we start to hate others.

Throughout history, armies had to heavily prescribe alcohol and drugs (like amphetamines, crystal meth, cocaine, heroin or psychedelics, etc.) to sufficiently numb and motivate soldiers to fight. But even then many conscript soldiers have shown the tendency to deliberately shoot into the air or freeze up in a crucial moment, often actually preferring to be killed rather than having to kill another human being.

Another sad but only natural reality of war is that a great many even professional soldiers keep committing suicide as they can't possibly live with themselves any longer, having done or witnessed things that are well, incredibly inhumane. Such suicides are not a consequence of what is downplayed to be post-traumatic stress disorder (PTSD), a term introduced in the 1970s to diagnose U.S. military veterans from the Vietnam War.

Quite many of today's military drone operators who have been heavily indoctrinated with sophisticated propaganda techniques and desensitized by playing incredibly brutal video games before starting to most cowardly kill for real from the safety of comfortable facilities located thousands of miles away (often while being drunk or high) still end up killing themselves. Such is *the power of our conscience* and the purity of our inherent goodness.

So in normal times and on a personal level, almost all of us are mostly friendly and good, generous and kind, supportive and loving – even while we are under the illusion of being a merely mortal physical body. However, the easier we are scared the more we can also panic and do harm, even against our very nature.

The currently still ongoing (as of March 2021) coronavirus pandemic has shown us a great many of the good, bad and ugly sides of humanity, including the widespread totalitarian impulses of panicked politicians. We were all suddenly and rather rudely reminded of our mortality; I have never seen so many normally cool, calm and collected people totally freak out in unison, even here in Australia, the land of the generally laid-back and easygoing.

The general public was induced to be in total panic mode rather than just being a bit more careful and cautious. Absolute fear was obvious in almost everybody's eyes. People often displayed an incredibly panicked demeanor and were almost too terrified to breathe or even look at others, desperately wanting to find some sense of normalcy by hoarding toilet paper and everything else, including guns and ammunition in the U.S.A.

As a society we were and partially still are once again in full survival of the fittest mode. With a lot of 'every man for himself' going on. Or countries against countries. Even regions or cities against other regions and cities. Should we really be surprised considering today's prevalence of Machine Man philosophy that has designated us to be just more or less strong or smart animals in need of fighting to stay alive?

Being in a more or less constant state of fear simply but surely lowers our cognitive abilities, including our intelligence quotients, and the mental faculties to use logic and reason. *The more fearful of death we are, the easier we can become conditioned and controlled, or otherwise convinced to do the bidding of the rich and powerful.*

All kinds of make-believe or exaggerated dangers and made-up enemies are supposedly lurking out there, everywhere and all the time, to be duly feared, hated and fought. All at our expense and their profit. For more centralized power and less individual freedom.

*The fewer of us who know who we really are, the more fears we will collectively have as a culture.* And the less peaceful and just our societies will continue to be. Racism will keep dividing us. Pollution will still shorten many lives and otherwise make life more unpleasant.

*Ultimately, knowing who we really are is not about who is right and wrong but a deciding factor about how free and happy we are while we are here.* And whether we are merely wasting our lives or worse, thoroughly screwing up both our present and future lives.

Living in fear basically means to live in unnecessary bondage and avoidable misery. Feeling increasingly insecure (and particularly so with growing age) instead of being well and truly confident. Suffering from ongoing mental anxiety and depression versus enjoying lasting inner peace and happiness. More joy. Or less. It's our choice.

Joy is our natural state of consciousness and a happy mind positively influences our overall physical health. In my first book, I've suggested that happy people have stronger immune systems and are otherwise healthier than the lesser happy or outright depressed:

"Increasingly, we become aware that our well being is influenced to a large degree by our mind. *Well balanced, strong and happy people have a stronger immune system and get less affected by sicknesses.* Disharmony in the energy field of one particular vibration level will negatively influence the energy fields of all other levels, while harmony too is expanding to benefit our total being." (1999; *Yes I Am Happy Now!* Page 61.)

In 2013, the results of various scientific studies were presented in the scientific journal *Nature*, confirming the strong physiological correlation between our personal happiness and physical health, including stronger immune systems and more favorable gene expressions.

*Fear clearly lowers our overall operating frequencies which in turn negatively affect our immune systems.* So the more fearful we are, the weaker our immune responses will be and the more likely we will pass away from infectious diseases, including the current pandemic sweeping the world. And of course, the opposite is true as well.

*Machine Man is commonly more fearful than the general specimen of Homo Credo, who in turn is generally more afraid than Mystic Man, who has essentially conquered fear for good.* The currently still ongoing and rather hysteric scaremongering campaigns by the corporate media, assorted governments and their pet scientists is certainly neither a very healthy nor a particularly happy affair. To put it mildly.

It is quite obvious that it is actually Homo Machina who gets first and foremost affected by this counterproductive, unhealthy peddling of fear. Small wonder the world's mega-rich have so quickly disappeared into their isolated castles, private luxury yachts, remote country estates or secure underground bunkers. They are literally fearing for their lives. The masses of course have to do with far more cramped and far less comfortable quarters.

But fear is fear no matter our surroundings. ***Mental anguish knows no limitations and also thrives in luxurious places.*** No one can help them escape the confines and limitations of their minds except they themselves. Whether we restrict our mind with limiting thoughts and beliefs or let it freely roam through the endless space of the Universe at large is completely up to us. It is an individual decision – if we are aware of it in the first place.

Now let's have a final look at ***the very latest scientific findings*** about the two sharply differing versions of reality (as always, see chapter *Notes* for more information):

### *The Machine Man reality:*
Researchers now claim that when we are dead – that is when our hearts have stopped beating and we can't move our bodies any longer, when all blood flow to the brain is cut off, and the brain stem reflexes (like pupil or gag reflex) are gone too – we are still conscious for up to six minutes as the brain takes some time to shut down completely.

In other words, they suggest that we do know that we have already died, but that we are trapped in our now dead body while little by little more of the remaining lights are switched off for good. So the dying is an ongoing agony as we slowly but surely lose consciousness.

This is Machine Man philosophy at its best, or worst. These scientists simply try to explain away truly amazing OBEs and NDEs as these just don't fit into their rigid belief system; they have no alternative explanation other than coming up with this rather distressing and depressing suggestion.

So a Machine Man who has already been terrified of death all life long now has further and greater anguish to look forward to; ***some final minutes of utter torment are said to await us beyond death.*** Wow. And good luck trying to be happy now, folks!

***The Mystic Man reality:***

A revolutionary new study has concluded that dying is actually a most euphoric experience filled with bliss, contentment and happiness.

Previously, scientific investigations into near-death experiences used questionnaires or asked potentially leading questions that quite possibly skewed the findings in favor of NDEs ("Did you feel separated from your body?" or "Did you have a feeling of peace and pleasantness?" etc.)

The latest research however used artificial intelligence and text mining techniques without asking specific questions of any kind. The fully automated and therefore entirely unbiased process analyzed the firsthand written accounts of 158 survivors, and found that positive words were used far more often of than negative ones.

The researchers from Canada's Western University and the University of Liège in Belgium consider their results to be the first quantitative scientific proof that most people respond very positively to their near-death experiences.

*"It was just like waking from a nap in a place I have always been and there was no fear or anything **just complete contentment and happiness**,"* Adam Tapp, Canadian paramedic who was certified dead for over 11 minutes.

Can Machine Man ever be truly happy? Quite apparently the answer is a simple No. Both on an individual personal level and collectively as a society. Why?

***Machine Man is simply not nourished on the soul level which indicates if not proves that we are a spiritual being in essence***: we have plenty of food for our bodies, an immense reservoir of mental stimulus for our intellectual needs, sheer endless forms of entertainment to amuse us, plentiful sexual opportunities to keep the hormonal juices flowing, an abundance of medications or food supplements to cure our ailments and deficiencies, ample varieties of booze and drugs to get or keep us in alternate spaces of reality, yet we are still not really fulfilled and happy as the rising numbers of anxious and depressed people confirm; what is missing is feeling our natural spiritual connections and thereby be properly and fully nourished in a world gone full-scale mad Machine Man!

Hopefully, the thoughts and information contained in this book will help to put the sparkle back into a great many eyes, invigorate countless tired minds, put the spring back in many of my readers' steps, cure thousands of broken hearts, free numerous souls from the needless scourge of fear, and enable a myriad of spirits to soar ever higher and set them free to live a most amazing life in the beautiful here and now!

It is my further hope that the perennial knowledge conveyed here will help bring about *a world that is free, fair and fun for all of us* temporarily living here on planet Earth.

Knowing who we really are has the potential to unite the deeply divided, to break the curse of racism, and solve the many social, economical and ecological problems still plaguing us today.

May this book also inspire broader thoughts about all that's really important in life, stimulate deeper explorations into the great mysteries of life, and encourage more truly innovative scientific research by formerly close-minded scientists who have now turned into genuinely open-minded skeptics.

There is not much difference between a real scientist and a true mystic after all; they equally share the genuine longing, deep passion and continuous search for finding ever deep truths.

And to every dear reader who upon reading this book still worries about the eventually approaching final day, let me repeat what I have told my dear father many years ago: when your time has come, you will have the best and most pleasant surprise of your life!

Best wishes,
Arne

**Epilogue**

Oh, and in the meantime, what happened to our dear Paul Schmitz, the now reformed but formerly so unlucky racist?

He got married to a lovely girl from Tajikistan. They have two beautiful daughters and adopted a nice boy from Tanzania who had lost his parents. He got appointed as the UN ambassador for Human Rights and still travels the world, telling everyone who is willing to listen about the idiocy of racism.

Paul is now teaching us *who we really are* and that all life is precious, and worthy of respect and love. He keeps pointing out that we are all part of the human race, planet Earth, and indeed, the Universe. And that therefore we should act accordingly. We really can and should live happily together in love, peace and harmony while equally enjoying the bounties and beauties of this wonderful planet, our current home away from home!

The End.

# NOTES
## Beyond Machine Man

### *The Three Perspectives*

My second book:
https://www.amazon.com/dp/1876538031/beampublishing
http://www.barnesandnoble.com/w/merry-christians-arne-klingenberg/1124795581

### *The Unfortunate Racist*

Paul Schmitz = 80 kg
transplanted bones 10% of body weight = 8kg (90%)
man-made parts 3 kg = approx. 3.5% (86.5%)
5 litres of blood = 6 kg = 7.5 % (79%)
liver = 1.560 kg average = 2% (77%)
skin 16% = 12.80 kg (61%)
lungs = 2.3 kg
+ heart = 0.35 kg
= 2.65 kg = approx. 3.5% (57.5%)
kidneys 0.3 kg
pancreas 0.1 kg
= 0.5% (57%)
water 60% = 48 kg

The liver is the second largest organ; its average weight in a normal human body is 1,560 gms. The spleen is the seventh largest or heaviest organ and weighs 170 grams heavy.
Your skin is your largest organ...it accounts for around 16 percent of your body weight.
http://www.bbc.co.uk/science/humanbody/body/factfiles/skin/skin.shtml

Th human skeleton may comprise between 12 and 20 percent of a person's total body weight with the average being 15 percent.
http://en.wikipedia.org/wiki/Human_skeleton
Each lung weighs 1.1 kilograms (2.4 lb), therefore making the entire organ about 2.3 kilograms (5.1 lb).
http://en.wikipedia.org/wiki/Human_lung
The human heart has a mass of between 250 and 350 grams and is about the size of a fist.
http://en.wikipedia.org/wiki/Human_heart
Each adult kidney weighs between 125 and 170 grams in males and between 115 and 155 grams in females.
http://en.wikipedia.org/wiki/Kidneys
Pancreas 100 grams
http://onlinelibrary.wiley.com/doi/10.1002/ar.1090320204/abstract
Arthur Guyton 's Textbook of Medical Physiology states that "the total amount of water in a man... averaging 60 percent of his total body weight.
http://en.wikipedia.org/wiki/Body_water


## *First Conclusions*

My first book:
https://www.amazon.com/exec/obidos/ASIN/1876538007/beampublishing/002-3757616-4304834


## *The DNA Question*

https://www.yourgenome.org/facts/what-is-dna
https://en.wikipedia.org/wiki/Genome
https://www.ancestry.com.au/lp/double-helix/dna-strands


"The mutation load essentially means that every functional part in your body or in your genome can experience changes that will be bad for them. Like in life, every functional entity, if left unchecked, will deteriorate and cease working – you cannot leave your television on and expect that in a

million years it will still work. The enemies of genes are mutations, and *the vast majority of mutations that happen in the functional portion of the genome are deleterious* (harmful, damaging)" – Dan Graur, Professor of the Department of Biology & Biochemistry at the University of Houston
https://sputniknews.com/science/201707221055792029-genome-junk-dna/
https://soundcloud.com/radiosputnik/our-genomes-are-the-product-of-evolution-dan-graur

https://en.wikipedia.org/wiki/C-value
http://www.genomenewsnetwork.org/articles/02_01/Sizing_genomes.shtml
https://en.wikipedia.org/wiki/Polychaos_dubium

https://www.scientificamerican.com/article/identical-twins-genes-are-not-identical/
http://www.uab.edu/newsarchive/39118-subtle-differences-in-dna-of-identical-twins-may-help-diagnose-disease
https://www.smithsonianmag.com/smart-news/identical-twins-arent-so-identical-which-makes-twin-studies-harder-119107266/

Phenotypically Concordant and Discordant Monozygotic Twins Display Different DNA Copy-Number-Variation Profiles
https://www.cell.com/ajhg/fulltext/S0002-9297(08)00102-X

https://www.researchgate.net/profile/Carl_Bruder

https://www.whatisepigenetics.com/

https://www.ted.com/talks/riccardo_sabatini_how_to_read_the_genome_and_build_a_human_being

In 2014, the American Academy of Microbiology published a FAQ that emphasized that the number of microbial cells and the number of human cells are both estimates, and noted that recent research had arrived at a new estimate of the number of human cells – approximately 37.2 trillion,

meaning that the ratio of microbial-to-human cells, if the original estimate of 100 trillion bacterial cells is correct, is closer to 3:1
https://en.wikipedia.org/wiki/Human_microbiome
https://www.cell.com/cell/fulltext/S0092-8674(16)00053-2

Human Virome: Scientists Say 380 Trillion Viruses Live Inside of Us
https://www.inverse.com/article/49747-what-is-the-human-virome
https://www.sciencedirect.com/science/article/abs/pii/S1879625711001908

The human virome is unique to each individual and includes many viruses, including previously uncharacterized bacteriophages, which may play a defensive role against pathogens (Minot et al., 2013).
https://www.sciencedirect.com/topics/immunology-and-microbiology/human-virome

DNA and RNA viruses that collectively make up the intestinal virome outnumber bacterial cells by as much as 10:1. The human gut virome includes a diverse collection of viruses that infect our own cells as well as other commensal organisms, directly impacting on our well-being. Despite its predominance, the virome remains one of the least understood components of the gut microbiota.
https://www.ncbi.nlm.nih.gov/pmc/articles/PMC6435874/
https://journals.sagepub.com/doi/10.1177/1756284819836620

### Brain Matters

"The gut can work independently of any control by the brain in your head—it's functioning as a second brain," says Michael Gershon, professor and chair of pathology and cell biology at Columbia. "It's another independent center of integrative neural activity."
https://www.psychologytoday.com/us/articles/201111/your-backup-brain

This "heart brain" is composed of approximately 40,000 neurons that are alike neurons in the brain, meaning that the heart has its own nervous

system. In addition, the heart communicates with the brain in many methods: neurologically, biochemically, biophysically, and energetically.
https://pubmed.ncbi.nlm.nih.gov/31728781/
https://link.springer.com/article/10.1007/s11916-019-0827-4

Characterization of the intrinsic cardiac nervous system
https://pubmed.ncbi.nlm.nih.gov/27568996/

The operation known as hemispherectomy—where half the brain is removed—sounds too radical to ever consider, much less perform. In the last century, however, surgeons have performed it hundreds of times for disorders uncontrollable in any other way. Unbelievably, the surgery has no apparent effect on personality or memory.
https://www.scientificamerican.com/article/strange-but-true-when-half-brain-better-than-whole/

Overall, hemispherectomy is a successful procedure. A 1996 study of 52 individuals who underwent the surgery found that 96% of patients experienced reduced or completely ceased occurrence of seizures post-surgery. Studies have found no significant long-term effects on memory, personality, or humor and minimal changes in cognitive function overall. For example, one case followed a patient who had completed college, attended graduate school and scored above average on intelligence tests after undergoing this procedure at age 5.5. This patient eventually developed "superior language and intellectual abilities" despite the removal of the left hemisphere, which contains the classical language zones.
https://en.wikipedia.org/wiki/Hemispherectomy

https://www.oecd.org/education/ceri/neuromyths.htm
https://www.psychologytoday.com/us/blog/the-athletes-way/201708/debunking-neuromyths-eight-common-brain-myths-set-straight
https://www.ncbi.nlm.nih.gov/pmc/articles/PMC3475349/
https://www.sciencedaily.com/releases/2017/08/170810104929.htm
https://www.edutopia.org/neuroscience-brain-based-learning-myth-busting

Neuroplasticity can be observed at multiple scales, from microscopic changes in individual neurons to larger-scale changes such as cortical remapping in response to injury. Behavior, environmental stimuli, thought, and emotions may also cause neuroplastic change through activity-dependent plasticity, which has significant implications for healthy development, learning, memory, and recovery from brain damage.
https://en.wikipedia.org/wiki/Neuroplasticity

In 1980, Roger Lewin published an article in Science, "Is Your Brain Really Necessary?", about Lorber studies on cerebral cortex losses. He reports the case of a Sheffield University student who had a measured IQ of 126 and passed a Mathematics Degree but who had hardly any discernible brain matter at all since his cortex was extremely reduced by hydrocephalus.
http://rifters.com/real/articles/Science_No-Brain.pdf
https://www.ncbi.nlm.nih.gov/pubmed/7434023
http://science.sciencemag.org/content/210/4475/1232.long

''The cerebral cortex of the brain is probably responsible for a great deal less than most people imagine." Professor John Lorber, British neurologist at Sheffield University, UK.

"To talk of redundancy is a cop-out to get around something you don't understand." Patrick Wall, neuroscientist and Professor of anatomy at University College, London.
https://en.wikipedia.org/wiki/Patrick_David_Wall


### *Neurofiction*

The author acknowledges and appreciates the amazing technical knowledge, deep insights, logical arguments, and meticulous research of neuroscientist, pharmacologist and whistleblower, Dr. Felix Hasler, in his must-read book (in German):
**Neuromythologie.** *Eine Streitschrift gegen die Deutungsmacht der Hirnforschung*, Oct 2012, 264 pp., ISBN 978-3-8376-1580-7

https://www.amazon.com/Neuromythologie-Felix-Author-Hasler/
dp/3837615804

https://www.researchgate.net/profile/Felix_Hasler
Berlin School of Mind and Brain, Humboldt-Universität zu Berlin,
Deutschland.
http://www.mind-and-brain.de/people/associated-researchers/
https://www.stichtingopen.nl/interview-felix-hasler-whats-missing-is-a-
holistic-view-on-the-psyche/

Felix Hasler über "Neuromythologie" (in German)
https://youtu.be/PQBLVVzikIo

David Kupfer, Chair of the DSM-5 Task Force, while defending the DSM
as a useful diagnostic tool in a press release, concedes that "biological and
genetic markers that provide precise diagnoses that can be delivered with
complete reliability and validity" are still "disappointingly distant. We've
been telling patients for several decades that we are waiting for biomarkers.
We're still waiting."
https://www.madinamerica.com/2013/05/chair-of-dsm-5-task-force-
admits-lack-of-validity/
https://www.madinamerica.com/wp-content/uploads/2013/05/Statement-
from-dsm-chair-david-kupfer-md.pdf

However, other studies have revealed the very opposite: an increase in
neuronal activity sometimes lead to less rather than more blood flowing
(as measured by the tightening of blood vessels instead of their expansion).
University of California San Diego (UCSD) Neurovascular Imaging
Laboratory
2008 Journal of Neuroscience: Anna Devor, Elizabeth M.C. Hillman et al.
http://www.jneurosci.org/content/28/53
http://www.jneurosci.org/content/28/53/14347

2009 Human Brain Mapping conference in San Francisco: The Salmon
of Doubt

Craig Bennett, Abigail Baird, Mike Miller, and George Wolford put an adult salmon into a fMRT scanner and showed it a range of pictures of various human interaction like shaking hands, hugging and so on. The authors of the study took the scan results and did a normal statistical interpretation; it showed higher brain activity in certain brain regions. The only problem was that the fish was already long dead.

http://prefrontal.org/files/posters/Bennett-Salmon-2009.jpg

http://prefrontal.org/blog/2009/06/human-brain-mapping-2009-presentations/

https://neuroskeptic.blogspot.com/2009/09/fmri-gets-slap-in-face-with-dead-fish.html

"90% of the brain are continually lying fallow" – a neuroscientist would immediately doubt that this statement is true for the following reasons:

1. Evolution does not allow any wastefulness. Wastefulness causes an exclusion of the gene pool. Like all other organs, our brain has been shaped by natural selection. While the brain only weighs 2% of the total body weight, it uses 20% of the whole energy. Thus, brain tissue is metabolically expensive to grow and run. A brain that only works with 10% of its power would not be worth the high costs and thereby human beings with their large brains would have already been excluded from the gene pool.

https://www.oecd.org/education/ceri/neuromyth4.htm

Hemispherectomy is a very rare neurosurgical procedure in which a cerebral hemisphere (half of the brain) is removed, disconnected, or disabled. Surgery does not appear to decrease a child's intellect. Intelligence sometimes, in fact, improves due, partly, to a lack of seizures and elimination of anti-seizure medications. Where there are no complications, many of these children leave the hospital for rehabilitation within two weeks of surgery.

http://hemifoundation.homestead.com/facts.html

You might not want to do it, but removing half of your brain will not significantly impact who you are. The operation known as hemispherectomy—where half the brain is removed—sounds too radical to ever consider, much less perform. In the last century, however, surgeons have performed it hundreds of times for disorders uncontrollable in any other way. Unbelievably, the surgery has no apparent effect on personality or memory. https://www.scientificamerican.com/article/strange-but-true-when-half-brain-better-than-whole/

Is your brain really necessary? This is the title of a famous paper published in the journal Science by Roger Lewin, concerning the research of the late Dr. John Lorber, professor of neurology at the university of Sheffield, UK.
http://www.supernoetics.com/tag/john-lorber/
http://rifters.com/real/articles/Science_No-Brain.pdf
https://www.ncbi.nlm.nih.gov/pubmed/7434023
http://science.sciencemag.org/content/210/4475/1232.long

https://www.newscientist.com/article/dn12301-man-with-tiny-brain-shocks-doctors/

## *Medical Tales*

"Let me remind you of a famous saying: "There are three ways to not tell the truth: lies, damned lies, and statistics." What you must do is ask yourself some questions: who did the study that came up with the statistics, what exactly are the statistics measuring, who was asked, how were they asked, and compared with what?" Richard Taflinger, Professor in the Communication department at Washington State University.
https://public.wsu.edu/%7Etaflinge/evistats.html

http://ahrp.org/lies-damned-lies-and-medical-science/
Much of what medical researchers conclude in their studies is misleading, exaggerated, or flat-out wrong. Dr. John Ioannidis has spent his career challenging his peers by exposing their bad science. How should we choose among these dueling, high-profile nutritional findings? Ioannidis suggests a simple approach: ignore them all.
http://www.theatlantic.com/magazine/archive/2010/11/lies-damned-lies-and-medical-science/8269/

John P. A. Ioannidis is a Professor of Medicine and of Health Research and Policy at Stanford University School of Medicine and a Professor of Statistics at Stanford University School of Humanities and Sciences. He is best known for his research and published papers on scientific studies, particularly the 2005 paper "Why Most Published Research Findings Are False". Ioannidis is one of the most-cited scientists across the scientific literature, especially in the fields of clinical medicine and social sciences, according to Thomson Reuters' Highly Cited Researchers 2015.
https://en.wikipedia.org/wiki/John_Ioannidis
https://www.ncbi.nlm.nih.gov/pmc/articles/PMC1182327/
https://www.ncbi.nlm.nih.gov/pmc/articles/PMC1182327/pdf/
pmed.0020124.pdf

Study Suggests Medical Errors Now Third Leading Cause of Death in the U.S. Analyzing medical death rate data over an eight-year period, Johns Hopkins patient safety experts have calculated that more than 250,000 deaths per year are due to medical error in the U.S.
10 percent of all U.S. deaths are now due to medical error.
Third highest cause of death in the U.S. is medical error.
Medical errors are an under-recognized cause of death.
https://www.hopkinsmedicine.org/news/media/releases/study_suggests_
medical_errors_now_third_leading_cause_of_death_in_the_us

Results Using a weighted average of the 4 studies, a lower limit of 210,000 deaths per year was associated with preventable harm in hospitals. ...the true number of premature deaths associated with preventable harm to patients was estimated at more than 400,000 per year. Serious harm seems to be 10- to 20-fold more common than lethal harm.
https://journals.lww.com/journalpatientsafety/Fulltext/2013/09000/A_
New,_Evidence_based_Estimate_of_Patient_Harms.2.aspx

Changes in midlife death rates across racial and ethnic groups in the United States: systematic analysis of vital statistics
https://doi.org/10.1136/bmj.k3096 (Published 15 August 2018)
https://www.bmj.com/content/362/bmj.k3096

https://www.theguardian.com/commentisfree/2018/aug/19/bad-news-is-were-dying-earlier-in-britain-down-to-shit-life-syndrome

In Baltimore, doctors at Mt. Washington Pediatric Hospital say babies born with Neonatal Abstinence Syndrome — a set of conditions caused by withdrawal from exposure to drugs — now account for 25% of the hospital's admissions. https://www.axios.com/the-youngest-victims-of-the-opioid-epidemic-7531ccf5-9ec4-431a-bb1e-991fc2fb0364.html
https://www.youtube.com/watch?v=3ncnetwVMHk

The increase in opioid overdose deaths has been dramatic, and opioids are now responsible for 49,000 of the 72,000 drug overdose deaths overall in the USA in 2017.
https://en.wikipedia.org/wiki/Opioid_epidemic

White House: True cost of opioid epidemic tops $500 billion
https://www.statnews.com/2017/11/20/white-house-opioid-epidemic/
https://www.drugabuse.gov/related-topics/trends-statistics/overdose-death-rates

Direct-to-consumer pharmaceutical advertising (DTCPA) has grown rapidly during the past several decades and is now the most prominent type of health communication that the public encounters. The U.S. and New Zealand are the only countries that allow DTCPA that includes product claims. Most other countries don't allow DTCPA at all.
https://www.ncbi.nlm.nih.gov/pmc/articles/PMC3278148/

A study by the prestigious Mayo Clinic and Olmsted Medical Center found that nearly 70 percent of all Americans are on at least one prescription drug, and more than half take two; twenty percent of all Americans are on five or more prescription drugs.
http://www.mayoclinic.org/news2013-rst/7543.html

*"The case against science is straightforward: much of the scientific literature, perhaps half, may simply be untrue. Afflicted by studies with small sample*

*sizes, tiny effects, invalid exploratory analyses, and flagrant conflicts of interest, together with an obsession for pursuing fashionable trends of dubious importance, science has taken a turn towards darkness."* Dr. Richard Horton, Editor-in-chief of the Lancet, the world's most respected medical journal. https://www.thelancet.com/pdfs/journals/lancet/PIIS0140-6736%2815%2960696-1.pdf

*"It is simply no longer possible to believe much of the clinical research that is published, or to rely on the judgment of trusted physicians or authoritative medical guidelines. I take no pleasure in this conclusion, which I reached slowly and reluctantly over my two decades as an editor of the New England Journal of Medicine."*
Dr. Marcia Angell, Physician and longtime Editor-in-Chief of the New England Medical Journal (NEMJ), a prestigious peer-reviewed medical journal.
https://www.ncbi.nlm.nih.gov/pmc/articles/PMC2964337/

*"The medical profession is being bought by the pharmaceutical industry, not only in terms of the practice of medicine, but also in terms of teaching and research. The academic institutions of this country are allowing themselves to be the paid agents of the pharmaceutical industry. I think it's disgraceful."*
Dr. Arnold Relman, a Harvard professor of medicine and editor of the New England Journal of Medicine (*NEJM*) from 1977 to 1991.
https://www.ncbi.nlm.nih.gov/pmc/articles/PMC1126053/

Doctors have diagnosed a 31-year-old US man with retinal toxicity, which affects the ability of the eyes to detect colors. The man was also diagnosed with irreversible erythropsia, which is characterized by red-hued vision, Vice reported.
They revealed that there had been a structural change in his retinas that might be irreversible and could be caused by sildenafil citrate.
*"To actually see these types of structural changes was unexpected, but it explained the symptoms that the patient suffered from,"* said Dr. Richard Rosen, the report's lead author and director of Retina Services at Mount Sinai Hospital.

*"While we know colored-vision disturbance is a well-described side effect of this medication, we have never been able to visualize the structural effect of the drug on the retina until now,"* Rosen added.
https://motherboard.vice.com/en_us/article/9k7n83/a-man-overdosed-on-an-erectile-dysfunction-drug-sildenafil-and-now-he-permanently-sees-red
https://journals.lww.com/retinalcases/Abstract/2018/01241/SILDENAFIL_CITRATE_INDUCED_RETINAL.9.aspx
https://www.mountsinai.org/about/newsroom/2018/irreversible-damage-to-color-vision-is-linked-to-a-popular-erectile-dysfunction-drug-mount-sinai-researchers-reveal

Selective Publication of Antidepressant Trials and Its Influence on Apparent Efficacy
Among 74 FDA-registered studies, 31%, accounting for 3449 study participants, were not published. Whether and how the studies were published were associated with the study outcome. New England Journal of Medicine (NEJM) January 17, 2008 N Engl J Med 2008; 358:252-260
http://www.nejm.org/doi/full/10.1056/NEJMsa065779#t=abstract

Angell M (January 15, 2009) Drug companies and doctors: A story of corruption. The New York Review of Books 56
FDA reviews of every placebo-controlled clinical trial submitted for initial approval of the six most widely used antidepressant drugs approved between 1987 and 1999 – Prozac, Paxil, Zoloft, Celexa, Serzone, and Effexor. The difference between drug and placebo was so small that it was unlikely to be of any clinical significance. The results were much the same for all six drugs: all were equally ineffective.
http://www.nybooks.com/articles/archives/2009/jan/15/drug-companies-doctorsa-story-of-corruption/
http://www.nybooks.com/articles/2009/01/15/drug-companies-doctorsa-story-of-corruption/
Irving Kirsch et al., "The Emperor's New Drugs: An Analysis of Antidepressant Medication Data Submitted to the US Food and Drug Administration," *Prevention & Treatment*, July 15, 2002.

Side Effects: A Prosecutor, a Whistleblower, and a Bestselling Antidepressant on Trial by Alison Bass
https://www.amazon.com/gp/product/1565125533/beampublishing

Our Daily Meds: How the Pharmaceutical Companies Transformed Themselves into Slick Marketing Machines and Hooked the Nation on Prescription Drugs by Melody Petersen
https://www.amazon.com/gp/product/0374228272/beampublishing

Shyness: How Normal Behavior Became a Sickness by Christopher Lane
https://www.amazon.com/gp/product/0300124465/beampublishing

The New York Times says that more than 30 million Americans are currently taking antidepressants.
https://well.blogs.nytimes.com/2013/08/12/a-glut-of-antidepressants

http://www.scientificamerican.com/article/the-medicated-americans/
http://www.zerohedge.com/news/2014-02-15/drugging-america-summarized-19-mind-altering-facts

"In a paper last year in the Lancet Psychiatry journal, Professor Gotzsche argued our use of antidepressants is causing more harm than good.
He said as the evidence against drugs such as Valium and Xanax emerged, they have been replaced with anti-depressants that are equally as addictive and their side-effects just as dangerous. Furthermore, he says research that showed small benefits over placebos was biased, as it did not properly hide whether patients were in the active or placebo group."
http://www.smh.com.au/national/health/peter-gotzsche-founder-of-the-cochrane-collaboration-visits-australia-to-talk-about-dangers-of-prescription-drugs-20150207-136nqc.html
http://www.thelancet.com/journals/lanpsy/article/PIIS2215-0366(14)70280-9/abstract
http://www.ncbi.nlm.nih.gov/pubmed/21810886?dopt=Abstract
http://www.deadlymedicines.dk/

Marketing the myth of serotonin, the 'happy chemical' by Adriana Barton
The Globe and Mail, Published Sunday, May. 17 2015
But the truth is, depression is not a serotonin deficiency. The idea that
depression is caused by low serotonin levels is based on flimsy evidence
dating to the 1950s. Pharmaceutical companies promoted the low serotonin
story to sell Prozac and related antidepressants.
https://www.theglobeandmail.com/life/health-and-fitness/health/
marketing-the-myth-of-serotonin-the-happy-chemical/article24457686/
https://www.theguardian.com/society/2008/feb/27/mentalhealth.health1

American Psycho - Has The United States Lost Its Collective Mind? by
Roberts Bridges
"The top-selling drug in America is an antipsychotic, happily named Abilify.
Aside from the fact that Americans are buying antipsychotic medication by
the truckload, there's another disturbing thing about Abilify: Nobody, not
even the Food and Drug Administration (FDA), has any idea what makes
it effective. According to the USPI label that accompanies each bottle: "The
mechanism of action of aripiprazole... is unknown."
http://www.zerohedge.com/news/2015-10-16/guest-post-american-
psycho-has-united-states-lost-its-collective-mind

A short excerpt from the list of possible side-effects as per the manufacturer's
website:
"Uncontrollable movements of face, tongue, or other parts of body, as these
may be signs of a serious condition called tardive dyskinesia (TD). TD
may not go away, even if you stop taking ABILIFY. TD may also start after
you stop taking ABILIFY." "High fever, stiff muscles, confusion, sweating,
changes in pulse, heart rate and blood pressure may be signs of a condition
called neuroleptic malignant syndrome (NMS), a rare and serious condition
that can lead to death."
https://www.abilify.com/
https://www.otsuka-us.com/media/static/Abilify-PI.pdf
https://www.medicinenet.com/aripiprazole/article.htm#what_are_the_
uses_for_abilify?
https://www.classaction.com/abilify/

"To be a top seller, a drug has to be expensive and also widely used," Steven Reidbord M.D. wrote in Psychology Today. "Abilify is both. It's the 14th most prescribed brand-name medication, and it retails for about $30 a pill. Annual sales are over $7 billion, nearly a billion more than the next runner-up." https://www.psychologytoday.com/blog/sacramento-street-psychiatry/201503/americas-top-selling-drug

...she began developing strange, fluttering tics around her eyes. The tics eventually grew to include involuntary chewing motions and twitching of her lips. Her tongue darted in and out uncontrollably. What happened to Maura is called "tardive dyskinesia," and it's one of the most worrisome side effects of many psychiatric drugs prescribed in America, including Prozac. https://www.webmd.com/depression/features/prozac-pro-con#1

Antidepressants and weight gain: What causes it? https://www.mayoclinic.org/diseases-conditions/depression/expert-answers/antidepressants-and-weight-gain/faq-20058127

Antidepressants have been associated with weight gain for about 50 years. https://www.psychologytoday.com/us/blog/the-antidepressant-diet/201007/reversing-antidepressant-weight-gain

According to the Centers for Disease Controls, every day in America, 44 people die from overdose of prescription painkillers.
In 2013, nearly two million Americans abused prescription painkillers. Each day, almost 7,000 people are treated in emergency rooms for abusing the medication. http://www.cdc.gov/drugoverdose/epidemic/index.html

A Brief History of Psychotropic Drugs Prescribed to Mass Murderers By Daren Savage
http://www.ladailypost.com/content/brief-history-psychotropic-drugs-prescribed-mass-murderers

There are 22 international drug regulatory agency warnings of psychiatric drugs causing violence—including mania, psychosis, depersonalization, aggression and even homicidal ideation.

https://www.cchrint.org/2014/05/26/will-lawmakers-investigate-elliot-rodgers-psychiatric-drug-use-or-ignore-it-that-is-the-question/
https://www.cchrint.org/psychiatric-drugs/drug_warnings_on_violence/

Prescription drug spending in the US exploded in 2014 to nearly $374 billion, a whopping 13.1 percent increase in growth, according to a new report from IMS Institute for Healthcare Informatics.
http://blogs.wsj.com/pharmalot/2015/04/14/why-did-prescription-drug-spending-hit-374b-in-the-us-last-year-read-this/

Suicide Rates Rise Sharply in U.S. By Tara Parker-Pope
"Another factor may be the widespread availability of opioid drugs like OxyContin and oxycodone, which can be particularly deadly in large doses."
http://www.nytimes.com/2013/05/03/health/suicide-rate-rises-sharply-in-us.html?_r=3&

Young people on antidepressants more prone to violence, study finds
Prozac and Seroxat may also make 15-24 year olds more likely to be involved in non-violent crime and to have alcohol problems
http://www.theguardian.com/world/2015/sep/16/study-finds-young-people-on-antidepressants-more-prone-to-violence
http://journals.plos.org/plosmedicine/article?id=10.1371/journal.pmed.1001875

Anti-depressant paroxetine linked to youth suicide and no more effective than a placebo, researchers find. The World Today By Nick Grimm
The study, published in the British Medical Journal, reviewed data used by pharmaceutical companies to help market the drug, which is sold in Australia under the names Aropax and Paxil. It is also known as paroxetine.
http://www.abc.net.au/news/2015-09-17/anti-depressant-linked-to-youth-suicide-in-damning-review/6783332

Antidepressant Nightmares
SSRI Stories is a collection of over 6,000 stories that have appeared in the media (newspapers, TV, scientific journals) in which prescription drugs

were mentioned and in which the drugs may be linked to a variety of adverse outcomes including violence.
https://ssristories.org/?sort=date

Lawmaker Calls For Study On Links Between Pharmaceuticals And Mass Killers
http://www.zerohedge.com/news/2015-10-07/lawmaker-calls-study-links-between-pharmaceuticals-and-mass-killers

'St John's Wort plant as effective as Prozac for treating depression', say scientists By Daniel Martin. The study's lead author, Dr Klaus Linde, from the Centre for Complementary Medicine in Munich, pooled data from 29 studies involving 5,489 patients with mild to moderately severe depression.
http://www.dailymail.co.uk/health/article-1072414/St-Johns-Wort-plant-effective-Prozac-treating-depression-say-scientists.html

Patients are being deceived into taking drugs they do not need, that do not work and even put lives at risk, according to a scathing review of the influence big drug companies have on healthcare. Drug companies ''masterfully influenced'' medicine, a review by Australian, British and US researchers has found.
European Journal of Clinical Investigation, Volume 43, Issue 5, pages 469–475, May 2013
Undue industry influences that distort healthcare research, strategy, expenditure and practice: a review By Emmanuel Stamatakis, Richard Weiler and John P.A. Ioannidis
http://onlinelibrary.wiley.com/doi/10.1111/eci.12074/abstract
http://onlinelibrary.wiley.com/doi/10.1111/eci.12074/pdf

Overdiagnosis is exposing healthy people to tests and treatments that are at best useless, and at worst trigger aggressive procedures with devastating side effects, a formidable alliance of peak doctors colleges, researchers, advocates and public health experts warned.
https://www.smh.com.au/healthcare/overdiagnosis-is-harming-patients-and-action-is-required-says-chief-medical-officer-20181014-p509jx.html

An analysis of HCF claims data for 21 procedures – including endoscopy in patients under 55 years of age, knee arthroscopy and spinal fusion – found up to 34 per cent of 32,900 admissions in 2016-17 were "low-value", unhelpful, and in some cases, potentially harmful.
https://www.smh.com.au/healthcare/how-inappropriate-surgeries-are-pushing-up-your-health-insurance-premiums-20180829-p500gl.html

Dangerous antipsychotic medicine being overprescribed for elderly patients Strong medications normally reserved for the very mentally unwell are being used too often and freely on elderly patients, causing damaging side effects and premature death."
http://www.abc.net.au/news/2018-09-18/dangerous-medicine-being-over-prescribed-for-elderly-patients/10261938
http://www.abc.net.au/radio/programs/am/anti-psychotic-drugs-may-be-overused-on-elderly-patients/10262108
https://www.kcl.ac.uk/ioppn/about/difference/32-Reducing-the-use-of-antipsychotics-in-dementia.aspx

https://en.wikipedia.org/wiki/Trepanning
https://en.wikipedia.org/wiki/Lobotomy

The bacterium Helicobacter pylori (H. pylori) was established as the leading cause of peptic ulcers in the early 1980s. It was also found to cause gastritis (inflammation of the stomach lining), and, in Asian populations, cancer of the stomach.
https://www.medicinenet.com/ulcers_what_causes_ulcers/views.htm

David Healy is a former secretary of the British Association for Psychopharmacology and author of over 120 articles and 12 books, including *The Antidepressant Era* and *The Creation of Psychopharmacology*. A chemical treatment was developed for one purpose, and as long as some theoretical rationale could be found, doctors administered it to the insane patients in their care to see if it would help. Why these treatments worked, Healy argues provocatively, was, and often still is, a mystery.
https://www.amazon.com/Creation-Psychopharmacology-David-Healy/dp/0674015991

https://www.ncbi.nlm.nih.gov/pmc/articles/PMC1279263/
http://www.hup.harvard.edu/catalog.
php?isbn=9780674015999&content=reviews

A must-view video for anyone on psychiatric drugs!
Robert Whitaker is a science and medical writer. He is the author of four
books, two of which tell of the history of psychiatry. His first, Mad in
America: Bad Science, Bad Medicine and the Enduring Mistreatment of the
Mentally Ill was named by Discover magazine as one of the best science
books of 2002, while the American Library Association named it one of the
best history books of that year. His newest book on this topic, Anatomy of
an Epidemic: Magic Bullets, Psychiatric Drugs, and the Astonishing Rise
of Mental Illness in America, won the Investigative Reporters and Editors
book award for best investigative journalism in 2010.
https://www.youtube.com/watch?v=5VBXWdhabuQ
https://www.amazon.com/Anatomy-Epidemic-Bullets-Psychiatric-
Astonishing-dp-0307452425/dp/0307452425/beampublishing

https://www.ncmhr.org/downloads/Anatomy-Of-An-Epidemic-Summary-
Of-Findings-Whitaker.pdf
https://www.salon.com/2010/04/28/interview_whitaker_anatomy_
of_an_epidemic/

https://www.nybooks.com/articles/2011/06/23/epidemic-
mental-illness-why/
https://www.nybooks.com/articles/2011/07/14/illusions-of-psychiatry/

https://en.wikipedia.org/wiki/Chlorpromazine
https://en.wikipedia.org/wiki/Henri_Laborit
https://en.wikipedia.org/wiki/Meprobamate
https://en.wikipedia.org/wiki/Librium
https://en.wikipedia.org/wiki/Iproniazid
https://en.wikipedia.org/wiki/Imipramine

The effectiveness of fluoxetine and other antidepressants in the treatment
of mild-to-moderate depression is controversial. A meta-analysis published

by Kirsch in 2008 suggests, in those with mild or moderate symptoms, the efficacy of fluoxetine and other SSRIs is clinically insignificant.
https://en.wikipedia.org/wiki/Fluoxetine

The United States Department of Justice fined GlaxoSmithKline $3 billion in 2012, including a sum for withholding data on paroxetine, unlawfully promoting it for under-18s and preparing an article, following one of its clinical trials, study 329, that misleadingly reported the drug was effective in treating adolescent depression.
https://en.wikipedia.org/wiki/Paroxetine
https://en.wikipedia.org/wiki/Sertraline

Meta-analyses of antidepressant medications have reported only modest benefits over placebo treatment, and when unpublished trial data are included, the benefit falls below accepted criteria for clinical significance.
https://www.ncbi.nlm.nih.gov/pmc/articles/PMC2253608/

"To propose that researchers can objectively identify a "chemical imbalance" at the molecular level is not compatible with the extant science. In fact, there is no scientifically established ideal "chemical balance" of serotonin, let alone an identifiable pathological imbalance." Jeffrey R. Lacasse, Jonathan Leo
https://journals.plos.org/plosmedicine/article?id=10.1371/journal.pmed.0050045
http://jeffreylacasse.com/

Antidepressants and the Chemical Imbalance Theory of Depression: A Reflection and Update on the Discourse
https://www.researchgate.net/publication/284720621_Antidepressants_and_the_Chemical_Imbalance_Theory_of_Depression_A_Reflection_and_Update_on_the_Discourse_with_Responses_from_Ronald_Pies_and_Daniel_Carlat

Serotonin and Depression: A Disconnect between the Advertisements and the Scientific Literature by Jeffrey R. Lacasse, Jonathan Leo.
https://journals.plos.org/plosmedicine/article/fileid=10.1371/journal.pmed.0020392&type=printable

288 Arne Klingenberg

https://www.ncbi.nlm.nih.gov/pubmed/16268734

*"Although it is often stated with great confidence that depressed people have a serotonin or norepinephrine deficiency, the evidence actually contradicts these claims."*
Elliot Valenstein, Professor Emeritus of Neuroscience at the University of Michigan in Blaming the Brain

*"We have hunted for big simple neurochemical explanations for psychiatric disorders and have not found them."*
Kenneth S. Kendler is an American psychiatrist best known for this pioneering research in psychiatric genetics, particularly the genetic causes of schizophrenia. Kendler is one of the highest cited psychiatry researchers. Kendler is a Banks Distinguished Professor of Psychiatry, Professor of Human Genetics, and Director of the Virginia Institute of Psychiatric and Behavioral Genetics at the Virginia Commonwealth University.
https://en.wikipedia.org/wiki/Kenneth_Kendler

Let Them Eat Prozac: The Unhealthy Relationship Between the Pharmaceutical Industry and Depression
https://www.amazon.com/Let-Them-Eat-Prozac-Pharmaceutical/dp/0814736971/beampublishing
https://davidhealy.org/

Side Effects: A Prosecutor, a Whistleblower, and a Bestselling Antidepressant on Trial
With meticulous research, Alison Bass shows us the underbelly of the pharmaceutical industry. She lays bare the unhealthy ties between the medical establishment, big pharma, and the FDA—relationships that place vulnerable children and adults at risk every day.
https://www.amazon.com/gp/product/1565125533/beampublishing

The New York Times and the ADHD epidemic:*"Drug companies were given the means, the motive, and the message to disease-monger ADHD and blow it up out of all proportion. They succeeded beyond all expectations in achieving a triumph of clever advertising over common sense."* Allen Frances MD,

Professor Emeritus of Psychiatry and former Chair at Duke University and DSM-IV.
https://www.researchgate.net/publication/270649984_The_New_York_Times_and_the_ADHD_epidemic
http://www.psychiatrictimes.com/authors/allen-frances-md
https://www.huffingtonpost.com/author/allen-frances

Australian doctors say it is time for a radical new approach to Alzheimer's disease after more than 100 drug trials and studies have failed to find a treatment that stops the devastating brain condition. Over the past 30 years, with all the drugs that have been developed globally to flush out this plaque, the failure rate has been nearly 100 per cent.
http://www.abc.net.au/news/2018-09-25/alzheimers-disease-research-questions-plaque-as-cause-of-disease/10299514

## *The Reality*

A placebo can be a sugar pill, saline infusion, fake surgery, and other methods; they work even when we know that we are taking a placebo. 'With altitude sickness, researchers have found that you can give people fake oxygen and then you will see a reduction in [the] chemicals that are behind many of the symptoms of altitude sickness.' 'if you respond to a fake painkiller there is a genuine release of endorphins in your brain.
http://www.abc.net.au/radionational/programs/allinthemind/science-of-mind-over-body-jo-marchant/7267100

The Nocebo Effect: Negative Thoughts Can Harm Your Health
In another study, patients about to undergo surgery who were "convinced" of their impending death were compared to another group of patients who were merely "unusually apprehensive" about death. While the apprehensive bunch fared pretty well, those who were convinced they were going to die usually did.
https://www.psychologytoday.com/blog/owning-pink/201308/the-nocebo-effect-negative-thoughts-can-harm-your-health

Lissa Rankin, MD explores the scientific literature, reviewing case studies of spontaneous remission, as well as placebo and nocebo effect data, to prove that our thoughts powerfully affect our physiology when we believe we can get well.
https://youtu.be/LWQfe__fNbs

Conclusions: In this controlled trial involving patients with osteoarthritis of the knee, the outcomes after arthroscopic lavage or arthroscopic débridement were no better than those after a placebo procedure.
https://www.ncbi.nlm.nih.gov/pubmed/12110735

Conclusions: In this trial involving patients without knee osteoarthritis but with symptoms of a degenerative medial meniscus tear, the outcomes after arthroscopic partial meniscectomy were no better than those after a sham surgical procedure. (Funded by the Sigrid Juselius Foundation and others; ClinicalTrials.gov number, NCT00549172.)
https://www.nejm.org/doi/full/10.1056/NEJMoa1305189

The Strange Powers of the Placebo Effect
https://youtu.be/yfRVCaA5o18

Spontaneous Remission Bibliography Project
http://noetic.org/research/projects/spontaneous-remission
Among those conditions that have proven responsive to placebo treatment are angina pectoris, cancer, rheumatoid arthritis, warts, asthma, ulcers, migraine headaches, allergies, multiple sclerosis, diabetes, and psychiatric disorders.
http://noetic.org/research/projects/spontaneous-remission/faqs

http://science.howstuffworks.com/life/inside-the-mind/human-brain/placebo-effect.htm
http://www.psychologytoday.com/blog/brain-sense/201201/the-placebo-effect-how-it-works

You Are the Placebo: Making Your Mind Matter Paperback by Dr. Joe Dispenza

http://www.amazon.com/You-Are-Placebo-Making-Matter/
dp/1401944590/beampublishing

*"When you look the papers up, you often find the drugs didn't even work better than a placebo. And no one tested how they worked in combination with the other drugs. Just taking the patient off everything can improve their health right away."*
Dr. John P. A. Ioannidis, Professor of Medicine and of Health Research and Policy at Stanford University School of Medicine, Professor of Statistics at Stanford University School of Humanities and Sciences.

Are All Placebo Effects Equal? Placebo Pills, Sham Acupuncture, Cue Conditioning and Their Association. The systematic study of placebo and ritual is still in its infancy.
"… sham injections were more powerful than placebo pills."
https://www.ncbi.nlm.nih.gov/pmc/articles/PMC3729687/

You Get What You Pay For? Costly Placebo Works Better Than Cheap One
A 10-cent pill doesn't kill pain as well as a $2.50 pill, even when they are identical placebos, according to a new provocative study.
https://www.sciencedaily.com/releases/2008/03/080304173339.htm

Placebos Do Work: Let's Consider Why
New research on the placebo effect has big implications.
https://www.psychologytoday.com/us/blog/side-effects/200906/placebos-do-work-lets-consider-why

Forty years ago, a young Seattle cardiologist named Leonard Cobb conducted a unique trial of a procedure then commonly used for angina, in which doctors made small incisions in the chest and tied knots in two arteries to try to increase blood flow to the heart. It was a popular technique – 90 percent of patients reported that it helped – but when Cobb compared it with placebo surgery in which he made incisions but did not tie off the arteries, the sham operations proved just as successful. See article for many more examples:
https://www.nytimes.com/2000/01/09/magazine/the-placebo-prescription.html

How placebos change the patient's brain. Different social stimuli, such as words and rituals of the therapeutic act, may change the chemistry and circuitry of the patient's brain.

The mechanisms that are activated by placebos are the same as those activated by drugs, which suggests a cognitive/affective interference with drug action.

https://www.ncbi.nlm.nih.gov/pubmed/20592717

Mind Over Medicine: Scientific Proof That You Can Heal Yourself
https://www.amazon.com/Mind-Over-Medicine-ScientificYourself/dp/1401939996/beampublishing
http://mindovermedicinebook.com/

https://www.popsci.com.au/science/medicine/yes-you-really-can-work-yourself-to-death,514345
https://www.theguardian.com/world/2017/oct/05/japanese-woman-dies-overwork-159-hours-overtime

Brave 15yo boy sacrifices himself while saving little cousin from bear in Russia
https://www.rt.com/russia/443222-bear-attacks-teenagers-kamchatka/

Men were trying to save boy in 'very selfless act' when they drowned at Teewah beach, near Noosa
https://www.abc.net.au/news/2020-12-06/teewah-two-men-drowned-trying-to-save-boy/12954856

### *Illusions*

https://en.wikipedia.org/wiki/Friedrich_Wilhelm_Joseph_Schelling

https://en.wikipedia.org/wiki/Samuel_Taylor_Coleridge
Samuel Taylor Coleridge (21 October 1772–25 July 1834) was an English poet, critic, and philosopher who consumed opium to address his health issues. His use of opium in his home country of England, as well as Sicily

and Malta, is extensively documented. Coleridge's opium use led to serious consequences.
https://en.wikipedia.org/wiki/Coleridge_and_opium

"Drawing on rarely consulted archives, Frederick Crews has assembled a great volume of evidence that reveals a surprising new Freud: a man who blundered tragicomically in his dealings with patients, who in fact never cured anyone, who promoted cocaine as a miracle drug capable of curing a wide range of diseases, and who advanced his career through falsifying case histories and betraying the mentors who had helped him to rise."
https://www.amazon.com/Freud-Making-Illusion-Frederick-Crews/dp/1627797173/beampublishing

Sigmund Freud apparently heartily endorsed Mantegazza's overwhelming positive observations on coca writing in his 1884 monograph "On Coca": "I have carried out experiments and studied, in myself and others, the effect of coca on the healthy human body,"; "my findings agree fundamentally with Mantegazza's description of the effect of coca leaves."
https://theskepticalcardiologist.com/2017/11/24/sigmund-freud-and-the-cocaine-cure-for-opiod-addiction/

He gave cocaine to his siblings, friends and colleagues, besides his fiancée, Martha, "to make her strong and give her cheeks some color."
https://psychcentral.com/blog/3-facts-you-might-not-know-about-freud-and-his-biggest-addiction/

https://thechart.blogs.cnn.com/2011/07/22/sigmund-freuds-cocaine-problem/
https://medium.com/history-of-yesterday/sigmund-freuds-scientific-cocaine-addiction-bd5cf9dec35c
https://www.nytimes.com/2011/07/24/books/review/an-anatomy-of-addiction-by-howard-markel-book-review.html

The Freudian Fallacy, first published in the United Kingdom as Freud and Cocaine, is a 1983 book about Sigmund Freud, the founder of psychoanalysis,

by the medical historian Elizabeth M. Thornton, in which the author argues that Freud became a cocaine addict and that his theories resulted from his use of cocaine.
https://en.wikipedia.org/wiki/The_Freudian_Fallacy

https://psychcentral.com/blog/3-facts-you-might-not-know-about-freud-and-his-biggest-addiction/

Critics have doubted the existence of the unconscious:
Thomas Baldwin (1995). Ted Honderich (ed.). The Oxford Companion to Philosophy. Oxford: Oxford University Press. p. 792. ISBN 978-0-19-866132-0.
https://archive.org/details/oxfordcompaniont00hond/page/792

"The Problem of Logic", Chapter 3 of Shrinking History: On Freud and the Failure of Psychohistory, published by Oxford University Press, 1980

"Exploring the Unconscious: Self-Analysis and Oedipus", Chapter 11 of Why Freud Was Wrong: Sin, Science and Psychoanalysis, published by The Orwell Press, 2005
https://en.wikipedia.org/wiki/Why_Freud_Was_Wrong

https://en.wikipedia.org/wiki/Unconscious_mind

https://www.psychologytoday.com/us/blog/supersurvivors/201707/does-the-unconscious-really-exist

Mandatory unconscious bias training has been ditched by UK government as experts say it makes people MORE prejudiced
https://www.rt.com/op-ed/509781-unconscious-bias-training-uk-government/
https://questions-statements.parliament.uk/written-statements/detail/2020-12-15/hcws652
https://www.telegraph.co.uk/politics/2020/12/14/exclusive-unconscious-bias-training-scrapped-review-finds-has/

Free Will is NOT An Illusion by W. R. Klemm, DVM, PhD, Professor of Neuroscience and Professor of Veterinary Integrative Biosciences at Texas A&M University.
http://brainblogger.com/2010/10/25/free-will-is-not-an-illusion/

Free will debates: Simple experiments are not so simple. William Klemm, Ph.D., is a senior professor of Neuroscience at Texas A&M University. The notion that free will is an illusion has achieved such wide acceptance among philosophers and neuroscientists that it seems to be acquiring the status of dogma. This review presents 12 categories of questionable conclusions that some scholars use to promote the idea that free will is an illusion.
https://www.ncbi.nlm.nih.gov/pmc/articles/PMC2942748/
https://www.ncbi.nlm.nih.gov/pmc/articles/PMC2942748/pdf/acp-06-047.pdf
https://www.researchgate.net/publication/46393932_Free_will_debates_Simple_experiments_are_not_so_simple

But free will provides another opportunity for programming in that some brain processing can consciously select and modify reactions to experience.
https://www.psychologytoday.com/us/blog/memory-medic/201606/free-will-is-not-illusion
https://www.psychologytoday.com/us/experts/william-r-klemm-phd
https://www.quora.com/What-is-difference-between-the-mind-and-the-brain-How-are-the-conscious-and-subconscious-minds-related-to-different-sections-of-the-brain/answer/W-R-Klemm?srid=GKVV

## *Feelings*

Takotsubo cardiomyopathy, also known as stress cardiomyopathy, is a type of non-ischemic cardiomyopathy in which there is a sudden temporary weakening of the muscular portion of the heart. This weakening may be triggered by emotional stress, such as the death of a loved one, a break-up, rejection from a partner or constant anxiety. Stress cardiomyopathy is now a well-recognized cause of acute heart failure, lethal ventricular arrhythmias, and ventricular rupture.
https://en.wikipedia.org/wiki/Takotsubo_cardiomyopathy

## *Memories*

On the "barcode" functionality of the DNA, or The phenomenon of Life in the physical Universe
https://arxiv.org/abs/physics/0111093
A Note on Science and NDE, By Simon Berkovich, Professor of Engineering and Applied Science at the George Washington University.
A scientific model why memory aka consciousness cannot reside solely in the brain
https://www.nderf.org/NDERF/Research/Berkovich.htm

Independent calculation show the brain could not store life's memories
https://www.nderf.org/NDERF/Research/Lancet%20von%20Lommel%20Review.htm

Terminal Lucidity in Patients With Chronic Schizophrenia and Dementia: A Survey of the Literature: Nahm, Michael PhD; Greyson, Bruce MD
http://journals.lww.com/jonmd/Abstract/2009/12000/Terminal_Lucidity_in_Patients_With_Chronic.12.aspx

The term was coined only five years ago by German biologist Michael Nahm. His 2009 article in The Journal of Near-Death Studies was the first modern review article on the curious subject of cognitively impaired people becoming clearheaded as their death approaches. According to him, cases of "terminal lucidity" had been recorded for millennia, from accounts by classical scholars such as Hippocrates, Cicero and Plutarch
https://blogs.scientificamerican.com/bering-in-mind/one-last-goodbye-the-strange-case-of-terminal-lucidity/

http://allnurses.com/hospice-nursing/sudden-improvement-before-73617.html

Terminal lucidity refers to an unexpected return of mental clarity and memory that occurs in the time shortly before death in patients suffering from severe psychiatric and neurologic disorder. This phenomenon has been noted in patients with schizophrenia, tumors, strokes, meningitis,

and Alzheimer's disease. It may be present even in cases of patients with previous mental disability. There are two subtypes: one that comes gradually (a week before death), and another that comes rapidly (hours before death). The former occurs in the majority of cases.
https://en.wikipedia.org/wiki/Terminal_lucidity

Dr. Batthyany uses Edward's example of Mrs. D to ask a different question in the light of the evidence from Terminal Lucidity: What if, "much like the moon eclipses the sun, the brain eclipses the self?" Is it possible that the severely damaged brain of an Alzheimer's patient constrains the consciousness; perverts and distorts the personality but does not inherently damage the mind behind it?

Dr. W. [Wittneben] stated over and over again: *"From a medical perspective, I am confronted with a mystery. Käthe has suffered so many severe infections of meningitis, that due to the anatomical changes in the cortical brain tissue, it is not comprehensible how the dying woman could suddenly sing so clearly and intelligibly."* (Stritter, 1930, pp. 176ff)
https://thesearchforlifeafterdeath.com/2017/10/22/terminal-lucidity-reveals-mysteries-about-consciousness/

The (re-)emergence of normal or unusually enhanced mental abilities in dull, unconscious, or mentally ill patients shortly before death, including considerable elevation of mood and spiritual affectation, or the ability to speak in a previously unusual spiritualized and elated manner. [Note: ignore the safety warning of your browser]
http://www.spiritualscientific.com/yahoo_site_admin/assets/docs/Lucidity_at_Death_Nahm_M.9131800.pdf

## *Living Magic*

https://www.merriam-webster.com/dictionary/life
https://en.wikipedia.org/wiki/Life
Abiogenesis, or informally the origin of life, is the natural process by which life arises from non-living matter, such as simple organic compounds.

While the details of this process are still unknown, the prevailing scientific hypothesis is that the transition from non-living to living entities was not a single event, but an evolutionary process of increasing complexity. https://en.wikipedia.org/wiki/Abiogenesis

"We are skeptical of claims for the ability of random mutation and natural selection to account for the complexity of life. Careful examination of the evidence for Darwinian theory should be encouraged."
https://dissentfromdarwin.org/scientists/
https://dissentfromdarwin.org/scientists/page/2/
https://www.discovery.org/m/2019/10/Scientific-Dissent-from-Darwinism-List-09302019.pdf

*"We are still in the dark about the origin of most major groups of organisms. They appear in the fossil record as Athena did from the head of Zeus — full-blown and raring to go, in contradiction to Darwin's depiction of evolution as resulting from the gradual accumulation of countless infinitesimally minute variations."*
Jeffrey Schwartz (anthropologist and professor at the University of Pittsburgh, and a fellow and President of the World Academy of Art and Science (WAAS) from 2008-2012.
Jeffrey Schwartz, Sudden Origins: Fossils, Genes, and the Emergence of Species, p. 3 (Wiley, 1999), ISBN 0-471-32985-1
https://en.wikipedia.org/wiki/Jeffrey_H._Schwartz

"Many species remain virtually unchanged for millions of years, then suddenly disappear to be replaced by a quite different, but related, form. Moreover, most major groups of animals appear abruptly in the fossil record, fully formed, and with no fossils yet discovered that form a transition from their parent group." C.P. Hickman, L.S. Roberts, and F.M. Hickman, Integrated Principles of Zoology, p. 866 (1988, 8th ed.)

*"New species usually appear in the fossil record suddenly, not connected with their ancestors by a series of intermediates."* Ernst Mayr (one of the 20th century's leading evolutionary biologists)
https://www.famousscientists.org/ernst-mayr/

https://en.wikipedia.org/wiki/Ernst_Mayr
Ernst Mayr, What Evolution Is, p. 189 (Basic Books, 2001)

See the following link for many more statements by luminaries of science:
https://dissentfromdarwin.org/resources-for-students/why-is-darwinian-evolution-controversial/

Loss of GULO activity in the primate order occurred about 63 million years ago, at about the time it split into the suborders Haplorhini (which lost the enzyme activity) and Strepsirrhini (which retained it). The haplorhines primates, which cannot make vitamin C enzymatically, include the tarsiers and the simians (apes, monkeys and humans). The strepsirrhines primates, which can still make vitamin C enzymatically, include lorises, galagos, pottos, and, to some extent, lemurs.
https://en.wikipedia.org/wiki/L-gulonolactone_oxidase
https://biology.stackexchange.com/questions/401/why-do-humans-not-produce-vitamin-c-like-other-mammals

In Why Animals Don't Get Heart Attacks, But People Do, Matthias Rath, M.D., an internationally respected cardiovascular researcher, asserts that high cholesterol is not the actual cause of heart disease. Bears, for example, have average cholesterol levels of 400 milligrams per deciliter of blood, but they don't suffer heart attacks because bears produce large amounts of vitamin C, which optimizes collagen production and ensures maximum stability of their artery walls.
https://www.amazon.com/Animals-Attacks-People-Fourth-Revised/dp/0967954681

Humans have the genes to regrow their own eyes – they just got switched off through evolution. According to Johns Hopkins University neuroscientist Seth Blackshaw, this ability is actually the default setting for many animals, including humans – we just lost it at several points on our evolutionary tree.
https://www.rt.com/news/502954-mammals-genes-regrow-eyes/
https://blackshawlab.com/
Gene regulatory networks controlling vertebrate retinal regeneration
https://science.sciencemag.org/content/early/2020/09/30/science.abb8598.full

The Mutant Says in His Heart, "There Is No God": the Rejection of Collective Religiosity Centred Around the Worship of Moral Gods Is Associated with High Mutational Load
https://doi.org/10.1007/s40806-017-0133-5

https://www.telegraph.co.uk/news/2017/12/21/atheists-likely-left-handed-study-finds/
https://edwarddutton.wordpress.com/academic-articles/
https://oulu.academia.edu/EdwardDutton

https://www.researchgate.net/profile/Guy_Madison
https://www.researchgate.net/profile/Curtis_Dunkel

Edward Peltzer Ph.D. Oceanography, University of California, San Diego (Scripps Institute), Associate Editor, Marine Chemistry
https://dissentfromdarwin.org/2008/09/02/edward_peltzer_university_of_c/

Why Is Darwinian Evolution Controversial?
https://dissentfromdarwin.org/resources-for-students/why-is-darwinian-evolution-controversial/

https://dissentfromdarwin.org/2008/08/11/chris_williams_phd_biochemistr/

https://dissentfromdarwin.org/2019/02/01/dr-marcos-eberlin-member-of-the-brazilian-academy-of-sciences-found-of-the-thomson-mass-spectrometry-laboratory/
Prof. Dr. Marcos Eberlin (member of the Brazilian Academy of Sciences, founder of the Thomson Mass Spectrometry Laboratory, author of Foresight: How the Chemistry of Life Reveals Planning and Purpose, endorsed by three Nobel Prize-winning scientists: Sir John B. Gurdon (Physiology or Medicine, 2012), Gerhard Ertl (Chemistry, 2007), and Brian D. Josephson (Physics, 1973).
https://www.amazon.com/Foresight-Chemistry-Reveals-Planning-Purpose/dp/1936599651/

Darwinian evolution struggles to explain the origin of this type of integrated complexity. Biochemist Franklin Harold admits in a book published by Oxford University Press: *"There are presently no detailed Darwinian accounts of the evolution of any biochemical or cellular system, only a variety of wishful speculations."*
Franklin M. Harold, The Way of the Cell: Molecules, Organisms and the Order of Life, p. 205 (Oxford University Press, 2001).

*"Scientific journals now document many scientific problems and criticisms of evolutionary theory and students need to know about these as well. ... Many of the scientific criticisms of which I speak are well known by scientists in various disciplines, including the disciplines of chemistry and biochemistry, in which I have done my work."*
Philip S. Skell, Member National Academy of Sciences, Emeritus Evan Pugh Professor at Pennsylvania State University.

*"Life cannot have had a random beginning ... The trouble is that there are about two thousand enzymes, and the chance of obtaining them all in a random trial is only one part in 1040,000, an outrageously small probability that could not be faced even if the whole universe consisted of organic soup."* Fred Hoyle and N. Chandra Wickramasinghe, Evolution from Space (London: J.M. Dent & Sons, 1981)

Published in his 1982/1984 books Evolution from Space (co-authored with Chandra Wickramasinghe), Hoyle calculated that the chance of obtaining the required set of enzymes for even the simplest living cell without panspermia was one in 10 to the power of 40,000. Since the number of atoms in the known universe is infinitesimally tiny by comparison (10 to the power of 80), he argued that Earth as life's place of origin could be ruled out. https://en.wikipedia.org/wiki/Fred_Hoyle

*"The chance that higher life forms might have emerged in this way is comparable with the chance that a tornado sweeping through a junk-yard might assemble a Boeing 747 from the materials therein."* Fred Hoyle on evolution, Nature, Vol. 294, No. 5837 (November 12, 1981), p. 105

*"The likelihood of the formation of life from inanimate matter is 1 to a number with 40,000 noughts after it (1040,000).... It is big enough to bury Darwin and the whole theory of evolution. There was no primeval soup, neither on this planet nor any other, and if the beginnings of life were not random, they must therefore have been the product of purposeful intelligence."* Fred Hoyle
http://www.azquotes.com/author/6972-Fred_Hoyle

*"Once we see, however, that the probability of life originating at random is so utterly minuscule as to make it absurd, it becomes sensible to think that the favorable properties of physics on which life depends are in every respect deliberate ... It is therefore almost inevitable that our own measure of intelligence must reflect ... higher intelligences ... even to the limit of God ... such a theory is so obvious that one wonders why it is not widely accepted as being self-evident. The reasons are psychological rather than scientific."*
Fred Hoyle, Evolution from Space
https://www.famousscientists.org/fred-hoyle/
https://en.wikiquote.org/wiki/Fred_Hoyle

Scientists estimate there are 10 to the power of 80 atoms in the universe.
https://www.thoughtco.com/number-of-atoms-in-the-universe-603795

The second law of thermodynamics
https://en.wikipedia.org/wiki/Second_law_of_thermodynamics

Directed Panspermia F.H.C.Crick, L.E.Orgel
Icarus Volume 19, Issue 3, July 1973, Pages 341-346
It now seems unlikely that extraterrestrial living organisms could have reached the earth either as spores driven by the radiation pressure from another star or as living organisms imbedded in a meteorite. As an alternative to these nineteenth-century mechanisms, we have considered Directed Panspermia, the theory that organisms were deliberately transmitted to the earth by intelligent beings on another planet.
http://www.sciencedirect.com/science/article/pii/0019103573901103
https://www.nobelprize.org/prizes/medicine/1962/crick/biographical/
https://www.the-scientist.com/daily-news/leslie-orgel-dies-45922

Cause of Cambrian Explosion - Terrestrial or Cosmic?
Progress in Biophysics and Molecular Biology Volume 136, August 2018, Pages 3-23
https://doi.org/10.1016/j.pbiomolbio.2018.03.004
https://www.sciencedirect.com/science/article/pii/S0079610718300798

A brief history of panspermia
The ancient history of a surprisingly resilient idea.
https://cosmosmagazine.com/biology/over-our-heads-a-brief-history-of-panspermia/

A group of international scientists has found evidence of rivers that existed on the surface of Mars some 3.7 billion years ago, a study published on Tuesday in the journal Nature Communications has revealed.
https://sputniknews.com/science/202005061079222455-scientists-discover-evidence-of-ancient-martian-rivers-by-reading-the-rocks/
https://edition.cnn.com/2020/05/05/world/mars-river-evidence-scn-trnd/index.html
Sustained fluvial deposition recorded in Mars' Noachian stratigraphic record
Published: 05 May 2020
https://www.nature.com/articles/s41467-020-15622-0#Abs1

ESA's Mars Express spacecraft has discovered several ponds of liquid water buried under the ice in the south polar region of Mars.
https://www.youtube.com/watch?v=Am0yFQJIGOs

NASA spacecraft orbiting Mars have returned clues for understanding seasonal features that are the strongest indication of possible liquid water that may exist today on the Red Planet.
https://www.jpl.nasa.gov/news/news.php?release=2014-042

23 Places We've Found Water in Our Solar System
Oceans, Ices, Vapors: Turns out the Solar System isn't so parched. We survey the moons and planets where scientists are finding water in all its forms.
https://www.popularmechanics.com/space/a14555/water-worlds-in-our-solar-system/

Scientists from the Earth-Life Science Institute (ELSI) at Tokyo Institute of Technology and the Institute of Space and Astronautical Science at Japan Aerospace Exploration Agency (JAXA) have discovered 4-billion-year-old organic molecules containing nitrogen in a Martian meteorite.
https://nypost.com/2020/05/05/meteorite-discovery-suggests-mars-might-have-once-been-blue/
https://www.nature.com/articles/s41467-020-15931-4

Russian Scientists Prove Life Can Survive on Mars, Venus, Jupiter's Ice Moon Researchers from the Russian Academy of Sciences' Space Research Institute findings were revealed in its latest annual report on its scientific and research activities.
https://sputniknews.com/science/202004261079098796-russian-scientists-prove-life-can-survive-on-mars-venus-jupiters-ice-moon/
http://www.iki.rssi.ru/sc_rep.htm

Extraterrestrial protein discovered in meteorite for the first time
https://newatlas.com/space/extraterrestrial-protein-meteorite/
http://astrobiology.com/2020/02/hemolithin-a-meteoritic-protein-containing-iron-and-lithium.html

1861 Paris Society for Chemistry: Sur les corpuscules organisés qui existent dans l'atmosphère: examen de la doctrine des générations spontanées: leçon professée à la Sociéte chimique de Paris le 19 mai 1861 by Pasteur, Louis, 1822-1895
https://archive.org/details/b30478248/mode/2up

The Earth is beaming with life and yet there is no consensus on how life arose or what life is. The origin of life is "one of the great unsolved mysteries of science" (Crick, F. Life Itself). Questions about the origin of life became more prevalent after Pasteur and others showed that life did not arise spontaneously.
https://blogs.scientificamerican.com/guest-blog/the-origins-of-directed-panspermia/

The human brain is unusually large. Brains incur high metabolic costs and accordingly a long-standing question is why the large human brain has evolved.
https://www.nature.com/articles/s41586-018-0127-x

*"The entire cell can be viewed as a factory that contains an elaborate network of interlocking assembly lines, each of which is composed of a set of large protein machines."*
Bruce Alberts, "The Cell as a Collection of Protein Machines: Preparing the Next Generation of Molecular Biologists," Cell, Vol. 92:291 (February 6, 1998).
https://brucealberts.ucsf.edu/

*"There are presently no detailed Darwinian accounts of the evolution of any biochemical or cellular system, only a variety of wishful speculations."*
Dr. Franklin Harold (biochemist, Professor Emeritus Department of Biochemistry and Molecular Biology, Colorado State University)
Franklin M. Harold, The Way of the Cell: Molecules, Organisms and the Order of Life, p. 205 (Oxford University Press, 2001).
https://www.franklinharold.com/

Kanzawa Tadashi controlling animals by the Power of Chi
https://www.youtube.com/watch?v=21Yh6C96AKo
Chi Energy master gets animals to sleep
https://www.youtube.com/watch?v=GNuPJEiEo5o
Japanese Qigong(kikou) doctor Kanzawa relaxes animals and puts them to sleep.
https://www.youtube.com/watch?v=SXsFndVCjMk
The Study of Kiryo: Awakening the Symbiotic Healing Power Paperback by Tadashi Kanzawa
https://www.amazon.com/Study-Kiryo-Awakening-Symbiotic-Healing/dp/0996192921
Healing with Kiryo: The Adventures and Teachings of Tadashi Kanzawa Paperback by Tadashi Kanzawa
https://www.amazon.com/Healing-Kiryo-Adventures-Teachings-Tadashi/dp/099619293X

Qigong Demo with Master "John Chang"
https://youtu.be/RAAB0dbc3Es

13 amazing antics of ants
https://www.mnn.com/earth-matters/animals/blogs/amazing-antics-ants
https://infogalactic.com/info/List_of_animals_by_number_of_neurons
http://www.daviddarling.info/encyclopedia/I/insect_senses.html
With their amazing necks, ants don't need 'high hopes' to do heavy lifting
https://www.sciencedaily.com/releases/2014/02/140210161230.htm
https://infogalactic.com/info/Ant

"One can only marvel at the intricacy, in a simple bacterium, of the total motor and sensory system." Robert Macnab, flagellar motor research pioneer. Bacterial Motility and Chemotaxis: The molecular Biology of a Behavioral System
https://www.tandfonline.com/Doi/abs/10.3109/10409237809177145
The Microbial Olympics
https://www.nature.com/articles/nrmicro2837
https://www.abc.net.au/news/science/2019-11-07/evolution-supported-by-bacterial-flagellar-motor/11635276

Energy Development from Elemental Transmutations in Biological Systems by Army research scientist Solomon Goldfein performed (Dec. 1977 – April 1978)
https://apps.dtic.mil/dtic/tr/fulltext/u2/a056906.pdf

https://www.thoughtco.com/mitochondria-defined-373367
https://www.britannica.com/science/mitochondrion

https://en.wikipedia.org/wiki/Value_of_life

## *The Conundrum*

Some philosophers of mind have argued that consciousness is a form of user illusion.

According to this picture, our experience of the world is not immediate, as all sensation requires processing time. It follows that our conscious experience is less a perfect reflection of what is occurring, and more a simulation produced unconsciously by the brain.
https://en.wikipedia.org/wiki/User_illusion

According to neuroscientist Anil Seth, we're all hallucinating all the time; when we agree about our hallucinations, we call it "reality."
https://www.ted.com/talks/anil_seth_how_your_brain_hallucinates_your_conscious_reality

It really is puppy love: Science finds dogs like you for you, not just your food
https://www.smh.com.au/technology/it-really-is-puppy-love-science-finds-dogs-like-you-for-you-not-just-your-food-20170912-gyfi0f.html

Jumbos mourn black rhino killed by poachers "The elephants were passing sticks to each other and Judy said you could see their tears running down their faces."
https://www.iol.co.za/news/africa/jumbos-mourn-black-rhino-killed-by-poachers-379267

Imire Rhino & Wildlife Conservancy is dedicated to protecting wildlife and strongly believe that rural communities and conservation programmes can successfully thrive side by side, working together to ensure the protection of our natural heritage.
http://www.im

Occurrence and variability of tactile interactions between wild American crows and dead conspecifics
https://royalsocietypublishing.org/doi/full/10.1098/rstb.2017.0259
https://doi.org/10.1098/rstb.2017.0259

What happens when two monkeys are paid unequally? Frans de Waal shares some surprising videos of behavioral tests, on primates and other mammals, that show how many of these moral traits all of us share.
https://www.ted.com/talks/frans_de_waal_do_animals_have_morals

https://www.youtube.com/watch?v=meiU6TxysCg

A study published on Thursday in Nature's Scientific Reports shows pet dogs may synchronise their stress levels with those of their owners.
More than just being man's best friend, it appears our pet dogs may be mirroring our mental state too, and that can be bad for their health.
https://www.abc.net.au/news/2019-06-07/your-mental-health-can-affect-your-dog/11188804
https://www.nature.com/articles/s41598-019-43851-x
The effects of fear and anxiety on health and lifespan in pet dogs
https://www.sciencedirect.com/science/article/abs/pii/S0168159110001243

Dogs are sentient animals. This means they can experience both positive and negative emotions, such as pleasure, comfort, fear, and anxiety.
https://theconversation.com/heres-what-the-science-says-about-animal-sentience-88047

http://variety.com/2018/film/news/barbra-streisand-oscars-sexism-in-hollywood-clone-dogs-1202710585/
https://www.smh.com.au/entertainment/celebrity/barbra-streisand-reveals-she-cloned-her-late-dog-20180228-p4z235.html

Perhaps the most surprising aspect of this area of study is that personality is discernible even in fish, which are often seen as being singularly lacking in emotional range.
http://journals.plos.org/plosone/article?id=10.1371/journal.pone.0062037
https://www.sciencedirect.com/science/article/pii/S0376635716303680#bib0060
https://onlinelibrary.wiley.com/doi/full/10.1002/ece3.2629

Corvids, or the crow and raven family of birds, are consciously aware of their environments and the short-term passage of time, which in turn, generates subjective experiences, the researchers found.
https://www.rt.com/news/501938-scientists-prove-crows-are-conscious/
A neural correlate of sensory consciousness in a corvid bird
https://science.sciencemag.org/content/369/6511/1626

Thus Spoke the Plant: A Remarkable Journey of Groundbreaking Scientific Discoveries and Personal Encounters with Plants
https://www.northatlanticbooks.com/shop/thus-spoke-the-plant/
https://www.researchgate.net/profile/Monica_Gagliano
https://www.monicagagliano.com/

Plant neurobiology is a newly focused field of plant biology research that aims to understand how plants process the information they obtain from their environment to develop, prosper and reproduce optimally. The behavior plants exhibit is coordinated across the whole organism by some form of integrated signaling, communication and response system. This system includes long-distance electrical signals, vesicle-mediated transport of auxin in specialized vascular tissues, and production of chemicals known to be neuronal in animals. Here we review how plant neurobiology is being directed toward discovering the mechanisms of signaling in whole plants, as well as among plants and their neighbors.
https://www.cell.com/trends/plant-science/fulltext/S1360-1385(06)00164-6

Inside the Vegetal Mind: On the Cognitive Abilities of Plants
… the idea that plants are also capable of learning by association had never been proven until recently. These recent findings that experimentally demonstrated associative learning in plants not only qualify them as proper subjects of cognitive research, but in so doing, they officially open the door for the empirical exploration of cognitive processes like learning, decision-making and awareness in plants.
https://www.researchgate.net/publication/324710399_Inside_the_Vegetal_Mind_On_the_Cognitive_Abilities_of_Plants

Study reveals plants can hear
https://www.youtube.com/watch?v=B2kDa6GnLjc

The Secret Life of Plants by Peter Tompkins and Christopher Bird explores plants' response to human care and nurturing, their ability to communicate with man, plants' surprising reaction to music, their lie-detection abilities, their creative powers, and much more.

https://www.amazon.com/Secret-Life-Plants-Fascinating-Emotional/
dp/0060915870

In 1962, Dr. T. C. Singh, head of the Botany Department at India's Annamalia
University, experimented with the effect of musical sounds on the growth
rate of plants. He found that balsam plants grew at a rate that accelerated by
20% in height and 72% in biomass when exposed to music. The size of crops
increased to between 25 to 60% above the regional average.
https://dengarden.com/gardening/the-effect-of-music-on-plant-growth
https://en.wikipedia.org/wiki/Jagadish_Chandra_Bose
After 30 days, the plant that received compliments was healthy and thriving,
while its insult-riddled counterpart was wilted and noticeably droopy.
https://globalnews.ca/news/4217594/bully-a-plant-ikea/
https://www.youtube.com/watch?v=Yx6UgfQreYY


https://www.smilinggardener.com/plants/music-and-plants/
https://www.classicfm.com/discover-music/playing-classical-music-plants/

"Quantum Shmantum" By Tim Folger
https://langanthology2017.wordpress.com/2017/04/21/quantum-
shmantum-by-tim-folger/


Quantum Shmantum: Physicist David Deutsch Shares the Best Kept Secret
in Physics, Alternate Universes. The Most Important Fish in the Sea: You've
Never Heard Of. Stardust: Who Parented Our Solar System. (Discover,
December 2001 - Volume 22, Number 9) Single Issue Magazine – January
1, 2001
https://www.amazon.com/Quantum-Shmantum-Physicist-Alternate-
Universes/dp/B003GUEHE6


"Naturally, it still makes no difference whether the observer is a man, an
animal, or a piece of apparatus." Statements of Niels Bohr after the Solvay
Conference of 1927, as quoted in Physics and Beyond (1971) by Werner
Heisenberg
https://en.wikiquote.org/wiki/Niels_Bohr

https://www.nobelprize.org/prizes/physics/1918/planck/biographical/

https://en.wikipedia.org/wiki/Uncertainty_principle
https://en.wikipedia.org/wiki/Observer_effect_%28physics%29
https://en.wikipedia.org/wiki/Quantum_entanglement

A team of physicists designed a quantum experiment that showed that facts actually change depending on your perspective on the situation. Physicists performed a sort of "coin toss" using photons in a tiny quantum computer, finding that the results were different at different detectors, depending on their perspectives.
https://www.livescience.com/most-important-surprising-quantum-physics-of-2019.html

One of the biggest problems with quantum experiments is the seemingly unavoidable tendency of humans to influence the situation and velocity of small particles. This happens just by our observing the particles, and it has quantum physicists frustrated.
http://science.howstuffworks.com/innovation/science-questions/quantum-suicide2.htm

The so-called EPR paradox supplies an even stranger example of quantum weirdness, in which two subatomic particles thousands of light-years apart can instantaneously respond to each other's motions. Scientists have observed this phenomenon, called entanglement, at the particle level, and in 2009, managed to produce the effect with linked superconductors.
http://science.howstuffworks.com/science-vs-myth/everyday-myths/quantum-weirdness.htm
http://www.wired.com/2009/09/quantum-entanglement/

Quantum Entanglement is a mysterious aspect of quantum mechanics: This phenomenon is so weird that even Einstein - who gave us black holes and warped space-time - couldn't believe it, disparagingly calling it "spooky action at a distance", because quantum entanglement allows distant particles to remain instantaneously connected.

http://www.abc.net.au/news/2016-02-08/mcfadden-it-seems-life-really-does-have-a-vital-spark/7148448

Physicists at the University of Geneva achieved the weird result by creating a pair of 'entangled' photons, separating them, then sending them down a fibre optic cable to the Swiss villages of Satigny and Jussy, some 18 kilometres apart. The researchers found that when each photon reached its destination, it could instantly sense its twin's behaviour without any direct communication. https://www.nature.com/news/2008/080813/full/news.2008.1038.html

Quantum "spooky action at a distance" travels at least 10,000 times faster than light
https://newatlas.com/quantum-entanglement-speed-10000-faster-light/26587/
Bounding the speed of 'spooky action at a distance'
http://arxiv.org/pdf/1303.0614v1.pdf

"For quantum networking, in this work, we have already achieved a two-photon entanglement distribution efficiency a trillion times more efficient than using the best telecommunication fibers," says Jian-Wei Pan, lead researcher on the project.
https://newatlas.com/quantum-entanglement-satellite-distance-record/50071/
Satellite-based entanglement distribution over 1200 kilometers
http://science.sciencemag.org/content/356/6343/1140
Jian-Wei Pan, a Chinese quantum physicist, led a team that used a satellite to send photon pairs through the near vacuum of space, successfully measuring the quantum keys at Tibetan receiving stations 1,203 kilometers apart.
https://english.cas.cn/newsroom/news/201902/t20190216_205404.shtml

In June 2017, Pan's team used their quantum satellite to demonstrate entanglement with satellite-to-ground total summed lengths between 1600km and 2400km and entanglement distribution over 1200km between receiver stations.
https://en.wikipedia.org/wiki/Pan_Jianwei

Here we demonstrate satellite-based distribution of entangled photon pairs to two locations separated by 1203 kilometers on Earth, through two satellite-to-ground downlinks with a summed length varying from 1600 to 2400 kilometers.
https://science.sciencemag.org/content/356/6343/1140

Quantum teleportation is a technique for transferring quantum information from a sender at one location to a receiver some distance away.
https://en.wikipedia.org/wiki/Quantum_teleportation

Prompt elasto-gravity signals (PEGS) and their potential use in modern seismology
Both processes induce gravity perturbations whose signals propagate with the speed of light and therefore can arrive at remote stations earlier than the fastest elastic P wave.
https://www.sciencedirect.com/science/article/abs/pii/S0012821X20300935
https://www.gfz-potsdam.de/en/home/
https://www.gfz-potsdam.de/medien-und-kommunikation/meldungen/alle-meldungen/article/wie-erdbeben-die-schwerkraft-verformen/

## Out There

Dr. Jeffrey Long - Near Death Experiences
Near Death Experience testimony from six people who tell their stories of the afterlife. Excellent short documentary.
http://youtu.be/LwyVFW9kT8k
Evidence of the Afterlife: The Science of Near-Death Experiences
http://www.amazon.com/dp/0061452572/?tag=iandsorg-20
https://www.near-death.com/science/experts/jeffrey-jody-long.html
http://www.nderf.org/

Can we survive death? What is the nature of our consciousness? *"Beyond Our Sight"* is an independant documentary by Anthony Chene that talks

about near-death experiences, human consciousness, and the possibility of communication with other dimensions. Interviews with Savonn Champelle, Lewis Brown Griggs, Karen Hanning, Alan Hugenot, Dean Radin, Terry Yoder.
https://youtu.be/xpSuO8DtiMM

Pam Reynold's Near Death Experience. This case comes the closest to hard evidence that consciousness survives physical death. During her brain operation, blood was drained from the brain and the heart stopped. She was incapable of hallucinating, yet she was out of the body and her observations come close to proving it. Debunkers have worked extra hard to try to disprove this case. But cardiologist Michael Sabom who studied this case and others says that Pam Reynolds was really out of the body and having a spiritual experience.
https://youtu.be/YO8UVebuA0g
https://vimeo.com/25629985
https://youtu.be/Bu1ErDeQ0Zw
http://www.near-death.com/science/evidence/people-have-ndes-while-brain-dead.html
https://www.near-death.com/science/evidence.html

Kim Clark Finds the Tennis Shoe and Proves Near Death Experiences Are Real
https://youtu.be/WPXK2Ls-xzQ

Reverend George Rodonaia (died October 12, 2004) underwent one of the most extended cases of a near-death experience ever recorded. Pronounced dead immediately after he was hit by a car in 1976, he was left for three days in the morgue. He did not "return to life" until a doctor began to make an incision in his abdomen as part of an autopsy procedure. Prior to his NDE he worked as a neuropathologist. He was also an avowed atheist. Yet after the experience, he devoted himself exclusively to the study of spirituality, taking a second doctorate in the psychology of religion.
http://www.near-death.com/science/evidence/some-people-were-dead-for-several-days.html
https://youtu.be/S8j2g-IsBPQ
https://youtu.be/jcEbQdy-BAM

The International Association for Near Death Studies. As an educational nonprofit organization, IANDS focuses most of its resources into providing the highest quality information available about NDE-related subjects. https://www.iands.org/

A Lawyer Presents the Evidence for the Afterlife Paperback by Victor Zammit & Wendy Zammit
https://www.amazon.com/Lawyer-Presents-Evidence-Afterlife/dp/1908733225/beampublishing

http://www.victorzammit.com/evidence/Outofbody.htm
http://www.victorzammit.com/evidence/nde.htm

Evidence of the Afterlife: The Science of Near-Death Experiences Paperback by Jeffrey Long
https://www.amazon.com/Evidence-Afterlife-Science-Near-Death-Experiences/dp/0061452572/beampublishing

Dr. Pim van Lommel of the Netherlands, world-renowned cardiologist, author, and university lecturer, has empirically investigated the near-death experiences (NDE) of his patients who survived cardiac arrest. His research suggests that our waking awareness does not always coincide with the functioning of the brain; moreover, it is possible to experience consciousness separate from the body.
https://pimvanlommel.nl/en/

Dr. Alan Ross Hugenot tells us about his near-death experience, explains the nature and capabilities of our consciousness, and why science has to change its viewpoint to really understand it.
https://youtu.be/Xug3tii0WaQ
http://www.afterlife.pro
http://afterlife.pro/video-audio/

Dr. Stanislav Grof, M.D., is a psychiatrist and one of the leading researchers into non-ordinary states of consciousness. In Tom Harpur's NDE

documentary, Life After Death, Dr. Grof explains a theory of consciousness based on these non-ordinary states. Dr. Grof theorizes consciousness to be nonlocalized and that the brain may instead function as a "reducing valve" minimizing the cosmic energy input bombarding our body. Consciousness then arises as a product of this reducing function of the brain.
http://www.near-death.com/experiences/out-of-body.html
https://www.near-death.com/experiences/triggers.html
https://www.consciouslifestylemag.com/non-local-consciousness-and-the-brain/

NDE Researcher Kenneth Ring: The Golden Rule Dramatically Illustrated
https://youtu.be/1tiKsKy7lFw
http://msv-nhne.org/jeffrey-mishlove-interviews-kenneth-ring/
Lessons from the Light: What We Can Learn from the Near-Death Experience
https://www.amazon.com/exec/obidos/ASIN/1930491115/beampublishing

After suffering from a terminal illness, in 1982 Mellen-Thomas Benedict died and for an hour and a half he was monitored showing no vital signs. Miraculously he returned to his body with a complete remission of the disease and what may be the most inspirational near-death experience story known to date.
http://www.mellen-thomas.com/
https://www.near-death.com/reincarnation/experiences/mellen-thomas-benedict.html

In this touching "Bonus interview" for the movie AWAKE IN THE DREAM, Mellen Thomas Bendict talks about his near death experience.
https://youtu.be/8VQiVQ4fa_4

Famous Cardiac Surgeon's Stories of Near Death Experiences in Surgery
Dr. Lloyd Rudy, a pioneer of cardiac surgery, tells stories of two patients who came back to life after being declared dead, and what they told him.
https://youtu.be/JL1oDuvQR08

Near Death Experience - Blind woman SEES while OUT OF BODY
https://youtu.be/5HbtoX3Q5OI

People Born Blind Can See During a Near-Death Experience
Vicki Umipeg, a forty-five year old blind woman, was just one of the more than thirty persons that Dr. Kenneth Ring and Sharon Cooper interviewed at length during a two-year study just completed concerning near-death experiences of the blind.
https://www.near-death.com/science/evidence/people-born-blind-can-see-during-nde.html

Anita Moorjani, Dying To Be Me, Interview by Renate McNay.
Anita worked in the corporate field before being diagnosed with terminal cancer. Four years after being diagnosed her body began shutting down. As her organs failed she entered into an extraordinary near-death experience where she realised the cause of her disease as well as waking up to who she truly is. On regaining consciousness she found her condition had improved so rapidly that she was released from hospital within weeks.
https://youtu.be/7jFN9XQeEn4
http://www.conscious.tv/text/27.htm

Mindsight: Near-Death and Out-of-Body Experiences in the Blind
This book investigates the astonishing claim that blind persons, including those blind from birth, can actually "see" during near-death or out-of-body episodes.
Kenneth Ring, Ph.D., is Professor Emeritus of Psychology at the University of Connecticut, and an internationally recognized authority on the subject of near-death experiences on which he has written five books and nearly a hundred articles.
https://www.amazon.com/Mindsight-Near-Death-Out-Body-Experiences/dp/0595434975

Dr Peter Fenwick, renowned neuro-psychiatrist, will discuss his research on the near-death experience.Dr Peter Fenwick is an internationally renowned neuropsychiatrist and a Fellow of the Royal College of Psychiatrists. He is Britain's leading clinical authority on near-death experiences and is president of the British branch of The International Association for Near-Death Studies.
https://youtu.be/M4PmjKn1zPE

http://whitecrowbooks.com/michaeltymn/entry/dr._peter_fenwick_
discusses_dying_death_and_survival/

NDE Stories: Every day, all over the world, an increasing number of people, from all walks of life, are reporting near-death experiences (and related phenomena). This website has been created to gather, study, and share the most compelling of these experiences.
http://ndestories.org

Transformed By The Light: The Powerful Effect Of Near-death Experiences On People's Lives. Written by bestselling authors Dr. Melvin Morse and Paul Perry, this book proves that those who return from the brink of death are profoundly changed for the better – spiritually and physically – for the rest of their lives.
https://www.amazon.com/Transformed-Light-Powerful-Near-death-Experiences/dp/0804111839/beampublishing
https://www.melvinmorsemd.com/

Some People Receive Verified Visions of the Future
https://www.near-death.com/science/evidence/some-people-receive-verified-visions-of-the-future.html

Skeptical Argument: Nothing Useful Comes From NDEs
https://www.near-death.com/science/skepticism/nothing-useful-comes-from-ndes.html

An Orthopedic Doctor's Near Death Experience - Dr Mary Neal (To Heaven and Back)
Dr. Mary Neal is a board-certified orthopaedic spine surgeon who drowned while kayaking on a South American river. She experienced life after death.
https://youtu.be/9-QjMRF1gkI

An international authority on near-death states, Dr. PMH Atwater, L.H.D. uses the culmination of her research to establish that the near-death phenomenon is not some kind of anomaly, but is rather part of the larger genre of transformations of consciousness.

http://www.pmhatwater.com/
https://youtu.be/v1mD10-CN34
https://www.near-death.com/science/evidence/people-are-dramatically-changed-by-ndes.html

This book contains over 100 reliable, often firsthand accounts of perceptions during NDEs that were later verified as accurate by independent sources. The Self Does Not Die: Verified Paranormal Phenomena from Near-Death Experiences
https://www.amazon.com/Self-Does-Not-Die-Experiences/dp/0997560800/beampublishing

Oprah Winfrey Interviews Betty Eadie
https://youtu.be/6uUiYFaawTU
https://www.embracedbythelight.com
https://www.youtube.com/playlist?list=PLB40021A30564950E&feature=plcp

Nurse Shares 30 Years Of Spiritual Experiences With Death & Dying
https://youtu.be/kl5cu1H4Hss
http://the-formula.org/resources/what-near-death-experiences-teach-us/
http://the-formula.org/ndes-hell/

Nancy Rynes NDE Atheist goes to Heaven
https://youtu.be/3VM9wcYvnCc
http://ndevideos.com/

Dr. Dianne Morrissey's Near-Death Experience
*"If I lived a billion years more, in my body or yours, there's not a single experience on Earth that could ever be as good as being dead. Nothing."* Dr. Dianne Morrissey
https://www.near-death.com/experiences/notable/dianne-morrissey.html
https://www.near-death.com/experiences/exceptional/dianne-morrissey.html

International Academy of Consciousness trainer Luis Minero talks to the South Bay Chapter of IANDS about the out-of-body experience and the near-death experience.

https://youtu.be/Ey8b9YnEzqk
Luis Minero (part two) OBEs and NDEs
https://youtu.be/ZgVlDh8q53k
Luis Minero (part three) OBEs and NDEs
https://youtu.be/zDWFVM5hRZ4

Demystifying the Out-of-Body Experience: A Practical Manual for Exploration and Personal Evolution by Luis Minero
http://www.amazon.com/Demystifying-Out-Body-Experience-Exploration/dp/0738730793/beampublishing

https://www.mayoclinic.org/tests-procedures/awake-brain-surgery/about/pac-20384913

Generally speaking, injuries begin at the one-minute mark, steadily worsening thereafter:
At three minutes, neurons suffer more extensive damage, and lasting brain damage becomes more likely. At five minutes, death becomes imminent.
https://www.spinalcord.com/blog/what-happens-after-a-lack-of-oxygen-to-the-brain

*"According to the current neuroscientific view, consciousness fails to survive brain death and, along with all other mental functions, is irrecoverably lost."* (https://en.wikipedia.org/wiki/Consciousness_after_death)

https://ndestories.org/category/miracle_healings/
Miraculous recovery for 13-year-old declared brain dead
https://www.youtube.com/watch?v=xnLMtouX2Fs

### Homo Digitalis

The average human life span is around 72 years, and billionaires are investing heavily in a handful of life science startups that hope to help people live longer.

https://www.forbes.com/sites/samshead/2019/08/19/billionaire-backs-uk-startup-trying-to-extend-human-lifespans/#70a3fdd05f03

Your body contains thousands of genes, but 90 per cent of biomedical research focuses on just 10 per cent of them. The study, published in PLOS Biology, created a large database that cross-referenced data on all human protein-coding genes — including chemical, physical, historical and experimental data.
http://www.abc.net.au/news/health/2018-09-30/disease-biomedical-research-why-study-the-same-genes-over-again/10287202

Large-scale investigation of the reasons why potentially important genes are ignored.
We find that biomedical research is primarily guided by a handful of generic chemical and biological characteristics of genes, which facilitated experimentation during the 1980s and 1990s, rather than the physiological importance of individual genes or their relevance to human disease.
http://journals.plos.org/plosbiology/article?id=10.1371/journal.pbio.2006643

And in a recent study on VEGF, a genetically engineered heart drug announced with much fanfare by its manufacturer, Genentech, the placebo actually performed better.
https://www.nytimes.com/2000/01/09/magazine/the-placebo-prescription.html

https://en.wikipedia.org/wiki/Publish_or_perish

A team of scientists from London's Francis Crick Institute attempted to genetically modify human embryos. They were deeply troubled by the results. After just fourteen days of embryonic development, half of the edited human embryos contained serious unintended genetic changes. When compared to embryos that had not undergone genetic modification, these edited embryos showed troubling signs of genetic damage and potential for birth defects and cancer later in life. "There's no sugarcoating this," says Fyodor Urnov, a gene-editing expert and professor of molecular and cellular

biology at the University of California, Berkeley. "This is a restraining order for all genome editors to stay the living daylights away from embryo editing." https://transhumanism.news/2020-06-19-london-scientists-genetically-alter-human-embryos-with-disastrous-results.html
https://onezero.medium.com/scientists-edited-human-embryos-in-the-lab-and-it-was-a-disaster-9473918d769d
Frequent loss-of-heterozygosity in CRISPR-Cas9-edited early human embryos
https://www.biorxiv.org/content/10.1101/2020.06.05.135913v1

The standard gene-editing tool, CRISPR-Cas9, frequently produces a type of DNA mutation that ordinary genetic analysis misses, claims new research published in the journal Science Advances. In describing these findings the researchers called such oversights "serious pitfalls" of gene editing (Skryabin et al., 2020). In all, the new results suggest that gene-editing is more error-prone than thought and, further, that identifying and discarding defective and unwanted outcomes is not as easy as generally supposed.
https://www.independentsciencenews.org/news/researchers-are-substantially-undercounting-editing-errors/
https://advances.sciencemag.org/content/6/7/eaax2941

https://www.nationalgeographic.com/news/2015/12/151203-gene-editing-terrific-terrifying-science/

CRISPR/Cas9-mediated gene editing in human tripronuclear zygotes
https://link.springer.com/article/10.1007/s13238-015-0153-5

Two studies published in mid-2018 found that cells edited by Crispr have the potential to seed tumors, raising the risk that they'd trigger cancer...
https://www.nature.com/articles/s41591-018-0049-z

Off-target Effects in CRISPR/Cas9-mediated Genome Engineering
https://www.sciencedirect.com/science/article/pii/S216225311630049X

We estimate a 21% increase in the all-cause mortality rate in individuals
https://www.nature.com/articles/s41591-019-0459-6

"What we found is that they had significantly increased mortality," lead researcher Rasmus Nielsen told NPR, breaking the unfortunate news that the twin girls are now 21 percent less likely to live until the age of 76 as a result of the CRISPR editing they were subjected to.
https://www.npr.org/sections/health-shots/2019/06/03/727957768/2-chinese-babies-with-edited-genes-may-face-higher-risk-of-premature-death

https://en.wikipedia.org/wiki/Gene_therapy#Adverse_effects,_contraindications_and_hurdles_for_use

Potential DNA Damage from CRISPR "Seriously Underestimated," Study Finds
https://www.scientificamerican.com/article/potential-dna-damage-from-crispr-seriously-underestimated-study-finds/

Our prescription drugs are the third leading cause of death after heart disease and cancer in the United States and Europe.
https://pubmed.ncbi.nlm.nih.gov/25355584/

The FDA has warned old people to stop infusing plasma from young people in order to slow down the aging process, saying it has "no proven clinical benefit" according to Bloomberg.
"There is no proven clinical benefit of infusion of plasma from young donors to cure, mitigate, treat or prevent these conditions, and there are risks associated with the use of any plasma product," reads a statement from FDA Commissioner Scott Gottlieb and Peter Marks, who leads the agency's biologics center.
https://www.bloomberg.com/news/articles/2019-02-19/beware-of-buying-young-people-s-blood-to-prevent-aging-fda-says
Hundreds of scientific research papers published by Australian scientists have been found to be unreliable or compromised... senior scientists claim it is just the tip of the iceberg. "The public should be aware the bulk of medical research in Australia is paid for by the taxpayer."
https://www.smh.com.au/national/bad-science-australian-studies-found-to-be-unreliable-compromised-20190719-p528ql.html

**2007**

We analysed 1016 completed systematic reviews. Of these, 44% concluded that the interventions studied were likely to be beneficial, of which 1% recommended no further research and 43% recommended additional research. Also, 7% of the reviews concluded that the interventions were likely to be harmful, of which 2% did not recommend further studies and 5% recommended additional studies. In total, 49% of the reviews reported that the evidence did not support either benefit or harm, of which 1% did not recommend further studies and 48% recommended additional studies. Overall, 96% of the reviews recommended further research.
https://pubmed.ncbi.nlm.nih.gov/17683315/

**2016**

High quality of the evidence for medical and other health-related interventions was uncommon in Cochrane systematic reviews
Overall, 1,394 SRs were identified. Of these, 608 (43.6%) incorporated GRADE. Within these reviews, only 13.5% (n = 82) reported a high quality and 30.8% (n = 187) a moderate quality of evidence for the first listed primary outcome, whereas 31.7% (n = 193) had low level and 24% (n = 146) had very low level of evidence.
https://pubmed.ncbi.nlm.nih.gov/27032875/

**2020**

Only one in ten medical treatments are backed by high-quality evidence
https://theconversation.com/only-one-in-ten-medical-treatments-are-backed-by-high-quality-evidence-145224
https://www.jclinepi.com/article/S0895-4356(20)30777-0/fulltext
The quality of evidence for medical interventions does not improve or worsen: a metaepidemiological study of Cochrane reviews
https://www.sciencedirect.com/science/article/abs/pii/S0895435620307770

*"Anesthetics have been used for 160 years, and how they work is one of the great mysteries of neuroscience."* Dr. James Sonner (Professor Emeritus, Anesthesia, University of California San Francisco)
Anaesthesia research "has been for a long time a science of untestable hypotheses," notes Neil L. Harrison (Professor of Anesthesiology, Professor of Pharmacology, Columbia University Medical Center)
https://en.wikipedia.org/wiki/Inhalational_anesthetic

https://anesthesia.ucsf.edu/people/jim-sonner
https://www.cumc.columbia.edu/mdphd/profile/nlharrison

... the regaining of consciousness is not understood either...
https://en.wikipedia.org/wiki/Inhalational_anesthetic
The biochemical mechanism of action of general anaesthetics is not well understood...
https://en.wikipedia.org/wiki/General_Anaesthesia

https://articles.mercola.com/sites/articles/archive/2020/09/13/peter-breggin-toxic-psychiatry.aspx
https://breggin.com/books/
https://www.youtube.com/user/PeterBreggin/
https://breggin.com/medication-madness/
https://www.mercola.com/forms/background.htm
https://articles.mercola.com/sites/articles/archive/2019/10/05/side-effects-of-antidepressants.aspx

Dr. Jeff Lichtman is a neuroscientist and Professor of Molecular and Cellular Biology at Harvard University who currently works with a team of experts to create a complete map of the brain's neural connections. He likens what we need to know about the brain as having to walk one mile, and what we actually do know as "about three inches."
Dr. Jeff Lichtman in: Beautiful 3-D Brain Scans Show Every Synapse by National Geographic
https://youtu.be/nvXuq9jRWKE

"First of all, you'd have to understand how the brain is doing it," says Chomsky. "That's preliminary. How is the brain constructing thoughts? We have barely any understanding of that." "You would have to have some kind of technology, which doesn't at all exist, to tap what the brain is doing when it's constructing thoughts," says Chomsky. "We're nowhere near even imagining what kind of technology that would be, even for much simpler things like how do you remember what you saw five minutes ago."
https://www.inverse.com/article/32395-elon-musk-neuralink-noam-chomsky

326 Arne Klingenberg

https://www.inverse.com/article/32422-facebook-elon-musk-neuralink-noam-chomsky
https://www.inverse.com/article/32369-facebook-mind-reading-noam-chomsky
https://www.inverse.com/science/blindsight
Noam Chomsky is an American linguist, philosopher, cognitive scientist, historian, social critic, and political activist.
https://en.wikipedia.org/wiki/Noam_Chomsky

Musk's Neuralink brain chip project is a fairy tale – Dr. Henry Marsh, one of Britain's top neurosurgeons
https://www.rt.com/shows/sophieco-visionaries/470673-musk-neuralink-brain-chip-project/
https://youtu.be/XymphPVP6y4

Elon Musk's Neuralink is neuroscience theater
To neuroscientists, it was nothing new; in their labs the buzz and crackle of electrical impulses recorded from animal brains (and some human ones) has been heard for decades.
https://www.technologyreview.com/2020/08/30/1007786/elon-musks-neuralink-demo-update-neuroscience-theater/

With Neuralink, Elon Musk Promises Human-to-Human Telepathy. Don't Believe It.
https://www.technologyreview.com/2017/04/22/242999/with-neuralink-elon-musk-promises-human-to-human-telepathy-dont-believe-it/

Levandowski started a new religion in Sept. 2015 called "Way to the Future," according to the report. Its mission is to "develop and promote the realization of a Godhead based on Artificial Intelligence."
https://www.businessinsider.com.au/anthony-levandowski-religion-worships-ai-god-report-2017-9
https://www.wired.com/story/anthony-levandowski-artificial-intelligence-religion/

Kurzweil does not believe in half measures. He takes 180 to 210 vitamin and mineral supplements a day, so many that he doesn't have time to organize them all himself. Kurzweil also spends one day a week at a medical clinic, receiving intravenous longevity treatments.
http://www.wired.com/2008/03/ff-kurzweil/

Robert Epstein is a senior research psychologist at the American Institute for Behavioral Research and Technology in California. A PhD of Harvard University, he is the author of 15 books and more than 250 scientific and mainstream articles, as well as the former editor-in-chief of Psychology Today.
https://aeon.co/essays/your-brain-does-not-process-information-and-it-is-not-a-computer

So a typical adult human brain runs on around 12 watts—a fifth of the power required by a standard 60 watt lightbulb.
https://www.scientificamerican.com/article/thinking-hard-calories/
Your three-pound brain runs on just 20 watts of power—barely enough to light a dim bulb.
https://www.gizmocrazed.com/2018/02/to-advance-artificial-intelligence-reverse-engineer-the-brain/

Traditional machine learning systems are not typically able to answer "what if" questions, DeepMind researcher Danilo Rezende explained.
http://www.abc.net.au/news/science/2018-06-15/googles-deepmind-algorithm-can-teach-itself-to-see/9861590
http://science.sciencemag.org/cgi/doi/10.1126/science.aar6170

Electromagnetic energy in the brain enables brain matter to create our consciousness and our ability to be aware and think, according to a new theory developed by Professor Johnjoe McFadden from the University of Surrey.
https://academic.oup.com/nc/article/2020/1/niaa016/5909853
https://neurosciencenews.com/electromagnetic-consciousness-17191/

Brain implants, AI, and a speech synthesizer have turned brain activity into robot words

At the moment the technology can only reproduce words that these five patients have heard—and it wouldn't work on anyone else. But there is the hope that technology like this could one day let people who have been paralyzed communicate with their family and friends, despite losing the ability to speak.
https://www.technologyreview.com/f/612843/brain-implants-ai-and-a-speech-synthesizer-have-turned-brain-activity-into-robot/
https://www.nature.com/articles/s41598-018-37359-z#Sec10
http://naplab.ee.columbia.edu/reconstruction.html

https://news.mit.edu/2018/computer-system-transcribes-words-users-speak-silently-0404
https://www.ted.com/talks/arnav_kapur_a_breakthrough_device_that_combines_mind_and_machine

## Who We Really Are

...subjects who show the highest values with respect to black humour preference and comprehension show the highest values with respect to intelligence, have higher education levels and show the lowest values regarding mood disturbance and aggression.
https://link.springer.com/article/10.1007/s10339-016-0789-y

Nick Bostrom's simulation hypothesis:
"The fraction of human-level civilizations that reach a posthuman stage (that is, one capable of running high-fidelity ancestor simulations) is very close to zero", or
"The fraction of posthuman civilizations that are interested in running simulations of their evolutionary history, or variations thereof, is very close to zero", or
"The fraction of all people with our kind of experiences that are living in a simulation is very close to one."
https://en.wikipedia.org/wiki/Simulation_hypothesis

https://en.wikipedia.org/wiki/Maya_(religion)

## *Beyond Machine Man*

The idea of dark matter was conjured up in the 1930s in response to astronomical observations that flew in the face of Newton's laws of gravity. Plenty of experiments have tried to detect particles of the elusive dark matter, or even create them, but so far none have been successful. Perhaps that's because it's not really there after all, and instead it might be that our models of gravity and physics need some tweaking.
https://newatlas.com/physics/modified-gravity-evidence-dark-matter/
https://iopscience.iop.org/article/10.3847/1538-4357/abbb96/meta

The standard model of our Universe may be showing some cracks. Several fundamental cosmological observations are contradicting each other. "The 'standard model of cosmology' is an admission of ignorance," admits Prof Abraham Loeb of Harvard University. "We label components whose nature we don't know as 'dark matter' and 'dark energy'. Since we don't know what they are, it's a very crude model that could easily be an oversimplification of reality."
https://www.sciencefocus.com/space/the-cracks-in-cosmology-why-our-universe-doesnt-add-up/
https://www.cfa.harvard.edu/~loeb/

Since the mid-90s, scientists have been trying to locate half of the universe's ordinary matter. They believed it was out there because of clues left over from the Big Bang, but it had never been seen. Astronomy is full of missing stuff. Most of the universe is understood to be "dark matter" and "dark energy", which nobody has ever directly seen.
https://www.abc.net.au/news/2020-05-28/astronomers-find-universe-missing-matter/12291788
More than three-quarters of the baryonic content of the Universe resides in a highly diffuse state that is difficult to detect, with only a small fraction directly observed in galaxies and galaxy clusters.
https://doi.org/10.1038/s41586-020-2300-2

This asymmetry of matter and antimatter in the visible universe is one of the great unsolved problems in physics.

https://en.wikipedia.org/wiki/Antimatter

Lost in Math: How Beauty Leads Physics Astray by Sabine Hossenfelder
A contrarian theoretical physicist argues that modern physicists' obsession
with beauty has given us wonderful math but bad science.
https://www.goodreads.com/book/show/36341728-lost-in-math

Think you have only 5 senses? You've actually got about 14 to 20.
https://bigthink.com/philip-perry/think-you-have-only-5-senses-its-
actually-a-lot-more-than-that
https://www.meditation24-7.com/page18/page18.html
https://www.wisegeek.com/how-many-human-senses-are-there.htm

Well, Michelson–Morley were not able to detect any difference! The
experiment has been repeated many times since 1887. Two possible
explanations were offered to account for the results:
(a) There is no aether. Somehow, photons can propagate for billions of
years, through the vastness of the universe, without a carrier, at a velocity
independent of photon frequency, and without an iota of attenuation.
(b) There is an aether that permeates all of space, but its local component is
stationary relative to the earth.
https://siddeutschwrites.wordpress.com/einsteins-greatest-mistake/

The Astrophysical Journal (2019; Volume 884, Number 2)
Mysterious Coherence in Several-megaparsec Scales between Galaxy
Rotation and Neighbor Motion. These profiles show unexpectedly strong
evidence of the dynamical coherence between the rotation of the CALIFA
galaxies and the average line-of-sight motion of their neighbors within
several-megaparsec distances.
https://iopscience.iop.org/article/10.3847/1538-4357/ab3fa3

Einstein's Greatest Mistake: Abandonment of the Aether
https://www.amazon.com/Einsteins-Greatest-Mistake-Abandonment-
Aether/dp/0595374816/beampublishing
https://siddeutschwrites.wordpress.com/about-sid-deutsch/
https://siddeutschwrites.wordpress.com/aether-theory/

https://www.nobelprize.org/prizes/physics/1998/laughlin/biographical/
https://en.wikipedia.org/wiki/Aether_theories

https://en.wikipedia.org/wiki/Vacuum_energy
https://en.wikipedia.org/wiki/Quintessence_(physics)
https://en.wikipedia.org/wiki/Fifth_force
This field, called the "Higgs Field", exists throughout space, and it breaks some symmetry laws of the electroweak interaction, triggering the Higgs mechanism.
https://en.wikipedia.org/wiki/Higgs_boson

Ice Man Wim Hof
https://youtu.be/8cvhwquPqJ0

Harvard researcher Herbert Benson, who has been studying a meditation technique known as "g Tum-mo" for 20 years, says that "Buddhists feel the reality we live in is not the ultimate one. Experiments with Buddhist monks practicing g Tum-mo produced dramatic results. Just using the power of their minds, the monks produced enough body heat to dry wet sheets placed on them as they relaxed in chilly rooms.
https://news.harvard.edu/gazette/story/2002/04/meditation-dramatically-changes-body-temperatures/
https://bensonhenryinstitute.org/about-us-dr-herbert-benson/
A 7 minute trailer for a longer documentary on the research of Dr. Herbert Benson.
https://vimeo.com/248297652
Neurocognitive and Somatic Components of Temperature Increases during g-Tummo Meditation: Legend and Reality
https://journals.plos.org/plosone/article?id=10.1371/journal.pone.0058244

https://www.abc.net.au/news/science/2019-02-19/mindfulness-changes-neuroscience-brain-imaging-meditation/10811320

Mindfulness meditation improves cognition: Evidence of brief mental training
https://www.sciencedirect.com/science/article/pii/S1053810010000681

Some evidence shows that compared to the wider population, long-time meditators have more brain volume in, for instance, the prefrontal cortex. https://www.ncbi.nlm.nih.gov/pmc/articles/PMC3184843/

Different meditation types train distinct parts of your brain https://www.newscientist.com/article/2149489-different-meditation-types-train-distinct-parts-of-your-brain/

Neuroscientists and Buddhist monks: The unusual collaboration between psychiatrist Richard Davidson and several Buddhist monks unveils the possibility that the brain, like the rest of the body, can be altered intentionally. Davidson and his colleagues put forth the idea that the phenomena of meditation can be translated into high-frequency gamma waves and brain synchronization, or coordination.
https://hopes.stanford.edu/meditation-and-hd/
https://www.crystalinks.com/medbrain.html

A Case of Xenoglossy and the Nature of Consciousness
APA TV spoke with Dr Samuel Sandweiss at APA 2015 about the strange case of a woman who was suddenly able to write in Sanskrit, without any previous awareness of the language - and what it means for our understanding of the mind.
https://www.youtube.com/watch?v=syX2X1QsRJI

Xenoglossy is the rare anomaly, mainly found in mediumship and reincarnation cases, of people being heard to speak correctly in a language they never learned, and could therefore not be expected to use to communicate.
https://psi-encyclopedia.spr.ac.uk/articles/xenoglossy-reincarnation-cases
https://psi-encyclopedia.spr.ac.uk/search/node/xenoglossy

Derek Amato, Sudden Musical Genius
"It's almost like the ghost of Beethoven jumped into my body, right, and took over and I just kinda went crazy."
https://www.youtube.com/watch?v=GTHDuZo7G3Y
https://www.npr.org/2016/02/22/467680296/stroke-of-genius-how-derek-amato-became-a-musical-savant

Amato, who can not read music, explained that he knew what to play as he could see black and white squares in his head that triggered his fingers to move.
https://www.dailymail.co.uk/news/article-2155919/Derek-Amato-Concussion-turns-Colorado-man-musical-genius-aged-40.html

Brain Gain: A Person Can Instantly Blossom into a Savant – and No One Knows Why
Some people suddenly become accomplished artists or musicians with no previous interest or training. Is it possible innate genius lies dormant within everyone?
https://blogs.scientificamerican.com/observations/brain-gain-a-person-can-instantly-blossom-into-a-savant-and-no-one-knows-why/

The savant syndrome: an extraordinary condition. A synopsis: past, present, future
https://www.ncbi.nlm.nih.gov/pmc/articles/PMC2677584/

TEDx talk by Darold Treffert, MD. His most recent book Islands of Genius: The Bountiful Mind of the Autistic, Acquired and Sudden Savant summarizes his 50 years of interest and research in both autism and savant syndrome.
https://www.youtube.com/watch?v=Wxe1PkyJev8

https://www.wonderslist.com/10-genius-child-prodigies-world/
https://www.nationalgeographic.com/magazine/2017/05/genius-genetics-intelligence-neuroscience-creativity-einstein/
http://content.time.com/time/health/article/0,8599,1879593,00.html

She has what's known as a highly superior autobiographical memory.
https://www.abc.net.au/radionational/programs/allinthemind/a-highly-superior-memory/11021088
https://en.wikipedia.org/wiki/Autobiographical_memory

To overcome this neural bias for negativity, we must repetitiously and consciously generate as many positive thoughts as we can.
https://www.psychologytoday.com/au/blog/words-can-change-your-brain/201208/the-most-dangerous-word-in-the-world

Part 1 of 3. We live in an experiential reality. The mind is not created by the brain, is not housed in the brain, and does not use the brain to function in the material realm.
https://youtu.be/F8RmBp5M9Z0
Part 2 explains that the brain is superfluous. The mind functions without the brain, so the mind has none of the limitations of the brain or physical realm. We create reality.
https://youtu.be/YrkgI2Bulkg
Part 3 - There Is Nothing but Mind and Experience
https://youtu.be/9HdMeg-KspA

Quantum superposition of molecules beyond 25 kDa
"Matter-wave interference experiments provide a direct confirmation of the quantum superposition principle, a hallmark of quantum theory, and thereby constrain possible modifications to quantum mechanics. Here, we report interference of a molecular library of functionalized oligoporphyrins with masses beyond 25,000 Da and consisting of up to 2,000 atoms. We demonstrate quantum superposition of these massive particles..."
https://www.nature.com/articles/s41567-019-0663-9

"Physicists have managed to produce hot clouds of trillions of entangled atoms, breaking quantity records and showing that entanglement isn't as fragile as previously thought.
Pairs or groups of particles can become so intertwined that measuring the state of one will instantly change properties of the others, no matter how far apart they are."
https://newatlas.com/physics/15-trillion-atoms-quantum-entanglement/
Measurement-induced, spatially-extended entanglement in a hot, strongly-interacting atomic system
https://www.nature.com/articles/s41467-020-15899-1

Telepathy proven in clinical trials:
Evidence for correlations between distant intentionality and brain function in recipients: a functional magnetic resonance imaging analysis
This study, using functional magnetic resonance imaging (fMRI) technology, demonstrated that distant intentionality (DI), defined as sending thoughts

at a distance, is correlated with an activation of certain brain functions in the recipients.

Significant differences between experimental (send) and control (no send) procedures were found (p = 0.000127). Areas activated during the experimental procedures included the anterior and middle cingulate area, precuneus, and frontal area. It was concluded that instructions to a healer to make an intentional connection with a sensory isolated person can be correlated to changes in brain function of that individual.
https://pubmed.ncbi.nlm.nih.gov/16398587/

Extrasensory electroencephalographic induction between identical twins
https://pubmed.ncbi.nlm.nih.gov/5890891/

The consistency of results across a huge number of tests done under a variety of circumstances balloons this divergence from chance to great proportions: "The overall odds against chance are a staggering 202 octodecillion (that's 2 x 1059) to 1," Radin wrote in his book "Entangled Minds: Extrasensory Experiences in a Quantum Reality."
https://www.theepochtimes.com/ability-to-sense-when-someones-staring-at-you-is-common-studies-show_917468.html

Effects of Distant Intention on Water Crystal Formation
This experiment tested the hypothesis that water exposed to distant intentions affects the aesthetic rating of ice crystals formed from that water.
http://www.noetic.org/research/projects/effects-of-distant-intention-on
Double-Blind Test of the Effects of Distant Intention on Water Crystal Formation
http://library.noetic.org/library/publication-scholarly-papers/double-blind-test-effects-distant-intention-water-crystal
Effects of Intentionally Treated Water on Growth of Arabidopsis thaliana Seeds With Cryptochrome Mutations
https://www.researchgate.net/publication/319400665_Effects_of_Intentionally_Treated_Water_on_Growth_of_Arabidopsis_thaliana_Seeds_With_Cryptochrome_Mutations

There is, without any doubt whatsoever, objective, repeatable, evidence for the existence of the afterlife. Retired lawyer and author Dr. Victor Zammit states that the evidence collected would be accepted by the highest court in any civilized country.

For the record, this is NOT religious crusading. Nor is there any attempt in any way to change your beliefs. It is a record of the work of some of the most brilliant scientists who ever lived.

https://victorzammit.com/evidence/index.html

http://deanradin.org/

Predicting the Unpredictable: 75 Years of Experimental Evidence

http://www.deanradin.com/evidence/Radin2011AAAS.pdf

Psychophysiological Evidence of Possible Retrocausal Effects in Humans

http://www.deanradin.com/papers/Radin_AAAS_final.pdf

Our main findings reported here in Part 1 of this work are: (1) the heart appears to receive and respond to intuitive information; (2) a significantly greater heart rate deceleration occurred prior to future emotional stimuli compared tocalm stimuli;

This study presents compelling evidence that the body's perceptual apparatus is continuously scanning the future.

http://www.deanradin.com/evidence/McCraty2004PartI.pdf

THE JOURNAL OF ALTERNATIVE AND COMPLEMENTARY MEDICINE Volume 10, Number 1, 2004, pp. 133–143

Dean Radin is an American scientist known for innovative experiments in the study of consciousness and psi phenomena. He is the author or co-author of over 250 technical and popular articles, four dozen book chapters, and four accessible books: The Conscious Universe (1997), Entangled Minds (2006), Supernormal (2013) and Real Magic (2018).

https://psi-encyclopedia.spr.ac.uk/sites/default/files/ebook/article/radin_dean-435.pdf

"A thought-provoking book. The author makes a convincing case for the reality and significance of magic." Brian Josephson PhD, Nobel Laureate in Physics

"It succeeds in blazing new trails. Well worth the read." Kary Mullis PhD, Nobel Laureate in Chemistry
https://www.realmagicbook.com/real-magic

Manifesto for a Post-MaterialistScience: We are a group of internationally known scientists, from a variety of scientific fields (biology, neuroscience, psychology, medicine, psychiatry), who participated in an international summit on post-materialist science, spirituality and society. We have come to the following conclusions:
https://opensciences.org/files/pdfs/Manifesto-for-a-Post-Materialist-Science.pdf
https://opensciences.org/

The Psi Encyclopedia is a new collection of articles and case studies about psi research, the scientific investigation of psychic phenomena. It's a work in progress, being created by the Society for Psychical Research in London.
https://psi-encyclopedia.spr.ac.uk/

THE SOCIETY for Psychical Research was set up in London in 1882, the first scientific organisation ever to examine claims of psychic and paranormal phenomena. We hold no corporate view about their existence or meaning; rather, our purpose is to gather information and foster understanding through research and education.
https://www.spr.ac.uk/

Afterlife Hall of Fame: Dedicated to those most brilliant scientists and dedicated mediums, psychics and researchers who made a most significant contribution towards promoting the pranormal and proving the existence of the afterlife.
https://www.victorzammit.com/hall/index.html

Respected scientists who investigated
https://www.victorzammit.com/book/4thedition/chapter02.html

The American Society for Psychical Research
http://www.aspr.com/index.html

An introduction to the evidence for the afterlife - with links to just a few of the fascinating videos and audios available.
https://www.victorzammit.com/evidence/index.html

https://www.debunkingskeptics.com/

334 trials of remote viewing, viewers were successful with odds against chance of 100 billion to 1. The Princeton Engineering Anomalies Research (PEAR) was a research program at Princeton University that studied parapsychology. Established in 1979 by then Dean of Engineering Robert G. Jahn,
https://psi-encyclopedia.spr.ac.uk/articles/princeton-engineering-anomalies-research-pear

"I think I can safely say I am the most tested Medium this country has ever produced... I have been boxed up, tied up, sealed up, gagged, bound and held – and still the voices have come to speak their message of life eternal." Leslie Flint, Independent Spirit Voice Medium.
https://www.leslieflint.com/
https://www.youtube.com/channel/UCpdkkzGOZwzAt89dlAls-Ag
https://www.youtube.com/user/LeslieFlintTrust
https://www.amazon.com/Voices-Dark-My-Life-Medium/dp/0333122011

The medium was tested hundreds of times using all manner of controls and never once was found to have produced the voices or had any collaborator produce the voices. "He held a certain amount of pink water in his mouth. Then his mouth was sealed by an adhesive strip. After the séance, he returned the entire amount of water--quite a difficult achievement!"
http://adcguides.com/validity2.htm

Closer To Truth's resource-rich website features over 4,000 video interviews with world-renowned scientists and philosophers searching the vital ideas of existence.
https://www.closertotruth.com/

The concept of multiple unperceived dimensions in the universe is one of the hottest topics in contemporary physics. It is essential to current attempts to explain gravity and the underlying structure of the universe.
https://www.amazon.com/Great-Beyond-Dimensions-Extraordinary-Everything/dp/0471741493

10 Real-Life Mystics Even Skeptics May Believe Have Paranormal Powers
https://www.toptenz.net/10-real-life-mystics-even-skeptics-may-believe-paranormal-powers.php

The Sense of Being Stared At
https://www.sheldrake.org/files/pdfs/papers/The-Sense-of-Being-Stared-At-Part-1-Is-it-Real-or-Illusory.pdf

Dean Radin's Extraordinary Synchronicity Story
https://youtu.be/Aan5hiQYlNs

Children Who Remember Previous Lives – Academic Publications
https://med.virginia.edu/perceptual-studies/publications/academic-publications/children-who-remember-previous-lives-academic-publications/
https://med.virginia.edu/perceptual-studies/wp-content/uploads/sites/360/2017/04/REI42-Tucker-James-LeiningerPIIS1550830716000331.pdf
https://med.virginia.edu/perceptual-studies/

The Science of Reincarnation
UVA psychiatrist Jim Tucker investigates children's claims of past lives
http://uvamagazine.org/articles/the_science_of_reincarnation

10 Reincarnation Stories
https://youtu.be/pq_AbsnAgH8

Chilling Reincarnation Stories: Meet 6 People Who Lived Before
https://www.rd.com/article/chilling-reincarnation-stories/

## *Why It Really Matters*

I am terrified of the thought of death. How do you guys deal with it? I am 18 years old, and I've been an atheist since I was 14.
https://www.reddit.com/r/TrueAtheism/comments/3a1els/i_am_terrified_of_the_thought_of_death_how_do_you/

I'm 25 and terrified of death. How do I overcome this fear and live life while I'm still alive?
https://www.quora.com/Im-25-and-terrified-of-death-How-do-I-overcome-this-fear-and-live-life-while-Im-still-alive?share=1

I don't believe in any sort of a god or an afterlife and the thought of dying terrifies me, I start to panic and find it hard to breath. I get hysterical and I can't bear to even think about it because it scares me so much.
https://uk.answers.yahoo.com/question/index?qid=20090531005947AAUhNqV

The poll carried out by New Scientist magazine found that 67% of British people are petrified by the prospect of dying.
http://news.bbc.co.uk/2/hi/health/2332601.stm

Academia considers cannibalism
Last year, a conference was held at the University of Warwick, entitled "Bites Here an There," where such topics as "Help Yourself: Autophagy as Response to Global Crises,""Cannibalism and Intimacy," and "'Ethical' Foodways: Justifying Cannibalism in Contemporary Speculative Fiction" were discussed.
https://www.rt.com/news/467685-cannibalism-promoted-by-academics/
https://warwick.ac.uk/fac/arts/hrc/confs/bites/
https://www.eurekalert.org/pub_releases/2017-07/lsu-can071017.php
https://theconversation.com/cannibalism-is-common-in-the-animal-kingdom-heres-why-for-humans-its-the-ultimate-taboo-121678

https://futurism.com/the-byte/scientist-cannibalism-climate-change

https://nypost.com/2019/09/09/scientist-suggests-eating-human-flesh-to-fight-climate-change/
https://www.jstor.org/stable/25064862
https://www.theepochtimes.com/swedish-researcher-pushes-human-flesh-eating-as-answer-to-future-climate-change-food-shortages_3068833.html

Composting of human bodies now legal in Washington state
Gov. Jay Inslee signed legislation Tuesday making Washington the first state to approve composting as an alternative to burying or cremating human remains.
https://www.nbcnews.com/news/us-news/composting-human-bodies-now-legal-washington-state-n1008606
https://www.businessinsider.com/washington-state-human-compost-bodies-into-soil-2019-5
https://www.bbc.com/news/world-us-canada-47031816

A team of scientists in the US has developed a DIY-meal kit branded "Ouroboros" which allows a consumer to grow edible meat from their own human cells... they will provide "everything you need to create cultivated food at home from your own cells"...
https://sputniknews.com/science/202011221081238833-us-scientists-roll-out-human-meat-eating-concept-that-is-technically-not-cannibalism/
https://www.dezeen.com/2020/11/13/ouroboros-steak-meal-kit-andrew-pelling-grace-knight-orkan-telhan/

https://www.telegraph.co.uk/royal-family/0/prince-philip-words/
https://www.azquotes.com/author/11607-Prince_Philip
https://www.azquotes.com/quote/1309522
https://www.azquotes.com/quote/609354

Drugs and warfare have always gone hand in hand – from Homeric warriors drinking wine and taking opium to Wehrmacht troops popping methamphetamines. The truth is, soldiers have been fighting while high for much of history. Alcohol is the oldest and likely most popular pharmacological motivator of fighting men.

342 Arne Klingenberg

https://militaryhistorynow.com/2018/05/08/combat-high-a-sobering-history-of-drug-use-in-wartime/

Thousands of Australians served in the army, navy and air force between 2001 and 2016.
From this group, 56 died during deployment and another 373 died by suicide.
https://www.abc.net.au/news/2019-04-24/anzac-day-surprising-truth-veteran-suicides-mental-health/10772720

https://www.news.com.au/lifestyle/health/mental-health/nine-adf-veterans-take-their-own-lives-in-three-weeks/news-story/6fd383b898ea6c58ea5643eef158a746

https://www.news.com.au/finance/money/wealth/heir-to-5-billion-fortune-john-gilbert-getty-dead-at-52-in-hotel/news-story/4c11a92007d6308d63918178536352d2

Southampton University scientists have found evidence that awareness continue for at least several minutes after clinical death which was previously thought impossible.
https://bioethics.georgetown.edu/2015/07/consciousness-after-clinical-death-the-biggest-ever-scientific-study-published/

When you die you know you're dead as your brain keeps working for some time, research shows. Haunting new research indicates we will actually know when we have died.
https://www.news.com.au/lifestyle/health/mind/when-you-die-you-know-youre-dead-as-your-brain-keeps-working-for-some-time-research-shows/news-story/8c1b4dc811db1f6738c0deee12a4dd48
https://www.thesun.co.uk/news/7819011/die-know-youre-dead-brain-keeps-working/

New research says when we die we know we are dead because our brains keep working and remain aware of what's happening.
https://www.theepochtimes.com/scientist-say-when-we-die-our-brains-know-we-are-dead_2883678.html

Major study shows mind still works after the body shows no signs of life
https://www.independent.co.uk/news/science/mind-works-after-death-consciousness-sam-parnia-nyu-langone-a8007101.html

'Complete contentment and happiness': Groundbreaking study finds death is a EUPHORIC experience
https://www.rt.com/news/479895-death-positive-experience-research/
"At some point in time when I was being electrocuted I went into cardiac arrest and I literally died and I was dead for eleven and a half minutes."
https://london.ctvnews.ca/i-died-for-eleven-and-a-half-minutes-new-study-looks-at-near-death-experiences-1.4792437
https://news.westernu.ca/2020/01/study-gets-up-close-with-near-death-experiences/

Characterization of near death experiences using text mining analyses: A preliminary study
https://journals.plos.org/plosone/article?id=10.1371/journal.pone.0227402

Immunology: The pursuit of happiness
By Jo Marchant, Nature magazine on November 27, 2013
https://www.nature.com/news/immunology-the-pursuit-of-happiness-1.14225
https://www.scientificamerican.com/article/how-happiness-boosts-the-immune-system/

CPSIA information can be obtained
at www.ICGtesting.com
Printed in the USA
BVHW030856070122
625448BV00037B/111